Ion-Molecule Reactions in the Gas Phase

A symposium sponsored
by the Division of Physical
Chemistry at the 152nd
Meeting of the American
Chemical Society, New York,
N. Y., Sept. 12-13, 1966

Pierre J. Ausloos, *Symposium Chairman*

ADVANCES IN CHEMISTRY SERIES **58**

AMERICAN CHEMICAL SOCIETY

WASHINGTON, D.C.   **1966**

Library of Congress Catalog Card 66-28609

PRINTED IN THE UNITED STATES OF AMERICA

Advances in Chemistry Series

Robert F. Gould, *Editor*

AMERICAN CHEMICAL SOCIETY PUBLICATIONS

FOREWORD

ADVANCES IN CHEMISTRY SERIES was founded in 1949 by the American Chemical Society as an outlet for symposia and collections of data in special areas of topical interest that could not be accommodated in the Society's journals. It provides a medium for symposia that would otherwise be fragmented, their papers distributed among several journals or not published at all. Papers are refereed critically according to ACS editorial standards and receive the careful attention and processing characteristic of ACS publications. Papers published in ADVANCES IN CHEMISTRY SERIES are original contributions not published elsewhere in whole or major part and include reports of research as well as reviews since symposia may embrace both types of presentation.

CONTENTS

PREFACE

Well before 1900, conductivity measurements on flames and on gases subjected to electric discharges or exposed to high energy radiation led researchers to conclude that ions were formed in such systems. As early as 1905 Langevin considered the interaction between an ion and a neutral molecule in the gas phase and formulated an expression for ion-molecule collision processes. In 1912 J. J. Thomson observed ions of molecular weight 3 when hydrogen was introduced into his cathode tube apparatus. This result was explained in 1925, when Hogness and Lunn demonstrated that H_3^+ is formed in the reaction $H_2^+ + H_2 \rightarrow H_3^+ + H$. A rate constant for this reaction was theoretically derived by Eyring, Hirschfelder, and Taylor in 1936. It was not until 20 years later, however, that this particular rate constant was determined experimentally. In fact, experimental determinations of ion-molecule reaction rates began only in 1952 with the investigations of Tal'roze, closely followed by the work of Stevenson (1955), Hamill (1956), and Lampe, Field, and Franklin (1957).

The rapid growth of free radical kinetics, starting in the 1930's, stands in sharp contrast to the slow development of ion-molecule reaction kinetics, a difference which can only partly be explained by insufficient development of experimental mass spectrometry in the first half of this century. A more important retarding factor was probably the fact that the importance of chemical reactions between ions and neutral molecules in many systems was not suspected. Lind realized as early as 1912 that ions formed by high energy radiation are responsible for chemical transformations, but rather than invoking specific chemical reactions, he suggested that the products observed were formed by neutralization of a cluster consisting of the primary ion surrounded by neutral molecules. Indeed, ion-molecule reactions were only inferred in interpreting radiolytic systems after it was demonstrated by mass spectrometry in the 1950's that such reactions can occur with high cross-sections. Moreover, only in the last three or four years has radiation chemistry been exploited as a means, complementary to mass spectrometry, of investigating ion-molecule reactions through an approach similar to that long used in kinetic studies of free radical reactions. Some of the papers presented at this symposium are concerned with studies of ion-molecule reactions by analyzing the neutral products.

However, because the mass spectrometer remains the most useful and for many systems the only possible tool for studying ion-molecule reactions, most of the papers describe mass spectrometric investigations. Present day mass spectrometry has acquired great versatility through the development of many sophisticated variations on the basic instrument of early investigators. In tandem mass spectrometers, for example, two mass spectrometers are coupled; the first produces ions of known identity and energy which are introduced into a reaction chamber of the second instrument which subsequently analyzes product ions. The wide applicability of this type of instrumentation, in several diverse forms, to ion-molecule reaction studies is illustrated at this symposium. Other papers demonstrate the feasability of studying ion-molecule reactions at elevated pressures in the mass spectrometer; the usefulness of the pulsed source technique for studying reactions of thermal ions is also explored. The kinetics of reactions of thermal ions are of course directly applicable and of interest to high energy radiation systems. In one paper, interesting analytical applications of ion-molecule reactions occurring in a mass spectrometer are considered. Since 1958 the mass spectrometer has also been used to identify the ions formed in flames; successful attempts to derive cross-sections of ion-molecule reactions occurring in flames as well as in electrical discharges are described in this volume.

Much of the interest of this symposium centers on the effect of the kinetic energy of the reacting ion on the reaction cross-section. A detailed examination of the effect of energy variations is essential to the development of a comprehensive theory for the kinetics of ion-molecule reactions.

The sophistication of the concepts being considered by this symposium points up the impressive advances which have been made in recent years in the understanding of ion-molecule reactions. Unfortunately, this knowledge is confined to that fraction of the scientific population which reads the current literature of mass spectrometry or radiation chemistry since writers of textbooks on kinetics have not yet discovered ion-molecule reaction kinetics as an area worthy of more than cursory mention. It is hoped that this symposium will help in some small way to remedy that situation.

Washington, D.C.   PIERRE J. AUSLOOS
June 1966

Charge Exchange and Ion-Molecule Reactions Observed in Double Mass Spectrometers

EINAR LINDHOLM

The Royal Institute of Technology, Stockholm 70, Sweden

Double mass spectrometers of different types have been used to investigate charge exchange and ion-molecule reactions. The recombination energies of positive ions with lifetimes of the order of 10^{-5} sec. are tabulated. Transfer of translational energy in charge exchange can be important, but for some applications one ought to try to avoid observing collisions in which such transfer has taken place. Selection rules are valid for charge exchange processes in distant collisions in contrast to the case with impact of slow electrons. Ion-molecule reactions take place during the collisions but can also be studied by increasing the pressure in the collision chamber.

In a double mass spectrometer several types of ion-molecule reactions can be observed: (a) charge exchange, $A^+ + B \rightarrow A + B^+$, often followed by dissociation of B^+; (b) transfer of part of A^+ or B (e.g., proton transfer or hydride ion transfer) during the collisions; (c) reactions at increased pressure in the collision chamber.

Two main types of experimental equipment which can be distinguished are: (a) the perpendicular type in which in the collision chamber the incident positive ions and the product ions move in paths perpendicular to each other; (b) the longitudinal type in which the paths are parallel.

The perpendicular type has been used in Stockholm (*1–27*), (Figure 1), Moscow (*28–32*), San Diego (*33–35*), Birmingham (*36–39*), Strasbourg (*40*), and in Baltimore (*41–45*), (Figure 2). The longitudinal type has been used in Chicago (*46–50*), (Figure 3), San Diego (*51*), and in Gainesville (*52*). Recently, in Gainesville (*53*) and San Diego (*54*) the angular distributions of the products have been completely determined.

Table I gives a compilation of the molecules other than monoatomic gases that have been investigated in these machines.

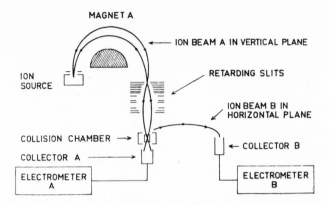

Figure 1.   Double mass spectrometer of perpendicular
type used in Stockholm (3, 26)

The ions A move in mass spectrometer A in a vertical plane
and then cross the collision chamber.   The reaction products
(the ions B) are extracted from the collision chamber at right
angles to the direction of the ion beam A and are analyzed by
mass spectrometer B, which is placed in a horizontal plane.
It therefore discriminates against secondary ions which have
acquired appreciable downward momentum from the ions A.
To avoid surface charges, all surfaces have been coated with
colloidal graphite in alcohol (7).   Radii of mass spectrom-
eter: 18 and 25 cm., respectively

Recombination Energies of Some Positive Ions

In charge exchange collisions the cross-section depends upon the
energetics of the reaction.   To compute the energy defect, the initial
and final states of the colliding particles must be specified.   This can
be done easily for the bombarded neutral molecule, which usually can
be assumed to be in the ground state before the collision, but not for the
incident ion which is often in one of its metastable states.

It seemed practical to assign to the ion definite recombination
energies (3) corresponding to transitions from the ground state or the
metastable states of the ion to the ground state or higher states of the
atom (or molecule).   A preliminary table of recombination energies
(RE) was given earlier (8).

Here an ion state must be considered metastable if its lifetime is of
the same order as the time between the formation of the ion and the
collision.   For the experiments on which Table II is based the ions are
produced in a mass spectrometer in which this time is about 10^{-5} sec.
Thus, a table of such recombination energies can be valuable in studying
ions in gases, although in such cases the corresponding time may be
shorter and the number of recombination energies larger.   In the upper atmosphere the time may be longer and the number of recombination energies smaller.

In our experiments the ions have been produced by electron impact
with 100-e.v. electrons.

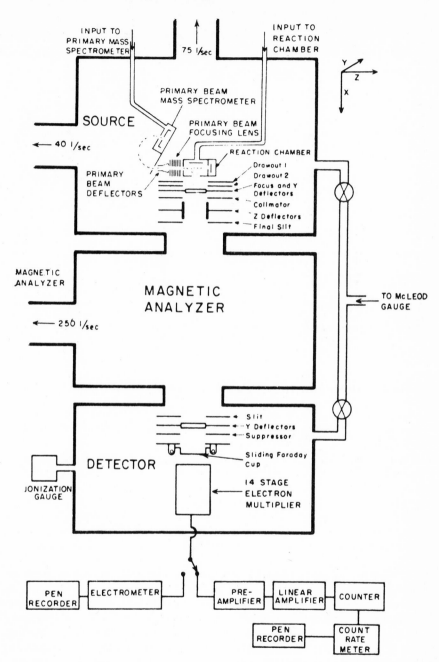

Figure 2.   Double mass spectrometer of perpendicular type used in Baltimore (45).   Radius of mass spectrometer A is only 1 cm. which makes possible work at very low velocities of the ions A (Journal of the American Chemical Society)

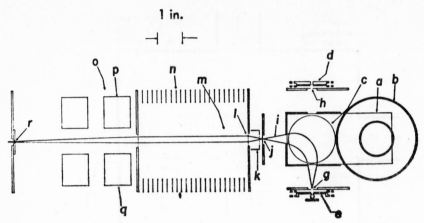

Figure 3.   Double mass spectrometer of longitudinal type used in Chicago
(47)

Radius of mass spectrometer A is only 2.5 cm so that very low velocities of the ions (A)
can be used.   In the collision chamber, k, reaction products (ions B) are formed from
the gas by charge exchange or ion-molecule reactions.   All ions move in the same
direction in the collision chamber and are accelerated by special electrostatic lenses;
hence, they all reach the slit r of mass spectrometer B (not shown) independently of
their initial velocities in the collision chamber.   The discrimination in mass spectrom-
eter B can therefore be considered negligible

Table I.   Molecules Investigated in Double Mass Spectrometers[a]

Molecule	Also Deuterated	Ions	Charge Exchange	Particle Transfer	Reactions at Increased Pressure
H_2		18	(2)		
		$H_2{}^+$, $N_2{}^+$	(52)	(52)	
		$H_2{}^+$		(47)	
D_2		Ar^+, $N_2{}^+$		(47)	
		Kr^+	(50)		
		$N_2{}^+$		(37)	
		$N_2{}^+$		(54)	
		Ar^+		(53)	
O_2		6	(18)		(18)
		H^+	(35)		
		He^+	(34)		
		N^+, O^+, $N_2{}^+$	(51)	(51)	
N_2		17	(4)		
		14	(2)		
		He^+	(34)		
		Ne^+, Ar^+	(49)		
		$D_2{}^+$		(47)	
		O^+	(51)	(51)	
CO		16	(5)		
		17	(2)		
		He^+, Ne^+, Ar^+	(48)		
H_2O		17	(3)		
		6	(17)		(17)
H_2S		17	(3)		

Table I. Continued

Molecule	Also Deuterated	Ions	Charge Exchange	Particle Transfer	Reactions at Increased Pressure
N_2O		16	(3)		
		Kr^+	(49)		
		Kr^+, Ar^+	(50)		
CO_2		14	(3)		
		4	(16)		(16)
NH_3		15	(3)		
		4	(29)		
		5	(42)		
C_2H_2		29	(9)	(9)	(9)
			(6)		
		7			(22)
		Ar^+	(50)		
CH_4	(23)	17	(3)		
		18	(23)	(23)	(23)
		He^+, Ne^+, Ar^+	(14)		(14)
		10			(21)
		13	(29)		
		7	(36) (38)		
		5	(44)		
CH_3Cl		6	(14)		(14)
CH_3I		3	(14)		(14)
CCl_4		4	(45)		
CCl_3F		Ne^+, F^+	(18)		
C_2H_4	(19)	29	(19)	(19)	
		11			(20)
		6	(40)		
		Xe^+, NH_3^+	(29)		
		Xe^+	(30) (31)		
		Xe^+	(50)		
CH_3OH		43	(27)	(27)	
	(10)	7		(10)	
		5			(17)
CH_3NH_2		19	(13)	(13)	
		6			(17)
C_2H_6	(24)	35	(24)	(24)	
		6	(40)		
		Xe^+, NH_3^+	(29)		
C_2H_5I	(25)	11	(25)		
C_2H_5OH		36	(26)		
		4	(27)		
C_3H_8		43	(12)	(12)	
	(6)		(6)		
	(25)	23	(25)		
		Xe^+, NH_3^+	(29)		
C_3H_7I	(25)	11	(25)		
iso-C_3H_7I	(25)	11	(25)		
C_3H_7OH		40	(11)	(11)	
C_4H_{10}		41	(1)	(1)	
$(CH_3)_2CO$		8	(29)		
B_5H_9		5	(43)		

[a] Monatomic gases are not included. Column 1 gives the gas in the collision chamber. If deuterated compounds were also used, this is marked in the second column by the reference number. Column 3 gives the incident ions or the number of different incident ions. A reference number in the fourth column shows that only charge exchange or dissociation after charge exchange has been measured. A reference number in the last two columns shows that either transfer of part of the ion or molecule or reactions at increased pressure has been observed.

Table II.   Recombination Energies of Positive Ions in e.v.

H $^+$: 13.60
He $^+$: 24.58
B $^+$ from BF$_3$:

$2s^2$ ^1S: 8.30	Usually too low to be of interest for charge exchange
$2p$ $^3P^0$: 12.92, 9.35, and 6.98	Abundant

C $^+$ from COS, CO$_2$, CO, CBrF$_3$, CBr$_2$F$_2$, or CCl$_3$F:

$2p$ $^2P^0$: 11.26, 10.00, 8.58	60%
$2p^2$ ^4P: 16.58, 12.40	40%

N $^+$ from N$_2$O, NH$_3$: (N$_2$ may give N$_2$ $^{+2}$)

$2p^2$ ^3P: 14.54, 12.16, 10.97	90%
$2p^2$ ^1D: 14.06, 12.87	0%
$2p^2$ ^1S: 15.03	10%
$2p^3$ $^5S^0$: 20.34	Low abundance

O $^+$:

	From CO	From CO$_2$	From COS and N$_2$O
$2p^3$ $^4S^0$: 13.62	30%	60%	Inter-medi-ate
$2p^3$ $^2D^0$: 16.94, 14.98	30%^{a}	30%^{a}	
$2p^3$ $^2P^0$: 18.64, 16.67, 14.45	40%^{a}	10%^{a}	
$3s'''$ $^6S^0$: 34.88	0%	0%	

F $^+$ from CBrF$_3$, SF$_6$, or other compounds:

$2p^4$ ^3P: 17.42	60%
$2p^4$ ^1D: 20.01	30%
$2p^4$ ^1S: 22.98	10%
$3s$ $^5S^0$: 26.60	Not yet observed

Ne $^+$: 21.56 and 21.66
Si $^+$ from SiF$_4$:

$3p$ $^2P^0$: 8.15, 7.36, 6.24	Too low to be of interest
$3p^2$ ^4P: 13.47, 9.35	Abundant

P $^+$ from POCl$_3$ (64):

$3p^2$ ^3P: 10.48, 9.05, 8.14	
$3p^2$ ^1D: 10.15, 9.24	
$3p^2$ ^1S: 10.81	
$3p^3$ $^5S^0$: 16.14	Low but not negligible abundance

S $^+$ from H$_2$S, COS, SF$_6$:

$3p^3$ $^4S^0$: 10.36	40%
$3p^3$ $^2D^0$: 12.20, 11.05	60%
$3p^3$ $^2P^0$: 13.40, 12.25, 10.65	0%
$3d$ ^4F: 15.64	0%

Cl $^+$ from CCl$_3$F:

$3p^4$ ^3P: 13.13, 13.01, 12.90	80%
$3p^4$ ^1D: 14.45, 14.34	20%
$3p^4$ ^1S: 16.47, 16.36	0%
$3d$ ^5D: 15.66, 15.21	0%

Ar $^+$:

$3p^5$ $^2P^0_{3/2}$: 15.76	66% Statistical weight
$3p^5$ $^2P^0_{1/2}$: 15.94	33% Statistical weight
High states: 18–20.	1% (60)

Br $^+$ from CBr$_2$F$_2$:

$4p^4$ ^3P: 12.32, 12.23, $\sim$ 11.80, 11.39	80%
$4p^4$ ^1D: 13.25, 12.80	20%
$4p^4$ ^1S: 15.32, 14.87 (estimated energy)	0%

Kr $^+$:

$4p^5$ $^2P^0_{3/2}$: 14.00	66% Statistical weight
$4p^5$ $^2P^0_{1/2}$: 14.67	33% Statistical weight
High states: 16–18	1% (60)

Table II.   Continued

I^+ from I_2:

$5p^4\ {}^3P$: 11.33, 11.25, 10.45, 10.40,
  10.32, 9.52   Abundant
$5p^4\ {}^1D$: 12.15, 11.22   Abundant
$5p^4\ {}^1S$: 14.49, 13.56   0%
$6s\ {}^5S^0$: 13.73, 12.96, 12.84   Not yet observed

Xe^+:

$5p^5\ {}^2P^0_{3/2}$: 12.13   66% Statistical weight
$5p^5\ {}^2P^0_{1/2}$: 13.44   33% Statistical weight
High states: 12.5–16.5   1% (60)

Hg^+:

$6s\ {}^2S$: 10.43   50%
$6s\ {}^2D_{5/2}$: 14.83   45%
$6s\ {}^2D_{3/2}$: 16.70   5%

Doubly charged ions (26, 27):

He^{+2}:

$He^{+2} \rightarrow 1s$: too high RE to be of interest for charge exchange
   $\rightarrow 2s$ or $2p$: about 11.0–12.5

Ne^{+2}:

$2s^2 2p^4 \rightarrow 2s 2p^5$: too high RE to be of interest
    $\rightarrow 2s^2 2p^4\ 3x$: about 10.5–12.0

Ar^{+2}:

$3s^2 3p^4 \rightarrow 3s^2 3p^5$: about 24 (Predominating)
    $\rightarrow 3s^2 3p^4\ nx$: about 9 (Usually too low to be of interest)
$3s^2 3p^4\ {}^3P \rightarrow 3s3p^6$: about 11.5–12.5. (Observed)
    ${}^1D \rightarrow$ about 13–14. (Abundance unknown)
    ${}^1S \rightarrow$ about 15.5–16.5. (Abundance unknown)

Kr^{+2}:

$4s^2 4p^4 \rightarrow 4s^2 4p^5$: about 21 (Predominating)
    $\rightarrow 4s^2 4p^4\ nx$: about 9 (Usually too low to be of interest)
$4s^2 4p^4\ {}^3P \rightarrow 4s4p^6$: about 10 (Abundance unknown)
    ${}^1D \rightarrow$ about 11 (Abundance unknown)
    ${}^1S \rightarrow$ about 13 (Observed)

Xe^{+2}:

$5s^2 5p^4 \rightarrow 5s^2 5p^5$: about 18–20 (Predominating)
    $\rightarrow 5s^2 5p^4\ nx$: about 9 (Usually too low to be of interest)
$5s^2 5p^4\ {}^3P \rightarrow 5s5p^6$: about 9 (Abundance unknown)
    ${}^1D \rightarrow$ about 10 (Abundance unknown)
    ${}^1S \rightarrow$ about 12.5 (Observed)

Hg^{+2}:

$5d^{10}\ {}^1S \rightarrow 5d^{10}\ ({}^1S)\ 6s\ {}^2S$: about 17
    $\rightarrow 5d^9\ 6s^2\ {}^2D_{5/2}$ or ${}^2D_{3/2}$: about 11–12

Molecular Ions:

H_2^+: (a) 16.4–17.4, (b) 13–14, (c) about 11

CH_2^+ from CH_4:
 10.4 or lower to 10.9

CH_3^+ from CH_4:
 9.0 or 9.5 to 10.5

CH_4^+: 9.0 or 9.5 to 12.0

OH^+ from H_2O:
 12.7

H_2O^+: 12.4

$C_2H_2^+$: 11.4

$C_2H_3^+$ from C_2H_4:
 much lower than 10.5

$C_2H_4^+$: somewhat lower than 10.5

N_2^+: 15.3

CO^+: 14.0

Table II. Continued

$C_2H_6^+$: perhaps 9.0 or 9.5 to 11.0

O_2^+: X $^2\Pi_g \to$ X $^3\Sigma_g^-$:   11.2–12.3   60%
$\quad \to$ $^1\Delta_g$ or $^1\Sigma_g^+$:   9.7–11.3
$\quad$ a$^4\Pi_u$: 14.0 and 17.0   40%

CH_3OH^+: 10.9 or lower to 12.0

SH^+ from H_2S:
  10.5–12.0

H_2S^+: 10.5, certainly below 11.0

N_2O^+: 12.7

CO_2^+: 13.8

COS^+: 11.2, perhaps range between 10.0 and 11.5

CS_2^+: range mainly below 10.0 (Mass spectrum in (11) erroneous)

$C_6H_6^+$: 9.2

$C_5H_5N^+$ (pyridine): 9.3

  [a] Uncertain

The recombination should be governed by the same selection rules as spectroscopic transitions. Let us consider the recombination of an oxygen ion $2s^2\,2p^3\,^4S°$. When one p electron is added to the ^4S ion we expect to obtain one of the states ^5P and ^3P. However, if the $2s^2\,2p^4$ state of the atom is obtained, it can only exist in the states ^3P, ^1D, or ^1S. Thus the recombination can only give $2s^2\,2p^4\,^3P$. Sometimes the selection rules are not strictly valid. In this case, however, no transitions $2s^2\,2p^3\,^4S°\,nx \to 2s^2\,2p^4\,^1D$ or ^1S have been observed by the spectroscopists (57) which shows that in this case the selection rules are strictly valid.

The selection rules obviously break down if the charge exchange takes place at very small distances between the colliding particles.

If the recombination leaves the atom in a high atomic state, the recombination energy will be so low that charge exchange cannot take place. Such recombination energies are not included in Table II.

In Table II the state of the ion and the recombination energies in electron volts (computed from (65)) are given. Some *very uncertain* information is included in the right hand column as to the relative abundances of the metastable states of the ions when produced by electron impact with 100-e.v. electrons from the indicated compounds.

Table II must be used with care in anomalous cases in which the transition probability for ionization of the molecule is very low in some energy ranges (e.g., acetylene, benzene, methylamine). In such cases higher RE's, not included in the table and normally of small importance, may be responsible for the charge exchange processes although with small cross-sections (cf. 9, 13).

Transfer of Translational Energy in Charge Exchange

If charge exchange occurs when the incident positive ion passes the neutral gas molecule with a certain velocity, transfer of translational energy will usually take place. This transfer of translational energy is especially important in nonresonant cases and is responsible for the fact that the cross-sections are different from zero in these cases. The relative importance of the transfer varies with the velocity, and when the velocity is small, the translational energy is also small so that the transfer is of minor importance.

In different applications the transfer of translational energy is of different interest. If the results of the investigations are to be applied to ordinary radiation chemistry in the gas phase, the velocities of all particles correspond to gas kinetic energies; therefore, it is necessary to perform the experiments in such a manner that no transfer of translational energy takes place. On the other hand, if the results are to be applied to a system with high velocities—e g., in the upper atmosphere— it is necessary to perform the experiments in such a manner, that the products are observed even if a large part of the cross-section is caused by the fact that transfer of translational energy has occurred in the collision. For the first kind of investigations the perpendicular type apparatus is suitable, but for the second kind of experiments the longitudinal type apparatus must be used.

Another aspect of the transfer of translational energy is concerned with investigating the energetics of the reaction. If it is possible to construct an apparatus in which only such processes are *observed* in which no or a very small transfer of translational energy takes place, the results of the measurements can be interpreted immediately since only such reactions will be observed for which $IP = RE$. On the other hand, if the apparatus allows such processes to be observed in which a large transfer of translational energy can take place, then the cross-sections will be large even if this condition is not satisfied; in order to determine the energetics it is necessary to decrease the velocity of the incident ion to obtain vanishing cross-sections (*48, 49, 50*). These two types of apparatus correspond approximately to the perpendicular and longitudinal types, respectively.

If no transfer of translational energy occurs, then the charge exchange process probably takes place when the distance between the ion and the molecule is large. This means, however, that the ion and the molecule can be considered as isolated from each other, and therefore, the recombination process of the ion and the ionization process of the molecule must obey the spectroscopic transition laws. On the other hand, if a large transfer of translational energy takes place, then the process probably takes place when the distance is small, and possibly then all selection rules break down.

The importance of the transfer of translational energy has been stressed by several authors (*31, 48, 49, 50*). The problem will be discussed below especially with regard to the difference in the results obtained in the perpendicular type apparatus in Stockholm and the longitudinal type apparatus in Chicago.

Giese and Maier (*48*) investigated the reaction: $Ne^+ + CO = Ne + C^+ + O$. This reaction had been investigated earlier by Gustafsson and Lindholm (*2*) down to a kinetic energy of 25 e.v., and they had found that the cross-sections increase with decreasing velocities of the incident ions.   Giese and Maier were now able to show that the cross-section decreases to zero when kinetic energies lower 5 e.v. are used. This shows that to obtain reliable results in a perpendicular apparatus it is necessary to perform measurements down to a kinetic energy of a few e.v.   This has been done in all later investigations in Stockholm (1, 6, 8–25, 27) and in all work in Baltimore (41, 42, 43, 44, 45).

Recently, Maier (50) thoroughly investigated the charge exchange between Ar^+ and C_2H_2.   His mass spectra are compared in Table III with partly unpublished measurements by Lindholm, Szabo, and Wilmenius (9).   The processes giving C_2H^+ and CH^+ are endothermic by 0.8 and 5.0 e.v., respectively.   According to Lindholm et al. the intensities of these ions increase only slowly with increasing velocity of the incident ions.   Therefore it must be possible in this case to extrapolate the mass spectra down to zero velocity and to interpret the extrapolated mass spectrum by assuming that the influence of the kinetic energy of the incident ion can be neglected.

Table III.   Relative Secondary Ion Currents as Percentages of the Total Secondary Ion Current for $Ar^+ + C_2H_2 \rightarrow$ Products

Secondary Ion	Author[a]	Kinetic Energy of the Incident Ion, e.v.						
		4	10	15	30	50	100	900
$C_2H_2^+$	LSW	93	84		74		71	74
	M	96	61	52	51	54		
C_2H^+	LSW	7	14		24		27	21
	M	4	39	48	31	27		
C_2^+	LSW	—	1		1		1	2
	M	—	—	0.3	3	0.6		
CH^+	LSW	—	0.3		1		1.5	2
	M	—	—	0.3	13	14		
C^+	LSW	—	0.1		0.3		0.7	1
	M	—	—	—	2	3		

[a] LSW = Lindholm, Szabo, and Wilmenius (9), M = Maier (50).

The intensities of the same fragment ions as measured by Maier increase rapidly from the threshold and attain such high values at even moderate velocities that the mass spectrum has no similarity with the extrapolated zero velocity mass spectrum.   Evidently utmost care is necessary in interpreting the mass spectra in this case, and Maier stresses that already at moderate velocities the total energy given to the target molecule by ion impact may well be greater than the recombination energy of the incident ion; hence, endothermic reactions can be observed with fairly large cross-sections.

Maier (50) also investigated the charge exchange between Xe^+ and C_2H_4.   These reactions were studied previously by Tal'roze et al. (29, 30, 31, 32) in a perpendicular type apparatus in which the geometry seems to result in a smaller discrimination in the second mass spectrometer than in the Stockholm apparatus.   Finally, the same reactions were observed in Stockholm by Szabo (19) during a detailed investigation of the charge exchange mass spectra of ethylene.   All mass spectra have been collected in Table IV.

The reaction that gives CH_2^+:

$$Xe^+ + C_2H_4 = Xe + CH_2^+ + CH_2$$

is endothermic by 5.0 e.v.   Despite this, Maier and Tal'roze observed fairly large relative intensities of this fragment, and both concluded that the kinetic energy of the incident ion is important in determining the species of the secondary ions produced in the reaction.   On the other hand, the CH_2^+ intensity observed by Szabo is small and decreases smoothly towards zero with decreasing velocity.   In this case also it must be possible to extrapolate Szabo's mass spectra to zero velocity and to interpret them by neglecting the kinetic energy of the incident ion.

The lower intensity of CH_2^+ observed by Szabo must be attributed to the larger discrimination in the Stockholm apparatus, and this explanation corresponds well to the higher intensities observed by Maier than by Tal'roze, as already pointed out by Maier (50).

In connection with their measurements, Giese and Maier (48, 49, 50) pointed out that only at extremely low velocity of the incident ion can its kinetic energy be neglected.   Of course, this is true, but it is also evident from the discussion above that by using a perpendicular type apparatus of appropriate construction it is possible to avoid observing most of the products from those collisions in which transfer of translation energy has occurred to an appreciable extent.   If the measurements are performed down to very low velocities of the incident ions, it is usually possible to extrapolate the results back to zero velocity and to interpret them by neglecting the kinetic energy of the incident ions. Then, the interpretation may be founded upon the assumption that the energy absorbed by the target molecule equals the recombination energy of the incident ion.

Table IV.   Relative Secondary Ion Currents as Percentages of the Total Secondary Ion Current for $Xe^+ + C_2H_4 \rightarrow$ Products

Secondary Ion	Author[a]	Kinetic Energy of the Incident Ion, e.v.								
		3	10	30	40	60	80	100	300	900
$C_2H_4^+$	S	60	60	58	57	57	57	57	59	60
	T				53	47	46	42		
	M	75	59	50	51	48	46	45		
$C_2H_3^+$	S	9	9	12	12	13	13	13	13	13
	T				18	22	23	22		
	M	7	12	17	16	16	15.3	15		
$C_2H_2^+$	S	31	31	31	31	30	30	29	27	26
	T				29	30	29	28		
	M	20	29	33	33	30	28.4	27		
CH_2^+	S	0	0	0	0	0.16	0.22	0.36	0.36	0.46
	T				0.1	0.8	2.2	3.4		
	M	0	0	0	0.44	5.8	10	12		
CH^+	S	0	0	0	0	0	0	0.01	0.02	0.05
	T				Not mentioned by Tal'roze					
	M	0	0	0	0.022	0.12	0.29	0.71		

[a] S = Szabo (19), T = Tal'roze (31), M = Maier (50).

Selection Rules in Ionization by Charge Exchange

If a charge exchange process, $A^+ + B \rightarrow A + B^+$, occurs when the distance between the two particles is large, we expect that no transfer of translational energy takes place in the reaction and that the same selection rules govern the ionization as in spectroscopic transitions. This means that if the molecule B is in a singlet state before the ionization, the ion B^+ will be formed in a doublet state after ionization of one electron without rearrangements of any other electrons, at least for small molecules.

Processes of this type can be expected to predominate when using a perpendicular type apparatus; in fact, it has been possible recently to observe the validity of selection rules when ionizing CO_2 and H_2O by charge exchange (16, 17).

In the electron impact mass spectrum of CO_2, O^+ ions are formed with an appearance potential (AP) 19.1 e.v. according to the process:

$$CO_2 + 19.1 \text{ e.v.} \rightarrow CO\ (X\ ^1\Sigma) + O^+\ (^4S) + e$$

In a potential energy diagram this dissociation limit must be connected with CO_2^+ in a quartet state according to the Wigner-Witmer correlation rules. Since the quartet states of CO_2^+ should have a comparatively high energy, the potential energy curve must be repulsive. Further, it will be impossible to reach such a state by simply ionizing one of the CO_2 electrons since simultaneous excitation of another electron is necessary to obtain a quartet state. We therefore expect that when the mass spectrum of CO_2 is studied by charge exchange, at least in a perpendicular type apparatus, the dissociation limit at 19.1 e.v. cannot be reached and the AP of O^+ must correspond to the next higher limit at 22.4 e.v. according to the process:

$$CO_2 + 22.4 \text{ e.v.} \rightarrow CO_2^+ \rightarrow CO\ (X\ ^1\Sigma) + O^+\ (^2D)$$

In agreement with this expectation Sjögren (16) found that when bombarding CO_2 with Ne^+ ions $(RE$ 21.6 e.v.) of low velocity and at low pressure, vanishing fractions of O^+ ions were obtained. This result indicates that when using electron or photon impact, O^+ (^4S) is formed at 19.1 e.v. after preionizing a highly excited triplet state of neutral CO_2.

In the electron impact mass spectrum of H_2O, OH^+ ions are formed with AP 17.9 e.v. according to the process:

$$H_2O + 17.9 \text{ e.v.} \rightarrow OH^+\ (^3\Sigma^-) + H + e$$

Fiquet-Fayard (59) has shown that this dissociation limit correlates with a repulsive quartet state of H_2O^+. Since such a state cannot be reached by simple ionization of one of the H_2O electrons, we expect that when the mass spectrum of H_2O is studied by charge exchange the dissociation products at 17.9 e.v. cannot be obtained. Therefore, the AP of OH^+ will correspond to the formation of OH^+ in an excited state at some higher energy. In agreement with this expectation Sjögren (17) obtained no OH^+ ions when bombarding with an ion with RE between

18 and 20 e.v. (Xe^{+2}) of low velocity although bombardment with Ne^+ (*RE* 21.6 e.v.) gave only OH^+. (The dissociation limit above correlates also with the $^2B_1$ state, but since this is the ground state of H_2O^+, formed by ionization of a nonbonding electron, no dissociation will take place via this state.)

Our finding that selection rules govern the ionization by means of charge exchange is interesting since other recent investigations seem to show that no selection rules are valid.

Lipeles, Novick, and Tolk (*63*) bombarded Ar gas with He^+ ions and observed the spectral line at 4764 A. The charge exchange reaction is therefore:

$$He^+ + Ar \rightarrow He + Ar^{+*} (3s^2\ 3p^4\ 4p)$$

followed by

$$Ar^+ (3s^2\ 3p^4\ 4p) \rightarrow Ar^+ (3s^2\ 3p^4\ 4s) + hf$$

The ionization of the argon atom means that one electron has been ionized, and another has been excited. This unusual process can be explained by assuming that the charge exchange process occurs when the distance between He and Ar is small. This assumption is necessary since the charge exchange process is strongly endothermic (*RE* 24.6 e.v., *IP* 35 e.v.). It is well known that all selection rules break down when the molecule in question is near another molecule. Further, the probably considerable initial kinetic energy of the Ar^{+*} ion causes no difficulties with spectroscopic observation. The hypothesis that such charge exchange reactions take place when the distance between the atoms is small is finally supported by the cross-section curve that has a high narrow maximum at low kinetic energy of He^+.

The discussion thus far indicates that the selection rules should be more valid for observations in a longitudinal type apparatus than in a perpendicular type apparatus.

In this connection it seems to be appropriate to point out that the spectroscopic selection rules do not seem to be valid in excitation by means of electron impact with slow electrons. In this case, exchange of the electrons is possible, and then the selection rules break down. This means that especially in appearance potential measurements no selection rules are valid, and therefore charge exchange and electron impact may give different appearance potentials. On the other hand, when using high energy electrons, scattered by small angles, only optically allowed transitions can be observed. The difference between slow and fast electrons is illustrated by recent work on electron impact excitation at low velocities (*66, 56*), at 70 e.v. (*58*), at 300 e.v. (*62*), at 25 k.e.v. (*55*), and in the range 13–50 e.v. (*61*).

We conclude, that the ionization processes by charge exchange in a perpendicular type apparatus or using electron impact at high energy are substantially similar, and therefore it is possible to calculate the electron impact mass spectrum from charge exchange observations by

integrating the intensities in the breakdown graph of the molecule
(1, 11, 12, 13, 19, 23, 24, 26, 27).

Ion-Molecule Reactions

Ion-molecule reactions can be investigated in a double mass spectrometer in two ways: (a) In the collision between the incident ion
and the gas molecule, transfer of part of one of these structures can
take place.   The pressure in the collision chamber must be low; (b) The
pressure in the collision chamber is increased.   The slow incident ions
ionize the gas molecules by charge exchange.   Then ion-molecule reactions take place between the ionized gas molecules or their fragment ions
and other gas molecules.

The major problem in method (a) is that in ion-molecule interchange, considerable momentum in the direction of travel of the incident
ion is imparted to both final products.   Hence, in a perpendicular type
apparatus only transfer of low weight particles can be observed at all
and only at very low velocities of the incident ions (1, 9, 10, 11, 12, 13,
19, 20, 23, 27).   Cross-sections cannot be measured.   The value of
these investigations is that some ion-molecule reactions—e.g., proton
transfer and hydride ion transfer—can be identified.   The energetics
and the competition between charge exchange and ion-molecule reactions can be discussed, and by using partially deuterated compounds,
one can obtain a detailed picture of the reaction.

In a longitudinal type apparatus the initial velocities of the products
are less important, and it is no longer necessary to restrict the observations to transfer of low weight particles (see Table I).   It is also possible
to determine cross-sections accurately.

Method (b) corresponds to the usual method of investigating
ion-molecule reactions in a high pressure mass spectrometer although
charge exchange with slow ions is used instead of electron impact.   After
preliminary work (9, 23), the method was fully developed by Szabo
(20, 21, 22).

In the first investigation (20), ethylene in the collision chamber was
bombarded with positive ions, and the intensities of the fragment ions,
obtained after the charge exchange, were recorded.   The mass spectra
were thus not normalized.   At low pressure only "primary" ions were
observed that were formed from ethylene in the charge exchange, but at
higher pressures also "secondary" and "tertiary" ions were obtained
as a result of ion-molecule reactions between the primary ions and the
ethylene molecules in the collision chamber.

In Figure 4 the logarithm of the observed ion intensities was plotted
as a function of the logarithm of the pressure in the collision chamber.
As the intensity of a product ion of a certain order increases propor-
tionally to the same power of the pressure, the curves in the diagram
corresponding to primary, secondary, and tertiary ions are represented
by straight lines of slopes equal to 1, 2, and 3, respectively.   Measurements were performed with 11 incident ions with different recombina-

tion energies.   The energy absorbed by the molecule was known in each case so that the results could be plotted as a function of this energy in Figure 5.

Figure 5 shows that at low absorbed energy $C_2H_4^+$ is primary and $C_2H_3^+$ and $C_2H_2^+$ are secondary ions, but at higher energy $C_2H_3^+$ and

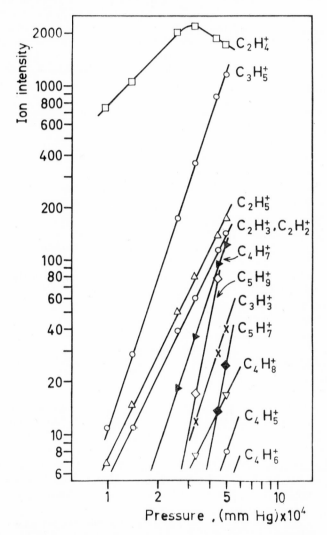

Figure 4.   Logarithmic ion intensity-pressure graph of ethylene obtained by bombarding with H_2S^+ of low kinetic energy

From the slopes it follows that $C_2H_4^+$ is primary; $C_2H_5^+$, $C_2H_3^+$, $C_2H_2^+$, and $C_4H_8^+$ are secondary; $C_3H_5^+$, $C_4H_7^+$, $C_3H_3^+$, $C_4H_5^+$, and $C_4H_6^+$ are tertiary; $C_5H_9^+$ and $C_5H_7^+$ are quaternary ions

$C_2H_2{}^+$ are primary and $C_2H_4{}^+$ is a secondary ion. It is difficult to observe such secondary ions in an electron impact mass spectrometer since they are hidden behind the primary ions. The reaction paths can often be determined directly from the unambiguous information in Figure 5. An important result is that the fragment ion $C_2H_2{}^+$ seems to be formed in an excited state above 20 e.v. This explains the form of the breakdown graph of ethylene (Figure 6), in which the $C_2H_2{}^+$ curve has a second maximum above this energy.

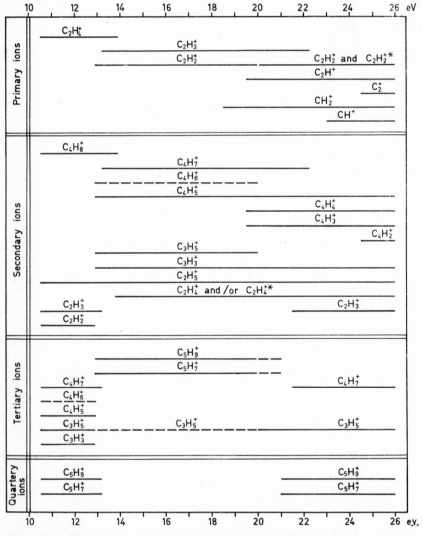

Figure 5. The nature of the product ions from ethylene as a function of the energy absorbed by the molecule during the charge exchange (20). (A dotted line has been used where the mode of formation is uncertain)

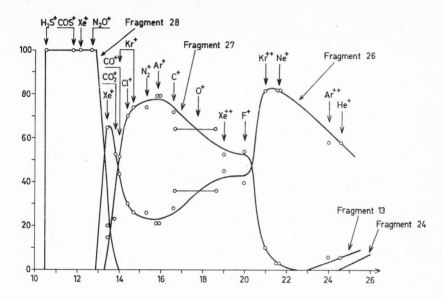

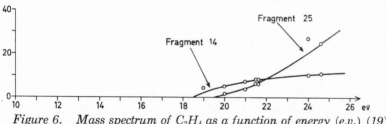

Figure 6. Mass spectrum of C_2H_4 as a function of energy (e.v.) (19)

A similar investigation of methane (*21*) has shown that between 15.5 and about 20 e.v. the fragment ion CH_2^+ is formed in the ground state, but above 20 e.v. in an excited state that can cause ion-molecule reactions of different kind.

Literature Cited

Perpendicular Type Apparatus

STOCKHOLM, SWEDEN

(1) Chupka, W. A., Lindholm, E., *Arkiv Fysik* **25**, 349 (1963).
(2) Gustafsson, E., Lindholm, E., *Arkiv Fysik* **18**, 219 (1960).
(3) Lindholm, E., *Z. Naturforsch.* **9a**, 535 (1954).
(4) Lindholm, E., *Arkiv Fysik* **8**, 257 (1954).
(5) Lindholm, E., *Arkiv Fysik* **8**, 433 (1954).
(6) Lindholm, E., *Bull. Soc. Chim. Belg.* **73**, 439 (1964).
(7) Lindholm, E., *Rev. Sci. Instr.* **31**, 210 (1960).
(8) Lindholm, E., Second International Conference on the Physics of Electronic and Atomic Collisions," p. 177, W. A. Benjamin, New York, 1961.
(9) Lindholm, E., Szabo, I., Wilmenius, P., *Arkiv Fysik* **25**, 417 (1963).
(10) Lindholm, E., Wilmenius, P., *Arkiv Kemi* **20**, 255 (1963).

(11) Pettersson, E., *Arkiv Fysik* **25,** 181 (1963).
(12) Pettersson, E., Lindholm, E., *Arkiv Fysik* **24,** 49 (1963).
(13) Sjögren, H., *Arkiv Fysik* **29,** 565 (1965).
(14) Sjögren, H., *Arkiv Fysik* **31,** 159 (1966).
(15) Sjögren, H., *Physics Letters* **19,** 210 (1965).
(16) Sjögren, H., *Arkiv Fysik,* in press.
(17) Sjögren, H., *Arkiv Fysik,* in press..
(18) Sjögren, H., Lindholm, E., *Arkiv Fysik,* **32,** 275 (1966).
(19) Szabo, I., *Arkiv Fysik* **31,** 287 (1966).
(20) Szabo, I., *Arkiv Fysik,* in press.
(21) Szabo, I., to be published.
(22) Szabo, I., to be published.
(23) Von Koch, H., *Arkiv Fysik* **28,** 529 (1965).
(24) Von Koch, H., *Arkiv Fysik* **28,** 559 (1965).
(25) Von Koch, H., to be published.
(26) Von Koch, H., Lindholm, E., *Arkiv Fysik* **19,** 123 (1961).
(27) Wilmenius, P., Lindholm, E., *Arkiv Fysik* **21,** 97 (1962).

Moscow, U.S.S.R.

(28) Frankevich, E. L., Tal'roze, V. L., *Pribory i Tekhnika Eksperimenta* **2,** 48 (1957).
(29) Lavrovskaya, G. K., Markin, M. I., Tal'roze, V. L., *Kinetika i Kataliz* **2,** 21 (1961).
(30) Tal'roze, V. L., *Izv. Akad. Nauk SSSR* **24,** 1001 (1960).
(31) Tal'roze, V. L., *Pure Appl. Chem.* **5,** 455 (1962).
(32) Tal'roze, V. L., *et al.*, *Pribory i Tekhnika Eksperimenta* **6,** 78 (1960).

San Diego, Cal.

(33) Fite, W. L., Brackman, R. T., Snow, W. R., *Phys. Rev.* **112,** 1161 (1958).
(34) Stebbings, R. F., Smith, A. C. H., Erhardt, H., *J. Chem. Phys.* **39,** 968 (1963).
(35) Stebbings, R. F., Smith, A. C. H., Erhardt, H., *J. Geophys. Res.* **69,** 2349 (1964).

Birmingham, England

(36) Homer, J. B., Lehrle, R. S., Robb, J. C., Takahasi, M., Thomas, D. W., *Advan. Mass Spectrometry* **2,** 503 (1962).
(37) Homer, J. B., Lehrle, R. S., Robb, J. C., Thomas, D. W., *Nature* **202,** 795 (1964).
(38) Homer, J. B., Lehrle, R. S., Robb, J. C., Thomas, D. W., *Advan. Mass Spectrometry* **3,** 415 (1966).
(39) Lehrle, R. S., Robb, J. C., Thomas, D. W., *J. Sci. Instr.* **39,** 458 (1962).

Strasbourg, France

(40) Abbe, J. C., Adloff, J. P., *C. R. Acad. Sci. Paris* **258,** 3003 (1964).

Baltimore, Md.

(41) Berta, M. A., Koski, W. S., *J. Am. Chem. Soc.* **86,** 5098 (1964).
(42) Hertel, G. R., Koski, W. S., *J. Am. Chem. Soc.* **86,** 1683 (1964).
(43) Hertel, G. R., Koski, W. S., *J. Am. Chem. Soc.* **87,** 404 (1965).
(44) Hertel, G. R., Koski, W. S., *J. Am. Chem. Soc.* **87,** 1686 (1965).
(45) Weiner, E. R., Hertel, G. R., Koski, W. S., *J. Am. Chem. Soc.* **86,** 788 (1964).

Longitudinal Type Apparatus

Chicago, Ill.

(46) Giese, C. F., Maier, W. B., *J. Chem. Phys.* **35,** 1913 (1961).
(47) Giese, C. F., Maier, W. B., *J. Chem. Phys.* **39,** 739 (1963).
(48) Giese, C. F., Maier, W. B., *J. Chem. Phys.* **39,** 197 (1963).
(49) Maier, W. B., *J. Chem. Phys.* **41,** 2174 (1964).
(50) Maier, W. B., *J. Chem. Phys.* **42,** 1790 (1965).

San Diego, Cal.

(51) Stebbings, R. F., Turner, B. R., Rutherford, J. A., *J. Geophys. Res.* **71,** 771 (1966).

Gainesville, Fla.

(52) Vance, D. W., Bailey, T. L., *J. Chem. Phys.* **44,** 486 (1966).

Investigations of Angular Distributions

(53) Bailey, T. L., Champion, R. L., Doverspike, L. D., Leventhal, J. J., IVth International Conference on the Physics of Electronic and Atomic Collisions, 1965.
(54) Turner, B. R., Fineman, M. A., Stebbings, R. F., *J. Chem. Phys.* **42**, 4088 (1965).

Further Literature

(55) Boersch, H., Geiger, J., *et al.*, *Z. Physik* **180**, 415 (1964) and *J. Chem. Phys* **43**, 4535 (1965).
(56) Bowman, C. R., Miller, W. D., *J. Chem. Phys.* **42**, 681 (1965).
(57) Edlén, B., *Kungl. Svenska Vetenskapsakad. Handl.* [3] **20**, No. 10 (1943).
(58) Erhardt, H., Linder, F., Meister, G., *Z. Naturforsch.* **20a**, 989 (1965).
(59) Fiquet-Fayard, F., *J. Chim. Phys.* **54**, 274 (1957), **57**, 453 (1960).
(60) Hagstrum, H. D., *Phys. Rev.* **104**, 309 (1956).
(61) Heideman, H. G. M., Kuyatt, C. E., Chamberlain, G. E., *J. Chem. Phys.* **44**, 440 (1966).
(62) Lassettre, E. N., *et al.*, *J. Chem. Phys.* **40**, 1208 (1964); **40**, 1271 (1964); **42**, 395 (1965); **42**, 3429 (1965); **42**, 3436 (1965).
(63) Lipeles, M., Novick, R., Tolk, N., *Phys. Rev. Letters* **15**, 815 (1965).
(64) Martin, W. C., *J. Opt. Soc. Am.* **49**, 1071 (1959).
(65) Moore, C. E., *Nat. Bur. Std., Circ.* **467**, (1949, 1952, and 1958).
(66) Schulz, G. J., *Phys. Rev.* **112**, 150 (1958); **116**, 1141 (1959).

RECEIVED April 29, 1966.

2

The Reaction $O^+ + N_2 \longrightarrow NO^+ + N$

CLAYTON F. GIESE

University of Minnesota, Minneapolis, Minn. 55455

The cross-section for the reaction, $O^+ + N_2 \to NO^+ + N$, as a function of the ion energy, has a maximum of about 4×10^{-16} sq. cm. at 10 e.v. and falls off for higher or lower ion energies. The low energy fall-off of the cross-section explains the persistence of O^+ ions in the ionosphere but is a puzzling and unexpected result. Some very tentative reasons for this fall-off are suggested.

The reaction $O^+ + N_2 \to NO^+ + N$ has until recently presented a great problem in understanding the ionosphere. Since the question has been adequately reviewed (6, 19), I will briefly sketch the nature of the problem. A theory (9, 13) for ion-molecule reaction cross-sections based on a classical trajectory governed by the classical electrostatic potential between an ion and a polarizable neutral gives a cross-section for intimate collisions varying as the reciprocal of ion velocity. Assuming that this reaction, which is highly exothermic (1.1 e.v. or 25 kcal./mole), proceeds whenever the reactants interact strongly, one expects a reaction cross-section which increases at low energies as $E^{-1/2}$, giving a rate constant which is large and independent of temperature. Using this predicted reaction rate or some earlier measured rates, one could calculate the time of removal of O^+ ions after sundown—i.e., after they are no longer produced by photoionization. Estimates differ according to just which N_2 concentration is used, but the O^+ ions on this basis should disappear in about 1 hour; instead, they persist all night. This puzzling disagreement has motivated a number of studies of the reaction $O^+ + N_2 \to NO^+ + N$. This report describes one such study.

Measurement

The apparatus used, as described previously (7), has modifications as described by Maier (16). A description also appears in this volume (15). A mass spectrometer of special design with 2-inch round poles, using 90° deflection with 1-inch magnetic radius, provides momentum-selected beams of low energy ions. These ions proceed at full energy or with moderate retardation into a differentially pumped reaction chamber. Emerging ions, either unreacted primary ions or secondary ions formed in reactions, pass into a second mass spectrometer of fairly standard design, a 60° sector field instrument with 12-inch magnetic radius.

A cross-section for a given reaction is determined from the formula:

$$\sigma(E) = \frac{I_s}{I_p n l} \left(\frac{A_s}{A_p}\right) K_1 K_2 \tag{1}$$

where I_s is the current of secondary ions, I_p the current of primary ions, n the number of target molecules per cc. determined by measuring the pressure of the target gas, l is the effective length of the reaction chamber. A_s is the area under a curve representing secondary ion intensity vs. a sweep voltage which deflects the ion beam across the entrance slit of the 12-inch mass spectrometer. This curve is normalized to unit intensity at its maximum. A_p is a similar quantity for the primary ions, and the ratio corrects the cross-section for the bias caused by the fact that the primary and secondary ions differ in their sharpness of focus. K_1 is the ratio of multiplier gain for primary ions to the gain for secondary ions. K_2 corrects for the fraction of secondary ions formed but not detected because they fail to emerge from the reaction chamber. The energy of the primary ions, E, is determined by a retardation technique (7).

For this reaction K_1 is 1.09, and A_s/A_p is readily measured, but the correction K_2 presents a real problem. Calculating this factor requires some assumption about the angular distribution of the product ions. Previous measurements of exothermic cross-sections (7) used a factor of K_2 calculated by assuming isotropy of the product angular distribution in the barycentric system. Measurement of endothermic cross-sections using a different reaction chamber (Figure 1 of Ref. 16) have been corrected by assuming that the secondary ion is highly forward-directed as it will be for an endothermic process near threshold. For these the factor K_2 is taken to be unity. The chamber used in this measurement is that described by Maier (16). Thus, the "pressure-length correction factor" of 2.09, essentially a factor which corrects for the pressure drop in the reaction zone compared with the pressure measured at a tap on the side, should apply. The shape of $\sigma(E)$ vs. E for this reaction is like that for the endothermic reactions of Maier (16), and until the angular distribution of NO^+ has been measured, K_2 is assumed to equal 1.

It is difficult to produce low energy beams of O^+ ions. All oxygen-containing gases seem to degrade the performance of a low energy ion source. Further, O_2 is a poor source of low energy O^+ ions because a substantial fraction of the ions is formed with appreciable kinetic energy (10). The best source gas proved to be carbon dioxide, which was used for most of the measurements.

An additional difficulty, especially noticeable when the product ion, NO^+ in this case, has a stable neutral counterpart is the presence of background ions. The vacuum pump used in this experiment, a titanium sputter pump, produced a background of NO^+ ions which were particularly bothersome at low energies where intensities of real secondaries were low.   Future attempts to study the reaction will use a mercury diffusion pump.

Results

The results obtained for the cross-section of the reaction O^+ + $N_2 \rightarrow NO^+ + N$ are shown in Figure 1.   The scatter of experimental points shows the measuring difficulties, particularly the problem of correcting for background NO^+ ions.   Numbers of the points included in Figure 1 are thought to be low but could not be discarded with

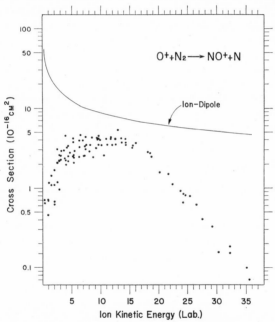

Measured cross-section for the reaction O^+ + $N_2 \rightarrow NO^+ + N$, compared with a theory (7) based on classical trajectories subject to an ion-induced dipole potential.   The assumptions involved in calculating the measured cross-sections are noted in the text

confidence.   The most probable curve of σ (E) vs. E would skirt the upper points shown.   The ionizing electron energy was varied from near threshold for O^+ formation, to 15 e.v. above threshold without any noticeable effect.   Therefore, there was no evidence for any importance of excited states of O^+, but this conclusion is weak because the combination of low electron energy *and* ion energy presents great experimental difficulties owing to the low intensities.

It is essential to remember the assumption that $K_2 = 1$. If the actual angular distribution of NO^+ ions in the laboratory system is widespread, the true cross-section could be larger than the values of Figure 1 by a factor of 2 or 3. Determining the angular distribution of NO^+ ions from this reaction is a most important area for future work. Measurement of angular distributions from ion reactions has just begun (1, 22).

The curve marked "ion-dipole" is based on the classical cross-section corresponding to trajectories which lead to intimate encounters (9, 13). The measured cross-sections differ more dramatically from the predictions of this theory than previously measured cross-sections for exothermic reactions (7). The fast fall-off of the cross-section at high energy is quite close to the theoretical prediction ($E^{-5.5}$) (2) based on the assumption of a direct, impulsive collision and calculation of the probability that two particles out of three will stick together. The meaning of this is not clear, however, since neither the relative masses of the particles nor the energy is consistent with this theoretical assumption. This behavior is, however, probably understandable in terms of competition of different exit channels on the basis of available phase space (24).

Turner et al. (23) have measured the cross-section for this reaction with a cross-beam apparatus using ion energies down to 4 e.v. These results are given in Table I. The agreement with the present results is gratifying in view of the uncertainties discussed above.

Table I.   Measured Cross-Section for the Reaction,[a]
$O^+ + N_2 \rightarrow NO^+ + N$

Ion Energy e.v.	Cross-Section 10^{-16} sq. cm.
4	2.4
8	4
10	4.4
15	5
20	3.8
25	1.2

[a] Turner et al. state that these cross-sections have an uncertainty of a factor of ca. 2 or 3 (23).

Paulson (18), using a single mass spectrometer in which the ions are produced and react in a single chamber, has studied the reaction $O^+ + N_2 \rightarrow NO^+ + N$. From the averaged cross-section, at different ion repeller voltages, one can extract a cross-section at definite ion energies (14). The results for this reaction are qualitatively like those in Figure 1 but with a larger maximum cross-section (17.5×10^{-16} sq. cm) occurring at an energy of 7 e.v. and more sharply peaked at this energy. Comparing this type of experiment with a cross-beam experiment is difficult since it depends on knowing the exact potential distribution in the ion source. However, the fact that Paulson finds a low energy dropoff in the cross-section is important because while a low energy backward-directed product could escape detection in a cross-beam experiment, it would not escape detection in an experiment with an ion chamber having a drawout field.

A low energy drop-off in the cross-section is also consistent with recent afterglow measurements of the apparent rate constant (4), 3×10^{-12} cc. sec.$^{-1}$, which is well below the predicted $(9, 13)$ ion-dipole rate, 9.7×10^{-10} cc. sec.$^{-1}$

Earlier measurements using a variety of techniques are summarized by Paulson (19) and Ferguson et al. (6). There seems to be no doubt now about the fall-off of the cross-section at low energies. This "window" for low energy O$^+$ ions explains their persistence in the ionosphere, but it remains a theoretical puzzle.

Further Discussion

The high energy behavior of the cross-section for this reaction—i.e., its rapid fall-off—can be explained by assuming that different exit channels compete on the basis of available phase space (24). The low energy behavior presents a greater mystery. Further possible reasons for this behavior are discussed below.

Consider first the states of the reactants and the products:

$$O^+(^4S) + N_2(^1\Sigma) \rightarrow NO^+(^1\Sigma) + N(^4S) \tag{2}$$

There does not seem to be any selection rule such as conservation of spin or orbital angular momentum which this reaction does not satisfy. It is also not clear that overall spin conservation, for example, is necessary in efficient reactions $(5, 16, 17, 20)$. Further, recent results (21) seem to show a greatly enhanced (20 times) reaction rate when the N_2 is in an excited vibrational state (vibrational temperature 4000 °K. or about 0.3 e.v.). This suggests the presence of an activation energy or barrier. A barrier of 0.3 e.v. is consistent with the low energy variation of the measured cross-section in Figure 1.

The possibility of a barrier which inhibits a reaction in spite of the attractive ion-dipole potential suggests that one should make even crude attempts to guess the properties of the potential hypersurface for ion reactions. Even a simple model for the long range behavior of the potential between neutrals (the "harpoon model") appears promising as a means to understand alkali beam reactions (11). The possibility of resonance interaction either to aid or hinder reactions of ions with neutrals has been suggested (8). The effect of possible resonance interaction on cross-sections of ion-molecule reactions has been calculated (25). The resonance interaction would be relatively unimportant for Reaction 2 because the ionization potential for O (13.61 e.v.) is so different from that for N_2 (15.56 e.v.). A case in which this resonance interaction should be strong and attractive is Reaction 3:

$$O^+(^4S) + CO_2(^1\Sigma) \rightarrow O_2^+(^2\pi) + CO(^1\Sigma) \tag{3}$$

because the ionization potential of CO_2 (13.79 e.v.) is just slightly greater than that of O. This reaction is fast $(5, 20)$ despite the fact that it does not conserve spin.

The behavior of the potential between ion and neutral at closer range, where molecular binding begins, may be decisive in determining whether or not a reaction will be fast. In particular, if the ion and neutral can combine to form the ground electronic state or a low lying state of that molecular ion which is the intermediate state, then they may follow an adiabatic potential curve which is strongly attractive. Of course, these intermediate states are almost always species about which nothing is known. Reaction 2 is unusual in that there is information about N_2O^+ (3). Suppose the reaction is written as follows:

$$O^+(^4S) + N_2(^1\Sigma) \rightarrow N_2O^+(^2\pi) \rightarrow NO^+ + N \tag{4}$$

At sufficient distance, it may be valid to regard the $^1\Sigma$ molecule as acting like a ^1S atom. Then, the Wigner-Witmer correlation rule (12) on spin says that the intermediate in this case cannot be formed from the reactants, nor can the other known (3) state of N_2O^+, $^2\Sigma$. The potential between the reactants may well be repulsive for distances down to some value where a crossing occurs with an attractive potential curve, this attractive curve connecting asymptotically with energy levels of the reactants in states of proper symmetry. This situation would produce a barrier to reaction. Seemingly, the barrier is low, and the reaction proceeds at moderate ion energies (Figure 1) or when the N_2 molecules are vibrationally excited (21). By contrast, consider Reaction 5:

$$N^+(^3P) + NO(^2\pi) \rightarrow N_2O^+(^2\pi) \rightarrow NO^+(^1\Sigma) + N(^4S) \tag{5}$$

Here the reactants can combine to form the ground state of the supposed intermediate. Since the ionization potentials of N (14.54 e.v.) and NO (9.25 e.v.) are very different, any resonance force of the type suggested by Giese (8) will be repulsive but weak. Thus, there should be no barrier to reaction (7), and it is known to be fast at low ion energies (23).

Whether or not $O^+(^2D)$ ions undergo fast reaction with N_2 at low energies is of great interest since they satisfy both rules. Unfortunately, the experimental evidence is not decisive. The resonance potential (8) in this case would be repulsive but weak since the ionization potential of O to this state, 16.94 e.v., is considerably greater than that of N_2, 15.56 e.v. The resonance potential may be strong enough to inhibit reaction of $O^+(^2D)$ ions at low energies.

These ideas are speculative only and cannot be considered conclusive until other cases are tested. Unfortunately, information on states of polyatomic ions is meager. Two ions which have been studied are CO_2^+ and CS_2^+, both of which have $^2\pi$ ground states and $^2\Sigma$ excited states. It would be interesting to look for ion-neutral reactions having these ions as possible intermediates.

Another possible reaction intermediate is NO_2^+. This is isoelectronic with CO_2, and one might guess its ground state to be $^1\Sigma$. We then have

$$O^+(^4S) + NO(^3\pi) \rightarrow NO_2^+(^1\Sigma) \rightarrow NO^+ + O \tag{6}$$

Here the combination of the reactants to form the intermediate violates both the spin rule and the orbital angular momentum rule. This reaction appears to be slow at low ion energy (23). Consider Reaction 7:

$$N^+(^3P) + O_2(^3\Sigma) \rightarrow NO_2^+(^1\Sigma) \rightarrow NO^+ + O. \qquad (7)$$

The spin rule is satisfied, but the orbital angular momentum rule is not. The reaction is apparently fast at low ion energies (4); hence, if there is an important selection rule in the combination of reactants, it is seemingly the spin rule. Conservation of spin in combining reactants is probably more likely than conservation of orbital angular momentum, since the latter will be more strongly coupled to collision angular momentum.

In conclusion, it is suggested that a spin combination rule may be an important criterion in determining whether or not reactants may follow an adiabatic, potential curve corresponding to a low lying state of an intermediate. This, in turn, may determine whether or not there will be strong attraction or weak, or even a barrier preventing fast reaction at low energy.

Acknowledgments

The research was supported jointly by the National Science Foundation and Office of Aerospace Research, U.S.A.F. Experimental results were obtained at the University of Chicago, Department of Physics.

Literature Cited

(1) Bailey, T. L., Champion, R. L., Doverspike, L. D., and Leventhal, J. J., International Conference on the Physics of Electronic and Atomic Collisions, 4th, 1965.
(2) Bates, D. R., Cook, C. J., Smith, F. J., Proc. Phys. Soc. 83, 49 (1964).
(3) Callomon, J. H., Proc. Chem. Soc. 1959, 313.
(4) Fehsenfeld, F. C., Schmeltekopf, A. L., Ferguson, E. E., National Bureau of Standards, Boulder, Colo., private communication.
(5) Fehsenfeld, F. C., Ferguson, E. E., Schmeltekopf, A. L., J. Chem. Phys. 44, 3022 (1966).
(6) Ferguson, E. E. et al., J. Geophys. Res. 70, 4323 (1965).
(7) Giese, C. F., Maier, W. B., J. Chem. Phys. 39, 739 (1963).
(8) Giese, C. F., Advan. Mass Spectroscopy 3, 321 (1966).
(9) Gioumousis, G., Stevenson, D. P., J. Chem. Phys. 29, 294 (1958).
(10) Hagstrum, H. D., Rev. Mod. Phys. 23, 185 (1951).
(11) Herschbach, D. R., Appl. Opt. Suppl. 2, 128 (1965).
(12) Herzberg, G., "Molecular Spectra and Molecular Structure," Vol. I, 2nd Ed., p. 315, D. Van Nostrand Co., Inc., New York, 1950.
(13) Langevin, P., Ann. Chim. Phys. 5, 245 (1905).
(14) Light, J. C., J. Chem. Phys. 41, 586 (1964).
(15) Lindholm, E., ADVAN. CHEM. SER. 58, 1 (1964).
(16) Maier, W. B., J. Chem. Phys. 42, 1790 (1965).
(17) Maier, W. B., J. Chem. Phys. 41, 2174 (1964).
(18) Paulson, J. F., Air Force Cambridge Research Laboratories, Bedford, Mass., private communication.
(19) Paulson, J. F., Ann. Geophys. 20, 75 (1964).
(20) Paulson, J. F., Mosher, R. L., Dale, F., J. Chem. Phys. 44, 3025 (1966).
(21) Schmeltekopf, A. L., Fehsenfeld, F. C., Gilman, G. I., Ferguson, E. E., "Abstracts of Papers," 18th Annual Gaseous Electronics Conference, Minneapolis, Minn., October 1965.

(22) Turner, B. R., Fineman, M. A., Stebbings, R. F., *J. Chem. Phys.* **42,** 4088
    (1965).
(23) Turner, B. R., Rutherford, J. A., Stebbings, R. F., "Abstracts of Papers,"
    18th Annual Gaseous Electronics Conference, Minneapolis, Minn., October
    1965.
(24) Wolf, F. A., *J. Chem. Phys.* **44,** 1619 (1966).
(25) Wolf, F. A., *Bull. Am. Phys. Soc.* **11,** 68 (1966).

RECEIVED May 16, 1966.

3

Some Negative Ion Reactions in Simple Gases

J. F. PAULSON

Air Force Cambridge Research Laboratories, Office of Aerospace Research, Bedford, Mass.

Reactions of D^- with D_2O and of O^- with O_2, N_2O, and NO_2 have been studied with a magnetic sector mass spectrometer. Competition between electron transfer and ion-atom interchange has been observed in the production of O_2^- by reaction of O^- with O_2, an endothermic reaction. The negative ion of the reacting neutral molecule is formed in O_2, N_2O, and NO_2 but not in D_2O. Rate constants have been estimated as a function of repeller potential.

Although low energy, positive ion-neutral collision reactions have been studied extensively during recent years, little is known of the reactions of even the simplest negative ions. This gap in our knowledge is caused largely by the relatively low negative ion currents available from conventional electron bombardment ion sources, reflecting the low two-body electron attachment cross-sections of most gases.

Nevertheless, in weakly ionized gases with predominantly thermal electrons, the loss of electrons by three-body attachment becomes an important process relative to molecular ion-electron recombination at pressures even below 1 torr. Charge transfer and ion-atom interchange reactions of these primary negative ions lead to the creation of different negative (and neutral) species, which, together with the primary negative ions, are ultimately destroyed by such processes as ion-ion recombination and associative detachment. The importance of negative ions in systems of chemical interest is most easily assessed if prior knowledge of the rates of these several reactions is available. This paper describes recent studies of the charge transfer and ion-atom interchange reactions of D^- and O^- ions with some simple molecules of interest, particularly in the chemistry of the lower ionosphere.

Experimental

The reactions were studied with a 6-inch 60°-sector mass spectrometer. The ion source is of the Nier type (*11*), machined from a block of stainless steel and equipped with narrow electron entrance and ion exit slits so that relatively high source pressures can be maintained.   The electron beam, produced by an emission regulated rhenium filament, enters the source through a 1.17 × 0.15 mm. slit, and except for some of the experiments involving D^- ions, is collimated by a 200-gauss magnetic field.   The beam passes midway between the repeller plate and the ion exit slit and impinges on a trap maintained at the source potential.   The electron current measured with a positive bias on the trap is 1 × 10^{-7} A.   The repeller forms one side of the source chamber and is 4.0 mm from the exit slit.   Gas enters the source behind the repeller plate and must collide many times with the walls before reaching the region of the electron beam.   The source block is maintained at 200° ± 10°C.   Ions exit from the source through a 7.15 × 0.114-mm. slit and are accelerated by a potential of 3500 volts.   The ion-accelerating region is evacuated with a 2-inch mercury diffusion pumping system which maintains this region at a pressure two orders of magnitude below that in the source chamber itself.   The analyzer is evacuated with a 6-inch mercury diffusion pumping system, maintaining a pressure below 1 × 10^{-6} torr when the pressure in the source is as high as 0.2 torr.   Ion currents are measured with an electron multiplier whose gain has been calibrated with the aid of a Faraday cup for all species reported here except N_2O^-, for which the gain is assumed to be the same as for NO_2^-.

Pressure in the source is measured with a micromanometer connected to the gas inlet line following a variable leak.   The micromanometer has been calibrated against molecular number densities in the source determined by collecting on the repeller all positive ions produced in each of several gases of known ionization cross-section (*14*) with an electron beam of known energy and intensity.   These calibrations agree to within 12% with pressure measurements made by connecting the micromanometer directly into the source chamber itself.

The mass spectrometer is equipped with an XY recorder and a motor-driven potentiometer on the ionizing voltage control, giving continuous traces of ion current as a function of electron energy.   Continuous traces are also obtained for ion current as a function of pressure.   For the studies described here, in which low electron energies were used, we had to adjust the nominal ionizing voltage as the repeller potential was varied so that the desired electron energy could be maintained.   Calibration curves obtained by observing the shift in the optimum nominal electron energy for production of O^- from CO_2 and in the half-width (full width at half maximum) of that peak are shown in Figures 1 and 2.   The electron energy scale has been normalized at a repeller potential of 1 volt to the electron energy, (8.2 e.v.), which Schulz (*18*) found to be optimum for CO_2 using a quasi-monochromatic electron beam.   The normalization involved increasing the nominal electron energy, read on a differential voltmeter, by 0.2 e.v.   The optimum electron energy for production of the O^- peak, whose onset was found by Schulz (*18*) to be 3.85 ± 0.1 e.v., is then 4.3 e.v. compared with Schulz's value of 4.4 e.v. and with 4.3 e.v. obtained by Rapp and Briglia (*13*).   The difference in optimum nominal electron energies for the two processes by which O^- is formed in CO_2 is independent of repeller potential (Figure 1).   The half-width increases from 1.6 e.v. at 1 volt to 3.4 e.v. at 16 volts repeller potential.

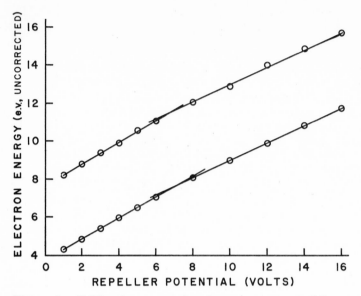

Figure 1.   Calibration curves for electron energy at different repeller potentials

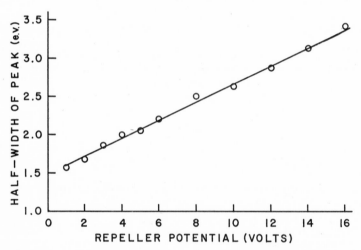

Figure 2.   Half-width of the O^- peak from CO_2 maximizing at an electron energy of 8.2 e.v., at different repeller potentials

Electron energies reported here are those obtained from the nominal values after correction with calibration curves shown in Figure 1.

Results

In this work the reacting negative ions were produced with electrons of low energy leading to resonance capture processes, rather than at higher energies where secondary electron capture and ion pair production occur. This method has the advantage that one ion species can be produced and its reactions studied largely to the exclusion of other processes possibly leading to the same product ion.   In order to obtain easily measurable ion currents, however, it was necessary to use electron energies above the capture threshold—a procedure which results in the products of the dissociative resonance capture process having kinetic energies above that of the ambient gas.   We assume that there is no spatial anisotropy in the velocity distributions of these products.   Initially then, negative ions produced at any point in the electron beam have velocity vectors whose envelope is a sphere.   If the repeller potential is sufficiently high, ions initially directed away from the plane of the exit slit are decelerated, their trajectories reversed, and finally accelerated toward the plane of the slit.   The ion residence time and path length in the source may be estimated if one assumes that the ion exit slit is infinitely thin and that the only ions collected are those whose initial motion is directed perpendicular to or away from the plane of the slit.   The average residence time, τ, for these ions is:

$$\tau = \frac{d}{V_r} \left[\frac{m}{e} \left(2E_i + V_r \right) \right]^{1/2} \tag{1}$$

and the average path length, λ is:

$$\lambda = \frac{d}{2V_r} \left(2E_i + V_r \right) \tag{2}$$

In Equations 1 and 2, d is the distance from repeller to exit slit, V_r is the repeller potential, E_i is the initial ion kinetic energy, and m/e is the mass-to-charge ratio of the ion.   Exact expressions for τ and λ for all the primary ions collected cannot be derived without information on the collection efficiencies for ions produced in the various regions of the source chamber, information not available for the type of source used here. Although data were taken over a range of repeller potentials, uncertainties in average residence times and in mass discrimination effects are more serious at low than at high V_r, and rate constants are therefore more reliable under the latter condition.   At repeller potentials high compared with the initial kinetic energy of the reacting ions, Equation 1 reduces to the usual expression for residence time of an initially thermal ion in a uniform electric field.

Discussion

D^- + D_2O.   Figure 3 shows the ion currents of D^-, O^-, and OD^- observed in D_2O as a function of electron energy.   Neither D_2O^- nor H_2O^- was observed.   The close similarity between the curves shown for D^- and OD^- suggests that the exothermic reaction

$$D^- + D_2O \rightarrow OD^- + D_2 \tag{3}$$

occurs.   This reaction has been suggested by Muschlitz (*10*).   The results of varying the pressure of D_2O are shown in Figure 4, where the currents of D^- and of OD^- vary with the first and second power, respectively, of pressure. The current of O^-, not shown, varied linearly with pressure. The electron energy used to produce the D^- ions, whose variation with pressure is shown in Figure 4, was 6.4 e.v.—i.e., the optimum energy shown in Figure 3. The initial kinetic energy with which these D^- ions are produced may be estimated from values of the electron affinity of D^- (assumed to be the same as that of H^- (12)) and the bond dissociation energy of D_2O (assumed to be the same as that of H_2O (8)) since, from conservation of energy and momentum:

$$E_i = (1 - \beta) [E_e - (D - A)] \qquad (4)$$

In Equation 4 E_i is the kinetic energy of the fragment ion; $\beta = m_i/M_o$ where m_i is the mass of the fragment ion, and M_o is the mass of the target molecule; E_e is the electron energy; D is the bond dissociation energy; and A is the electron affinity. Applying Equation 4 to the present case gives a value of $E_i = 1.9$ e.v. The residence time from Equation 1 is 2.14×10^{-7} sec. at $10V_r$. Rate constants for Reaction 3 derived from the relation:

$$k = \frac{i_2}{(i_1 + i_2)n_o\tau} \qquad (5)$$

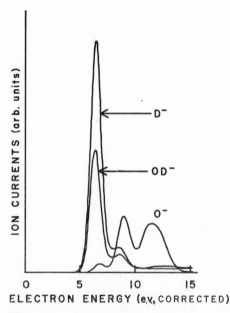

Figure 3. Ion currents of D^-, O^-, and OD^- from D_2O as functions of electron energy. The curves are traced from XY recordings and do not show relative intensities

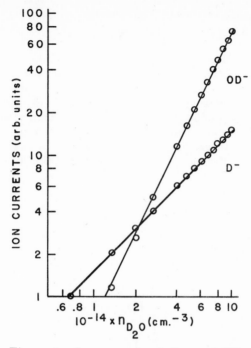

Figure 4. Ion currents of D^- and OD^- from D_2O as functions of D_2O number density, using an electron energy of 6.4 e.v.

are shown in Table I. In Equation 5, i_1 and i_2 are the ion currents of reactant and product ions, respectively, and n_o is the number density of reactant neutral species. Although mass discrimination effects are particularly troublesome for such low mass ions as D^- and may lead to erroneously large rate constants, it appears that Reaction 3 is very rapid, occurring essentially at every collision.

Table I. Rate Constants

Repeller Potential V_r	k (cc. molecule^{-1} sec.$^{-1}$) $\times 10^{11}$					
	Reaction 3	Reaction 6	Reaction 14	Reaction 18	Reaction 20	Reaction 22
4	454	1.7	3.4	0.20	103	1.8
5	466	2.3	3.6	0.23	119	2.0
6	463	3.0	3.7	0.24	130	2.0
7	468	4.3	3.5	0.27	128	2.1
8	457	5.6	3.7	0.34	130	2.3
9	433	6.4	3.6	0.44	122	2.4
10	380	7.6	3.6	0.55	119	2.7
11	375	8.7	3.5	0.63	131	2.9
12	364	9.3	3.6	0.74	143	3.3
13		10.8				
14		10.9				
15		12.1				

$O^- + O_2$. The reaction:

$$O^- + O_2 \rightarrow O_2^- + O \tag{6}$$

was suggested by Burch and Geballe (2) to explain their data from a pulsed Townsend discharge in oxygen.   Although Reaction 6 is endothermic by about 1 e.v., the production of O_2^- was observed in this work even at low repeller potentials probably because of the excess kinetic energy of O^- ions produced by dissociative electron attachment to O_2 at electron energies above threshold.   Figure 5 shows the data on O^- and O_2^- ion currents with varying electron energy.   The curves maximize at electron energies differing by about 1 e.v., reflecting the fact that Re-

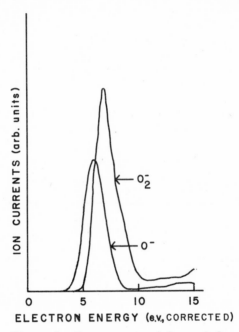

Figure 5.   Ion currents of O^- and O_2^- from O_2 as functions of electron energy. Traced from XY recordings

action 6 is endothermic and that O^- ions in the high energy end of the distribution react much more rapidly than those with lower kinetic energy. The possibility that O_2^- might be formed by the three-body attachment process

$$e + O_2 + O_2 \rightarrow O_2^- + O_2$$

as suggested by Muschlitz (10) rather than by Reaction 6, cannot be unequivocally eliminated since the same second power dependence of O_2^- ion current upon sample pressure (Figure 6) would be observed in either case.   However, it is extremely improbable that the optimum electron energy for the three-body attachment process would be as high as shown in Figure 5—i.e., 6.9 e.v.

The initial kinetic energy of O^- ions produced by dissociative attachment in O_2 at an electron energy of 6.9 e.v. may be determined from Equation 4 to be 1.64 e.v. using values of 1.465 e.v. (*1*) for $A(O)$ and 5.09 e.v. (*7*) for $D(O—O)$. The residence time for O^- ions calculated from Equation 1 is 6.0 $\times$ 10^{-7} sec. at 10 volts repeller potential. Rate constants for Reaction 6 determined from data at varying V_r are shown in Table I and are seen to increase sharply with increasing repeller potential, as expected for an endothermic process.

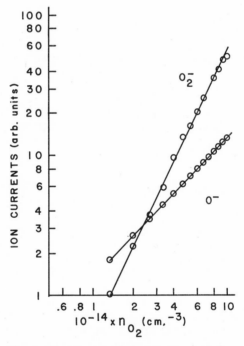

Figure 6. Ion currents of O^- and O_2^- from O_2 as functions of O_2 number density, using an electron energy of 6.9 e.v.

Reaction 6 might conceivably proceed through either an ion-atom interchange mechanism (Reaction 7) or a charge transfer mechanism (Reaction 8),

$$^{16}O^- + {}^{18}O_2 \rightarrow {}^{16}O\ {}^{18}O^- + {}^{18}O \tag{7}$$

$$^{16}O^- + {}^{18}O_2 \rightarrow {}^{18}O\ {}^{18}O^- + {}^{16}O \tag{8}$$

Using an equimolar sample mixture of $^{16}O_2$ and $^{18}O_2$, together with a small amount of ^{16}O ^{18}O impurity, the following set of reactions contributing to the ion-atom interchange mechanism must be considered:

$$^{16}O^- + {}^{16}O_2 \rightarrow {}^{16}O_2^- + {}^{16}O$$
$$^{18}O^- + {}^{18}O_2 \rightarrow {}^{18}O_2^- + {}^{18}O$$
$$^{16}O^- + {}^{18}O_2 \rightarrow {}^{16}O\ {}^{18}O^- + {}^{18}O$$
$$^{18}O^- + {}^{16}O_2 \rightarrow {}^{16}O\ {}^{18}O^- + {}^{16}O$$
$$^{16}O^- + {}^{16}O\ {}^{18}O \rightarrow {}^{16}O\ {}^{18}O^- + {}^{16}O$$
$$^{16}O^- + {}^{16}O\ {}^{18}O \rightarrow {}^{16}O_2^- + {}^{18}O$$
$$^{18}O^- + {}^{16}O\ {}^{18}O \rightarrow {}^{16}O\ {}^{18}O^- + {}^{18}O$$
$$^{18}O^- + {}^{16}O\ {}^{18}O \rightarrow {}^{18}O_2^- + {}^{16}O$$

The following set contribute to the charge transfer mechanism:

$$^{16}O^- + {}^{18}O_2 \rightarrow {}^{18}O_2^- + {}^{16}O$$
$$^{16}O^- + {}^{16}O_2 \rightarrow {}^{16}O_2^- + {}^{16}O$$
$$^{18}O^- + {}^{16}O_2 \rightarrow {}^{16}O_2^- + {}^{18}O$$
$$^{18}O^- + {}^{18}O_2 \rightarrow {}^{18}O_2^- + {}^{18}O$$
$$^{16}O^- + {}^{16}O^{18}O \rightarrow {}^{16}O^{18}O^- + {}^{16}O$$
$$^{18}O^- + {}^{16}O^{18}O \rightarrow {}^{16}O^{18}O^- + {}^{18}O$$

Realizing that the last four reactions of the ion-atom interchange mechanism listed each have only one-half the statistical probability of occurring as do the first four and assuming no isotope effect on the rate constants, we can write the following set of rate equations:

$$\frac{di_{34}}{dt} = k_1 i_{16} n_{36} + k_1 i_{18} n_{32} + \frac{1}{2} k_1 i_{16} n_{34} + \frac{1}{2} k_1 i_{18} n_{34} + k_2 i_{16} n_{34} + k_2 i_{18} n_{34} \quad (9)$$

$$\frac{di_{32}}{dt} = k_1 i_{16} n_{32} + \frac{1}{2} k_1 i_{16} n_{34} + k_2 i_{16} n_{32} + k_1 i_{18} n_{32} \quad (10)$$

$$\frac{di_{36}}{dt} = k_1 i_{18} n_{36} + \frac{1}{2} k_1 i_{18} n_{34} + k_2 i_{16} n_{36} + k_2 i_{18} n_{36} \quad (11)$$

In Equations 9, 10, and 11, i_j is the number density of the ionic species of $m/e = j$, and n_{32}, n_{34}, and n_{36} are the number densities of $^{16}O_2$, $^{16}O^{18}O$, and $^{18}O_2$, respectively, in the ion source. The rate constants are k_1 and k_2 for the ion-atom interchange and charge transfer mechanisms, respectively.

Assuming equal collection efficiencies for all ionic species, we found experimentally that $i_{16} \approx i_{18}$, $n_{32} \approx n_{36}$, and $n_{34} = 4.3 \times 10^{-2} n_{32}$ in the sample mixture. Realizing that at $t = 0$, $i_{32} = i_{34} = i_{36} = 0$, and that the consumption of reactant ions is negligible, we can write from Equation 9,

$$\frac{i_{34}}{i_{16}} = 2.043\ k_1 n_{32}\tau + 0.086\ k_2 n_{32}\tau \quad (12)$$

and from Equation 10

$$\frac{i_{32}}{i_{16}} = 1.0215\ k_1 n_{32}\tau + 2k_2 n_{32}\tau \quad (13)$$

For simplicity the residence times, τ, of $^{16}O^-$ and of $^{18}O^-$ are assumed to be equal here.   With Equations 12 and 13 it is now possible to determine the rate constants k_1 and k_2 at different V_r.   The results are shown in Table II and agree fairly well with the rate constants obtained using ordinary oxygen.   The ratios of the rate constants for the two mechanisms are constant in the range of repeller potentials from 7 to 12 volts.

Table II.   Rate Constants[a] for $O^- + O_2 \rightarrow O_2^- + O$

	Repeller Potential, V_3								
	4	5	6	7	8	9	10	11	12
Ion-Atom Interchange	0.7	0.9	1.2	1.5	1.8	1.9	2.1	2.2	2.2
Charge Transfer	2.5	3.1	3.9	4.4	5.1	5.5	5.9	6.4	6.6

[a] Rate constants given as: k (cc. molecule $^{-1}$ sec. $^{-1}$) $\times 10^{11}$

$O^- + N_2O$.   The high pressure negative ion mass spectrum of N_2O contains peaks at m/e 16, 30, 32, 44, and 46 in addition, of course, to the corresponding isotope peaks.   The currents of m/e 16 and m/e 30 as functions of electron energy are shown in Figure 7.   The data show only a small shoulder instead of a well defined peak in the current of O^- at electron energies below 1 e.v., as obtained by Schulz (*18*) and by Curran and Fox (*5*) using a quasi-monochromatic electron beam.   The electron current falls away rapidly in our source at energies below 1 e.v., and we have not attempted to correct the data for this effect.

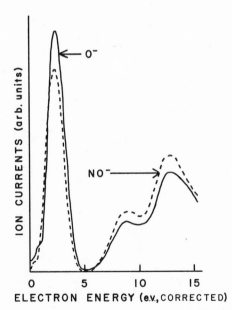

Figure 7.   Ion currents of O^- and NO^- from N_2O as functions of electron energy.   Traced from XY recordings

The dependence of the currents of m/e 16 and m/e 30 upon sample pressure, using an electron energy of 2.3 e.v., is shown in Figure 8.   The linear variation of m/e 16 and the quadratic variation of m/e 30 with pressure, together with the results shown in Figure 7, indicate the occurrence of Reaction 14.

$$O^- + N_2O \rightarrow NO^- + NO \qquad (14)$$

Reaction 14 is 1.0 e.v. exothermic.   Using equation 4, with E_e = 2.3 e.v., $D(N_2-O)$ = 1.68 e.v. (8), and $A(O)$ = 1.465 e.v. (1),   the initial kinetic energy of the O^- ions is calculated as 1.34 e.v.   However, Schulz (19) has shown that the kinetic energy of O^- ions from N_2O is independent. of electron energy in the range 1.5–3 e.v. and has the value 0.65 e.v. This unusual behavior is ascribed (19) to increasing vibrational excitation of the N_2 fragment with increasing electron energy.   Such behavior is possible in principle whenever an atomic ion is produced from a triatomic or larger parent.

Using a value of E_i = 0.65 e.v. (19), rate constants for Reaction 14 have been calculated and are shown in Table I.

A sample of $^{14}N^{15}NO$ was used to investigate whether Reaction 14 proceeds through a dissociative charge transfer mechanism involving an

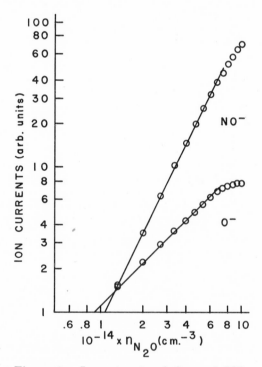

Figure 8.   Ion currents of O^- and NO^- from N_2O as functions of N_2O number density, using an electron energy of 2.3 e.v.

unstable intermediate (Reaction 15) or by abstraction of N by O^- (Reaction 16).

$$O^- + {}^{14}N^{15}NO \rightarrow (O^{14}N^{15}NO)^- \rightarrow {}^{14}NO^- + {}^{15}NO \quad \text{and}$$

$${}^{15}NO^- + {}^{14}NO \quad (15)$$

$$O^- + {}^{14}N^{15}NO \rightarrow {}^{14}NO^- + {}^{15}NO \quad (16)$$

The ratio of negative ion currents, i_{31}/i_{30}, was found to be 0.80 ± 0.05. Although production of $^{15}NO^-$ might occur partly by abstraction of the ^{15}N rather than the ^{14}N as shown in Reaction 16, this mechanism appears less probable than that indicated. We tentatively conclude that Reaction 15 predominates.

Reaction 14 has been proposed by others workers (*3*, *15*) to account for the NO^- observed in N_2O. It has also been suggested (*15*) that NO^- is formed in low abundance by dissociative attachment in N_2O at an electron energy of 25 e.v. Using values of $A(NO) = 0.9$ e.v. (*6*) and $D(N—NO) = 4.72$ e.v. (*8*) the minimum electron energy for this process is 4.07 e.v. In the experiments described here, a nominal electron energy of 2.9 e.v. was used. Although the energy spread is sufficiently large that some NO^- might be formed by the dissociative attachment reaction, our data do not indicate a process linear with pressure, producing NO^- at 2.9 e.v. in the pressure range investigated.

As mentioned above, negative ion currents at m/e 32, 44, and 46 were observed. The current at m/e 32 varied with the second power of the sample pressure and showed the same dependence upon electron energy as the m/e 16 current. The reaction:

$$O^- + N_2O \rightarrow O_2^- + N_2 \quad (17)$$

which has been suggested by Burtt and Henis (*3*), is exothermic by 2.4 e.v. The ion current ratio i_{32}/i_{16} increased rapidly with increasing repeller potential. The rate constants obtained in this work for Reaction 6 permit one to estimate the impurity level of O_2 required to produce the observed ion current of O_2^-. The result is that an O_2 impurity level of 1% would be sufficient. The observed O_2 impurity level in the positive ion spectrum is 0.8%. Therefore, the O_2^- observed here probably arises from Reaction 6 rather than Reaction 17.

The ion currents at m/e 44 and 46 were also directly related to the current at m/e 16 in their dependence upon electron energy. In a sample of $^{14}N^{15}NO$ these peaks shifted to m/e 45 and m/e 47, respectively, and are therefore ascribed to N_2O^- and NO_2^-. An approximately second-power pressure dependence of the ion current of N_2O^- was observed both in samples of N_2O alone and in an equimolar mixture of N_2O and O_2, and Reaction 18 is therefore suggested.

$$O^- + N_2O \rightarrow N_2O^- + O \quad (18)$$

Rate constants for this process are given in Table I. The electron affinity of N_2O is unknown. However the results indicate that the reaction is endothermic, and therefore the affinity of the state produced is less than that of O^-.

The origin of the NO_2^- observed is uncertain. Reaction 19, proposed by Burtt and Henis (3), is calculated to be exothermic by at least 0.5 e.v., assuming the electron affinity of NO_2 is ≥ 3.8 e.v. (4).

$$O^- + N_2O \rightarrow NO_2^- + N \tag{19}$$

Our data give a rate constant of 4×10^{-13} cc. molecule $^{-1}$ sec., $^{-1}$ assuming the production of NO_2^- solely by this reaction. However, one must consider the probability that NO_2, present as a minor impurity or produced by pyrolysis or N_2O of or near the hot filament, would react by Reaction 20.

$$O^- + NO_2 \rightarrow NO_2^- + O \tag{20}$$

Using a rate constant for the latter reaction of 1×10^{-9} cc. molecule^{-1} sec. $^{-1}$ (see below), it is estimated that the NO_2^- current observed could be explained by an NO_2 impurity level of 0.2%.

In an equimolar mixture of $^{14}N^{15}N^{16}O$ and $^{18}O_2$ run at an electron energy of 5.9 e.v.—i.e., the optimum energy for production of O^- from O_2, the negative ion current ratio, i_{18}/i_{16}, was found to be 4.06. The predominant negative ion above m/e 44 in this sample was m/e 45, $^{14}N^{15}N^{16}O^-$, indicating that Reaction 18 proceeds principally through a charge transfer mechanism. Ions observed at higher m/e are of ambiguous composition and do not permit elucidation of the origin of the NO_2^- observed. The positive ion spectrum showed no isotope exchange occurring in the sample mixture.

$O^- + NO_2$. Production of NO_2^- by Reaction 20

$$O^- + NO_2 \rightarrow NO_2^- + O \tag{20}$$

has been observed previously (4, 7), and its cross-section was estimated (7) to be 2.9 times larger than that of the positive ion-molecule reaction

$$H_2O^+ + H_2O \rightarrow H_3O^+ + OH \tag{21}$$

at a repeller field of 4 volts cm. $^{-1}$ Although the rate constant and energy dependence of Reaction 21 are the subjects of some question (16, 17, 20), the calculated rate constant for Reaction 20 is approximately 1×10^{-9} cc. molecule^{-1} sec.$^{-1}$ at low ion energies on the basis of these earlier results.

Figure 9 shows the ion currents of O^-, NO^-, O_2^- and NO_2^- as functions of electron energy observed in a sample of NO_2 at a number density of 3×10^{14} cc. $^{-1}$. The ion currents of both m/e 16 and m/e 30 varied linearly with sample pressure when the respective optimum electron energies shown in Figure 9 were used. The ion current of O_2^-, using the lower of the two optimum electron energies shown in Figure 9 (i.e., 2.2 e.v.) varied as the second power of the sample pressure whereas that at 5.2 e.v. varied linearly with pressure. The ion current of NO_2^- at an electron energy of 2.2 e.v. varied as the square of the sample pressure. These results are consistent with Reactions 20, 22, and 23.

$$O^- + NO_2 \rightarrow O_2^- + NO \tag{22}$$

$$e + NO_2 \rightarrow O_2^- + N \tag{23}$$

The O_2 impurity level was well below that required to produce the observed O_2^- by Reaction 6. Using Equation 4 and the values $D(NO—O)$ = 3.11 e.v. (8) and $A(O) = 1.465$ e.v. (1), the kinetic energy of O^- ions produced from NO_2 at an electron energy of 2.2 e.v. is 0.36 e.v. Rate constants for Reactions 20 and 22 calculated from the data at varying repeller potentials are shown in Table I. Attempts to elucidate the mechanisms of these reactions by using a sample of NO_2 and $^{18}O_2$ were unsuccessful because isotope exchange occurred in the sample reservoir. With increasing repeller potential there is increasing electron energy band width and therefore increasing overlap between the O_2^-

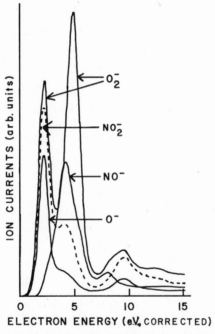

Figure 9. Ion currents of O^-, NO^-, O_2^-, and NO_2^- from NO_2 as functions of electron energy. Traced from XY recordings

peaks produced by Reactions 22 and 23. The data for Reaction 22 (Table I) have not been corrected for this effect. Corrections based on the variation of half-widths of peaks with varying repeller potential, shown in Figure 2, indicate that the estimated rate constants for Reaction 22 are independent of repeller potential.

The production of NO_2^- by charge transfer from either SF_6^- or SF_5^-, previously observed by Curran (4), has been confirmed during this work. The attachment cross-section curves for SF_6^- and for SF_5^- closely overlapped in the low energy range, and it was impossible to determine whether SF_6^- or SF_5^- was the reacting ion.

Conclusion

The work described here is preliminary in the sense that the rate constants obtained are averages over a wide range of interaction energies and may not apply to ions having well defined kinetic energies. The assumption of isotropic spatial distributions of the reactant and product ions may lead to seriously erroneous rate constants at low repeller potentials but becomes unnecessary at high repeller potentials. Similarly, the expression used to estimate ion residence times becomes more accurate at high repeller potentials. Finally, a high field strength ensures that anisotropic reactive scattering effects are minimized. Unfortunately, the width of the reactant ion kinetic energy distribution increases with increasing field strength, and defocusing of the ion beam also occurs, leading to decreased signal levels. However, except for Reaction 6, known to be endothermic, and Reaction 18, the rate constants obtained here show only a weak dependence upon repeller potential, the effect observed most probably being caused largely by a slowly varying ion collection efficiency. Nevertheless, it is clear that definitive tests of the dependence of these rate constants upon kinetic energy can only be carried out using ion beam techniques in which angular distributions of the products are measured.

Acknowledgements

The assistance of F. Dale and J. Welsh in performing the work described in this paper is gratefully acknowledged.

Literature Cited

(1) Branscomb, L. M., Burch, D. S., Smith, S. J., Geltman, S., *Phys. Rev.* **111**, 504 (1958).
(2) Burch, D. S., Geballe, R., *Phys. Rev.* **106**, 188 (1957).
(3) Burtt, B. P., Henis, J., *J. Chem. Phys.* **41**, 1510 (1964).
(4) Curran, R. K., *Phys. Rev.* **125**, 910 (1962).
(5) Curran, R. K., Fox, R. E., *J. Chem. Phys.* **34**, 1590 (1961).
(6) Farragher, A. L., Page, F. M., Wheeler, R. C., *Discuss. Faraday Soc.* **37**, 203 (1964).
(7) Henglein, A., Muccini, G. A., "Chemical Effects of Nuclear Transformations," pp. 89–98, International Atomic Energy Agency, Vienna, 1961.
(8) McBride, B. J., Heimel, S., Ehlers, J. G., Gordon, S., "Thermodynamic Properties to 6000°K. for 210 Substances Involving the First 18 Elements," NASA Scientific Publication SP-3001, Lewis Research Center, Cleveland, 1963.
(9) Moiseiwitsch, B. L., "Advances in Atomic and Molecular Physics," D. R. Bates ed., p. 61, Academic Press, New York, 1965.
(10) Muschlitz, E. E., *J. Appl. Phys.* **28**, 1414 (1957).
(11) Nier, A. O., *Rev. Sci. Instr.* **18**, 398 (1947).
(12) Pekeris, C. L., *Phys. Rev.* **126**, 1470 (1962).

(13) Rapp, D., Briglia, D. D., *J. Chem. Phys.* **43,** 1480 (1965).
(14) Rapp, D., Englander-Golden, P., *J. Chem. Phys.* **43,** 1464 (1965).
(15) Rudolph, P. S., Melton, C. E., Begun, G. M., *J. Chem. Phys.* **30,** 588 (1959).
(16) Ryan, K. R., Futrell, J. H., *J. Chem. Phys.* **42,** 824 (1965).
(17) Ryan, K. R., Futrell, J. H., *J. Chem. Phys.* **43,** 3009 (1965).
(18) Schulz, G. J., *Phys. Rev.* **128,** 178 (1962).
(19) Schulz, G. J., *J. Chem. Phys.* **34,** 1778 (1961).
(20) Tal'roze, V. L., Frankevich, E. L., *Zh. Fiz. Khim,* **34,** 2709 (1960).

RECEIVED May 13, 1966.

4

Vibrational Relaxation of Molecular Ions

H. SHIN

University of Nevada, Reno, Nev.

The vibrational relaxation of simple molecular ions M^+ in the M^+-M collision (where $M = O_2$, N_2, and CO) is studied using the method of distorted waves with the interaction potential constructed from the inverse power and the polarization energy. For M-M collisions the calculated values of the collision number required to de-excite a quantum of vibrational energy are consistently smaller than the observed data by a factor of 5 over a wide temperature range. For M^+-M collisions, the vibrational relaxation times of M^+ (τ^+) are estimated from $300°$ to $3000°K$. In both N_2 and CO, τ^+'s are smaller than τ's by 1-2 orders of magnitude whereas in O_2 τ^+ is smaller than τ less than 1 order of magnitude except at low temperatures.

In studying ion-molecule reactions it is important to know the details of energy transfer between translational and internal motions of the collision partners. In the charge transfer process (e.g., $O_2^+ + O_2 \rightarrow O_2 + O_2^+$), which is often a glancing one and occurs at comparatively large impact parameters except at high energies, in ion-neutral collisions in aftergrows, or in the ionosphere process (e.g., $N_2^+ + O_2 \rightarrow NO^+ + NO$), the molecular ions are probably found in vibrationally excited states (4,11,19,31,32). Since the states of both the reactant and product involve molecular ions, the collisional characteristics can be markedly different from reactions involving neutral molecules, owing to the enormous electric field near the ions. Since the fate of the ions and hence the overall process will depend upon the vibrational state of the molecular ions, it is important to evaluate the vibrational relaxation times or the number of collisions required for the molecular ions to return to the Boltzmann distribution for the given gas temperature. For example, in an electrical discharge in helium gas, the molecular ion He_2^+ may be formed in a vibrationally excited state, and the rate of dissociative recombination of $He_2^+ + e \rightarrow He + He$ may depend on the vibrational state. Similarly, since O_2^+ has an appreciably small internuclear distance (1.123 A.) compared with O_2 (1.207 A.), the ionization of O_2 will probably lead to a vibrationally excited molecular ion.

In recent years measurements of cross-sections for ion-molecule collisions have become one of the active fields in physics and chemistry, and continued efforts have led to ingenious experimental techniques. In spite of the concentrated effort in this area, relatively few theoretical studies deal with estimating the vibrational transition probabilities, relaxation times, or collision numbers for excited molecular ions (*29,31*). To gain a thorough insight into ion-molecule reactions, these collision quantities must be estimated from relevant interaction parameters. Our study deals with this aspect, extending our previous work (*29*) on the effect of the polarization energy on ion-molecule collisions to calculate the vibrational collision numbers of simple molecular ions and to estimate their vibrational relaxation times.

Vibrational Transition Probability

The main difference between a molecule-molecule (M-M) collision and an ion-molecule (M$^+$-M) collision is the presence of a polarization force in the latter system owing to the attraction between the static charge on M$^+$ and the dipole moment induced on M. For a large intermolecular separation, the polarization energy is known as

$$U_p(r) = -\frac{\alpha e^2}{2r^4} \tag{1}$$

where α is the angle-average polarization of M, e is the electronic charge, and r is the distance between centers of mass of the collision partners. The polarization energy can significantly increase the depth of the potential well between an ion and a molecule so that the relative kinetic energy is increased. Obviously, such a deep potential well will modify the slope of the repulsive part of the potential on which the probability of energy transfer depends. At present, however, the short range value of the polarization energy is not known; therefore, it is difficult to analyze the role of polarization forces in ion-molecule inelastic collisions, and this prevents us from evaluating the vibrational transition probabilities and related quantities with accuracy.

When Equation 1 is introduced into a typical intermolecular interaction energy potential such as a Morse type or an inverse power type, as a Lennard-Jones (LJ) potential, the resulting potential energy curve appears strongly repulsive with a deep attractive well at a close separation so that it may be used to describe M$^+$-M collisions. Therefore, we express the intermolecular interaction by introducing Equation 1 into an inverse power potential. The short range exponential potentials represent inelastic collisions well because strong repulsive terms give better insight into the collision than do inverse power potentials. However, as shown below the results of the inverse power potential can be reduced easily to those of the exponential potentials. The assumed form of the potential for this study is

$$U(r) = 4D\left[\left(\frac{\sigma}{r}\right)^{12} - \left(\frac{\sigma}{r}\right)^6\right] - \frac{\alpha e^2}{2r^4} \tag{2}$$

where $U_{LJ}(\sigma) = 0$, and D is the depth of the potential well of the 12-6 function. Although the inverse power function or the Lennard-Jones (LJ) 12-6 function is known to be inadequate for "close-in" inelastic collisions, it is the potential used most often for inelastic collisions in a thermal energy range because the perturbation integral for this potential is easy to evaluate (6,23,30). As discussed below this method evaluates the perturbation integral of the method of distorted waves essentially by considering only the collision partners close to each other where the repulsive interaction potential varies rapidly.

We consider a general inverse power potential function of the form

$$U(r) = \sum_{i=m,n,p\ldots} \frac{C_i}{r^i} \tag{3}$$

For the present 12-6-4 potential we then have $C_{12} = 4D\sigma^{12}$, $C_6 = -4D\sigma^6$, and $C_4 = -\alpha e^2/2$. The WKB evaluation of the perturbation integral of the method of distorted waves results in the (temperature) average transition probability in the form (29):

$$
\begin{aligned}
\mathbf{P} = \rho^2 \, & \frac{4\pi^2 m\hbar C_m{}^{3/2}}{M\epsilon^2} \sqrt{\frac{2m\pi\mu}{2+3m}} \left(\frac{\epsilon}{m+2}\right) \sqrt{\frac{2\mu}{C_m}} \frac{1}{\hbar}\right)^{\frac{3m+2}{m+2}} \sqrt{\frac{\chi_m}{kT}} \\[2mm]
& \times \exp\left[-\left(\frac{2+3m}{2+m}\right)\frac{\chi_m}{kT} - \sum_{i=n,p\ldots} \frac{\Gamma\!\left(\frac{1}{m}+1\right)\Gamma\!\left(\frac{1-i}{m}+\frac{3}{2}\right)}{\Gamma\!\left(\frac{1}{m}+\frac{3}{2}\right)\Gamma\!\left(\frac{1-i}{m}+1\right)} \right. \\[2mm]
& \times\left(\frac{C_i}{C_m{}^{i/m}}\right)\frac{\chi_m{}^{i/m}}{kT} + \sum_{i=n,p\ldots} \left\{ \left(\frac{m}{2+3m}\right) \left[\frac{\Gamma\!\left(\frac{1}{m}+2\right)\Gamma\!\left(\frac{1-i}{m}+\frac{5}{2}\right)}{\Gamma\!\left(\frac{1}{m}+\frac{3}{2}\right)\Gamma\!\left(\frac{1-i}{m}+1\right)} \right]^2 - \right. \\[2mm]
& \left(\frac{2-2i+3m}{4m}\right)\left[\frac{\Gamma\!\left(\frac{1}{m}+1\right)\Gamma\!\left(\frac{1-2i}{m}+\frac{3}{2}\right)}{\Gamma\!\left(\frac{1}{m}+\frac{3}{2}\right)\Gamma\!\left(\frac{1-2i}{m}+1\right)} \right]\right\}\left(\frac{C_i}{C_m{}^{i/m}}\right)^2\frac{\chi_m{}^{\frac{2i}{m}-1}}{kT} - \\[2mm]
& \sum_{i=n,p\ldots}\sum_{j\neq i\neq m} \left[\frac{\Gamma\!\left(\frac{1}{m}+1\right)\Gamma\!\left(\frac{1-i-j}{m}+\frac{5}{2}\right)}{\Gamma\!\left(\frac{1}{m}+\frac{3}{2}\right)\Gamma\!\left(\frac{1-i-j}{m}+1\right)} \right]\left(\frac{C_iC_j}{C_m{}^{\frac{i+j}{m}}}\right)\frac{\chi_m{}^{\frac{i+j-1}{m}}}{kT} + \frac{\epsilon}{2kT} \right]
\end{aligned}
\tag{4}
$$

where
ρ = $m_B/(m_A + m_B)$, if we express M by AB
μ = reduced mass of the collision partners
ϵ = magnitude of the change in the oscillator's energy owing to the transition, $h\nu$ (ν is the frequency of the oscillator)
M = "effective" reduced mass of the oscillator and

$$\chi_m = \left[\frac{\Gamma\left(\dfrac{1}{m} + \dfrac{3}{2}\right) \sqrt{2\pi\mu} \; \sigma \epsilon k T}{\Gamma\left(\dfrac{1}{m} + 1\right) m\hbar} \right]^{\frac{2m}{2+3m}}$$

For the 12-6-4 potential, this reduces to:

$$\mathbf{P} = 1.612\rho^2 \left(\frac{D^{1/7}\mu^{13/7}\epsilon^{5/7}}{M} \right) \left(\frac{\sigma}{\hbar} \right)^{12/7} \left(\frac{\chi}{kT} \right)^{1/2} \exp\left[-2.714\,\frac{\chi}{kT} + \right.$$

$$\left. 1.346\,\frac{\sqrt{D\chi}}{kT} + 0.254\left(\frac{\alpha e^2}{D^{1/3}\sigma^4}\right)\frac{\chi^{1/3}}{kT} + 0.362\,\frac{D}{kT} + \frac{\epsilon}{2kT} \right] \quad (5)$$

with

$$\chi = \left[\frac{\Gamma(^{19}/_{12})}{\Gamma(^{1}/_{12})} \; \frac{\sqrt{2\pi\mu}\;(4D)^{1/12}\sigma\epsilon kT}{\hbar} \right]^{12/19}$$

The time constant τ, appearing in the simplest frequency equation for the velocity and absorption of sound, is related to the transition probabilities for vibrational exchanges by $1/\tau = P_e - P_d$, where P_e is the probability of collisional excitation, and P_d is the probability of collisional de-excitation per molecule per second. Dividing P_d by the number of collisions which one molecule undergoes per second gives the transition probability per collision $\mathbf{P}$, given by Equation 4 or 5. The reciprocal of this quantity is the number of collisions Z required to de-excite a quantum of vibrational energy $\epsilon = h\nu$. This number can be explicitly calculated from Equation 4 since $Z \equiv 1/\mathbf{P}$, and it can be experimentally derived from the measured relaxation times.

Since there are no experimental values of Z for M^+-M collisions available at present, we first calculate Z for the M-M collisions for N_2, CO, and O_2 whose experimental values are well established (7,21). After establishing the usefulness of this approach for the M-M collisions, we then calculate the collision numbers for the M^+-M systems, Z^+.

Molecule-Molecule Collisions

For numerical illustrations we use the potential parameters (9,14) and vibrational frequencies (12) given in Table I.

In Figures 1–3 the calculated values of Z for M-M and for M^+-M are shown as (log Z *vs.* $T^{-7/19}$) for M = N_2, O_2, and CO, respectively. We will first discuss the M-M collisions.

From 500° to 760°K. the impact tube method of Huber and Kantrowitz (15) used nitrogen containing 0.05% water vapor. Their work on the relaxation of N_2 in water yields $\mathbf{P}(N_2 - H_2O)/\mathbf{P}(N_2 - N_2) = 1100$ at 560°K., and their data are smaller than the calculated values by a factor of 4. The values of Lukasik and Young (17) are obtained from the resonance method between 770° and 1190°K. using the sample containing <0.005% water. Their values at 1020° and 1186°K. agree well

Table I.   Potential Parameters and Vibrational Frequencies

$M^+ - M$	σ (A.)	D/k (°K.)	α (A.³)	ν (cm.⁻¹)	ν^+ (cm.⁻¹)
M = O_2	3.433	113	1.60	1580.36	1876.4
CO	3.590	110	1.95	2170.21	2214.24
N_2	3.681	91.5	1.76	2359.61	2207.19
H_2O	2.824	230.9	1.48	1595	
CO_2	3.996	190	2.65	672.2	
CH_4	3.882	137	2.56	1306	

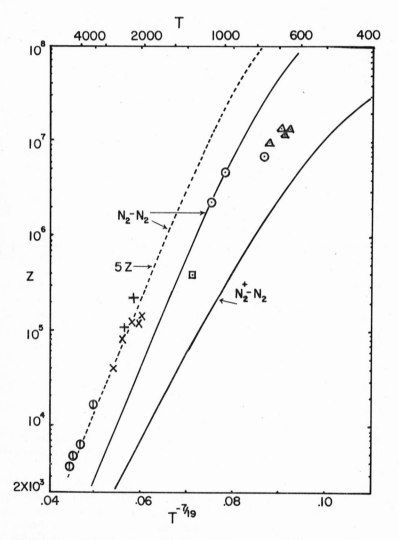

Figure 1.   Calculated collision number Z as a function of $T^{-7/19}$ for the N_2-N_2 and N_2^+-N_2 systems.   Experimental data are: ⊕ Ref. 3; + Ref. 5; × Ref. 10; △ Ref. 15; ⊙ Ref. 17; ▫ Ref. 24

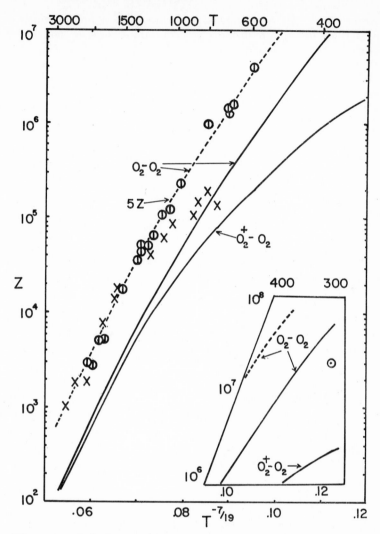

Figure 2. Calculated collision number Z as a function of $T^{-7/19}$ for the O_2-O_2 and O_2^+-O_2 systems. Experimental data are: × Ref 3; ⊙ Ref. 16; ⓘ Ref. 21

with our calculated values. Other experimental values (references are given in Figure 1) using relatively pure nitrogen at higher temperatures are about five times the calculated values. Blackman's results (3) are obtained using the sample containing water of less than one part in 10^5. Since these experiments were carried out with considerably pure nitrogen, the error of our calculation may be considered real. Figure 1 shows that the experimental data of Blackman (3) and of Gaydon and co-workers (5,10) are consistently larger than our calculations by a factor of 5. The calculated values of Z by introducing this factor are also plotted in

Figure 1. In N_2-N_2, however, no accurate data at lower temperatures are available; hence, a realistic comparison does not seem possible.

An extensive study by Blackman (3) and a recent study by Millikan and White (21) on the vibrational relaxation of O_2 are shown in Figure 2. The impurity of Blackman's sample varied from 1–5%, but the bulk impurity was nitrogen. Blackman's data at lower temperatures are significantly different from Millikan and White's values. The latters' data have the same temperature dependence as Equation 5 over the

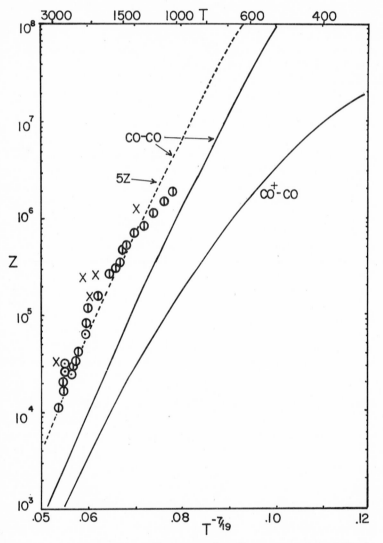

Figure 3. Calculated collision number Z as a function of $T^{-7/19}$ or the CO-CO and CO⁺-CO systems. Experimental data are: ⊙ Ref. 10; ① Ref. 21; × Ref. 34

entire temperature range studied, and they are larger than the calculated values by a factor of 5. Blackman's data at higher temperatures follow the same temperature dependence. The value of Knoetzel and Knoetzel (16) at 288°K. is about one-half of the calculated value. The latter experimental value is obtained by extrapolating the measured absorption maxima to zero concentration of additive polar molecules such as H_2O and NH_3 to obtain the relaxation times for pure O_2; hence, it may be considered inaccurate.

The temperature dependence of Z for CO is very similar to the above two systems (Figure 3). Experimental data of Millikan and White and of Gaydon and Hurle (10) at temperatures above 1000°K. are again larger than our values by a factor of 5. Windsor, Davidson, and Taylor (34) obtained a larger Z value than the ones above.

Ion-Molecule Collisions

The above study shows that Equation 5 is satisfactory in predicting the T dependence of Z and can also be used to calculate Z and vibrational relaxation times of diatomic molecules if we introduce a factor of 5. Based on this success and the hope that the essential part of M^+-M collisions can be represented by the strong attractive term, Equation 1, and the strong repulsive energy which occurs at small r, we calculate Z^+ for N_2^+, O_2^+, and CO^+ (Figures 1–3). Note that the polarization energy given by Equation 1 is significantly larger than the attractive term of the 12-6 function. The collision numbers for the molecular ions are generally much smaller than those for the molecules. Figure 4 is a plot of the ratio $Z^* = Z/Z^+$.

The collision numbers for N_2^+-N_2 are smaller than those for N_2-N_2 by 2 orders of magnitude at lower temperatures; for example, at 300°K. $Z^* = 434$, and at 1000°K. it is 15. On the other hand, in O_2^+-O_2 the ratio is significantly smaller: 20.6 and 1.6 at 300° and 1000°K., respectively. The variation of Z^* for CO^+ with temperature lies between these two cases. The small Z^* values for O_2^+ compared with other ions can be easily understood in terms of its electron configuration. In O_2 there are six bonding electrons (two $p\sigma_g$ and four $p\pi_u$ electrons) and two anti-bonding electrons ($p\pi_g$) whereas in O_2^+ one of the anti-bonding electrons is removed. Therefore, the number of anti-bonding electrons is decreased by 1, and the vibrational energy quantum is increased from O_2 to O_2^+ by 294.04 cm.$^{-1}$ On the other hand, N_2 has six bonding electrons whereas N_2^+ has five bonding electrons; therefore, bond weakening occurs when N_2 is converted to N_2^+. The vibrational energy quantum is decreased by 152.42 cm.$^{-1}$ The species CO and CO^+ are isoelectronic to N_2 and N_2^+, respectively, but the bond strengthening process increases the vibrational energy quantum only by 44.03 cm.$^{-1}$ From the difference between the collision numbers for O_2 and O_2^+, we note that the effect of the polarization term in the exponent is seriously counteracted by the large leading term which resulted from the repulsive part of $U(r)$. In N_2^+ and CO^+ both polarization energy and the bond weakening effect, however, facilitate the relaxation of the excited ions compared with the neutrals. Even at a temperature as high as 3000 °K. N_2^+ still relaxes faster than N_2 by a factor of 3.8. The corresponding factors for carbon monoxide and oxygen are 2.1 and 1.1.

If we assume that the same discrepancy between theory and experiment in M-M enters in M^+-M, we can estimate the vibrational relaxation times for the molecular ions. Table II shows the estimated vibrational relaxation times τ^+ at various temperatures. The values are shorter than those for the neutrals by factors given in Figure 4.

We may also apply the above expressions to polyatomic molecular ions. However, the effective reduced mass M of the oscillator in Equation 5 is a function of the definition of normal coordinate, and it is diffi-

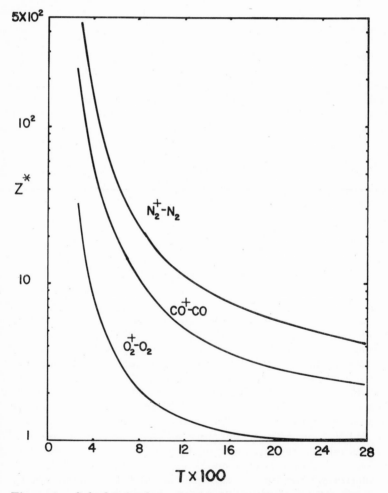

Figure 4. Calculated values of the reduced collision number Z^* as a function of temperature for N_2^+-N_2, O_2^+-O_2, and CO^+-CO

Table II.   Estimated Values of the Relaxation Times[b] τ^+

T, °K.	$N_2^+ - N_2$	$O_2^+ - O_2$	$CO^+ - CO$
300	7.93(−2)[a]	5.53(−3)	1.49(−2)
400	2.89(−2)	8.68(−4)	6.82(−3)
600	7.20(−3)	2.70(−4)	1.65(−3)
800	1.42(−3)	1.95(−4)	5.33(−4)
1000	5.32(−4)	4.60(−5)	2.21(−4)
1500	8.82(−5)	1.06(−5)	2.16(−5)
3000	5.74(−6)	5.26(−7)	3.31(−6)

[a] Numbers in parentheses denote the exponent of 10 – e.g., 7.93(−2) = 7.93 × 10⁻². Values given in seconds for 1 atm. pressure.

cult to evaluate.   In a simple oscillator roughly half the molecule vibrates with respect to the other half; hence, M may be approximated as one-fourth the molecular mass.   When the molecule is composed of very dissimilar atoms or radicals, this approximation can give an erroneous value for M.   The evaluation of ρ suffers a similar difficulty.   In poly-atomic molecules there are many vibrational modes, and most often the lowest vibration is degenerated.   In addition, the collision between M^+ and M may not be linear so that introducing a "steric" factor becomes considerably more complex.   This study suffers from these difficulties which are common to most formal theories.   In calculating Z Herzfeld (*13*) introduced a "steric" factor of 3 for direct de-excitation of longitudinal vibrations, $^3/_2$ for direct de-excitation of doubly degenerate bending vibrations, and $2j/3$ for complex de-excitations, where j is an undetermined parameter.

From Equation 5 we obtain the ratio Z^* as

$$Z^* = \frac{1}{\delta^{2.815}} \exp\left[-\frac{2.714\chi^+(1 - \delta)}{kT} + \frac{1.346\sqrt{D\chi^+}(1 - \sqrt{\delta})}{kT} + \right.$$
$$\left. 0.254\left(\frac{\alpha e^2}{D^{1/3}\sigma^4}\right)\frac{\chi^{+1/3}}{kT} + \frac{\epsilon^+}{2kT}(1 - \delta)\right] \quad (6)$$

where $\delta = \dfrac{\nu}{\nu^+}$.   This is equal to the ratio of the corresponding relaxation times.   When $\delta \simeq 1$, such as in CO^+-CO, the ratio reduces to

$$Z^* \simeq \exp\left[0.254\left(\frac{\alpha e^2}{D^{1/3}\sigma^4}\right)\frac{\chi^{+1/3}}{kT}\right] \quad (7)$$

If the removal of an electron does not significantly change the bond strength, Equation 7 can be used to estimate the importance of polarization energy.   Figure 5 is plot of Equation 7 for H_2O^+, CH_4^+, and CO_2^+. Since we do not know accurate values of the vibrational frequency of the ions, this ratio gives the Z^*-T variation only qualitatively, but it may lead to a correct temperature dependence of Z^+.   Table III presents estimated relaxation times for H_2O^+, CH_4^+, and CO_2^+ based on the observed data and the ratio Z^*.   The water molecule has a significantly large α/σ^4 compared with the others.   In general, the effect of polariza-

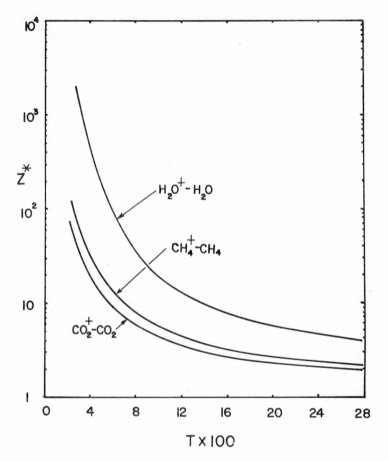

Figure 5. Calculated values of the reduced collision number Z^* as a function of temperature for H_2O^+-H_2O, CO_2^+-CO_2, and CH_4^+-CH_4

tion energy on the relaxation process is largely controlled by the competing effect of α and σ.

We will now compare the numerical results obtained from our study with those obtained by other methods. Assuming a Morse potential Takayanagi (*31*) calculated $Z^* \simeq 10$ at 300 °K. for O_2^+ whereas we obtained 20.8. Takayanagi introduced a constant polarization energy evaluated at a distance in the most important region of the interaction, which he assumed as 7 a.u.; therefore, he modified the depth of the potential well of the Morse potential only by adding this constant factor. The exponential range parameter is assumed as $a \simeq \sigma/17$ at 300 °K. Our study shows $a = \sigma/15.4$ which is obtained by comparing the vibration transition probability per collision for the Morse and the LJ(12-6) potential at the most probable distance of the vibrational transitions.

Table III.   Estimated Values of the Relaxation Times[a]

T, °K.	$H_2O^+ - H_2O$	$CO_2^+ - CO_2$	$CH_4^+ - CH_4$
300	3.0(−11)	1.2(−7)	1.7(−7)
400	1.0(−10)	1.9(−7)	1.5(−8)
600	4.3(−10)	2.3(−7)	2.3(−8)
800	4.5(−10)	3.9(−8)	...
1000	...	1.4(−8)	...

[a] We estimated τ^+ from widely scattered experimental data for M − M (p. 90, 97, 100 of Ref. 7). In addition, τ^+ for CO_2^+ and CH_4^+ are estimated from the experimental data of different sources. All values are in seconds for 1 atm. pressure.

Steric Factor

In Equation 5 we note that a steric factor which considers the effect of nonlinear collisions on energy transfer is not introduced. In several previous studies on M-M collisions, the exponential interactions were used (1, 9, 22, 27, 28). In such systems, the exponential range parameter a, which occurs when the interaction potential is represented by $U(r) = A \exp(-r/a)$, is commonly chosen by fitting the exponential function to LJ potential functions obtained from transport property measurements. If the fitted parameters are used, the transition probabilities are generally of the correct order of magnitude, but the slope of the curve in the probability *vs.* temperature (*log* P *vs.* $T^{-1/3}$) plot is often poor. On the other hand, if a is chosen to reproduce the experimentally observed temperature dependence, the probabilities are generally found to be an order of magnitude too large. This has been explained in terms of a "steric" factor of the order $1/_{30}$, which seems too small for simple diatomic molecules (18, 20). However, these studies have not considered the important role of the correction terms resulting from the attractive forces between the collision partners. These terms, as shown in Equation 5, are 1.346 $(D\chi)^{1/2}/kT$ and 0.362 D/kT for M-M collisions. The first term can affect seriously the over-all value of the transition probability at low temperatures particularly for polar molecules—i.e., the log P *vs.* $T^{-1/3}$ plot will not yield a straight line; therefore, the fitting procedure can give an erroneously small value for a. Schwartz and Herzfeld (28) have calculated the transition probability for the most favorable orientation and then multiplied by $1/_3$ to account for the less favorable possibilities. However, if a steric factor must be used, this introduces a somewhat nebulous feature into the theory since it is usually difficult to evaluate. Of course, we do not expect exact agreement between theory and experiment. As Figures 1–3 show, our calculation seems to give the correct temperature dependence and results in Z consistently smaller than "accurate" experimental data by a factor of 5. Therefore, if the discrepancy between theory and experiment is solely caused by the so-called steric factor, this study suggests that it should be approximately 5.

Over-All Interaction Energy

Another important aspect of our study is that assuming the over-all interaction energy $V(x,r)$ between the ion and the molecule as a function of $r - \rho x$, Equation 5 is obtained where x is the displacement of the oscillator from its equilibrium position. With this assumption $V(x,r)$ is expanded as

$$V(x,r) = V(0,r) + x(\partial V/\partial r)_{x=o} + \cdots \qquad (8)$$

where $V(0,r) = U(r)$. Neglecting the higher order terms and thereby assuming that the amplitude of vibration is small compared with the range of the potential, we considered that the perturbation of the oscillator energy levels and wave functions varies by $x \cdot (\partial V/\partial r)_{x=o}$. However, when $V(x,r) \neq V(r - \rho x)$ or when the higher order terms are not small, we may have to use the over-all interaction energy of the form $V(x,r) = B \cdot V(x) \cdot U(r)$, where $V(x)$ may now be assumed by the exponential form $\exp\,(x/b)$, and B is a constant. Then the ratio of $\mathbf{P}$ for this interaction energy to Equation 5 can be calculated as

$$f = \left[\frac{r^*}{12} \frac{\displaystyle\int_{-\infty}^{\infty} \varphi_i(x) V(x) \varphi_f(x) dx}{\displaystyle\int_{-\infty}^{\infty} \varphi_i(x) x \varphi_f(x) dx} \right]^2 \qquad (9)$$

where $\varphi_i(x)$ and $\varphi_f(x)$ are the wave functions of the unperturbed initial and final states of the oscillator and r^* is the most probable distance for the energy transfer introduced in obtaining Equation 5; it is

$$r^* = \left(\frac{14\hbar}{\epsilon} \sqrt{\frac{2D}{\mu}} \; \sigma^6 \right)^{1/7}$$

For $i = 0$ and $f = 1$, the integrals in Equation 9 are (20, 26)

$$\int_{-\infty}^{\infty} \varphi_i(x) V(x) \varphi_f(x) dx = \frac{\hbar}{b(2M\epsilon)^{1/2}} \exp \left(\frac{\hbar^2}{4b^2 M \epsilon} \right)$$

$$\int_{-\infty}^{\infty} \varphi_i(x) x \varphi_f(x) dx = \frac{\hbar}{b(2M\epsilon)^{1/2}}$$

so that

$$f = \left(\frac{r^*}{12b} \right)^2 \exp \left(\frac{\hbar^2}{2b^2 M \epsilon} \right) \qquad (10)$$

For N_2-N_2 we obtain $r^* = 2.215$ A.; by assuming $b = 0.2$ A. we obtain $\hbar/(2M\epsilon)^{1/2}b = 0.16$. Therefore, $f = 0.99$. Similar calculation gives $f = 0.95$ for O_2-O_2, so that here the assumption that $V(x,r) = V(r - \rho x)$ may be considered as a satisfactory treatment.

Transition Probability for Large m

We may also obtain the transition probability for $U(r)$ with very large m. As $m \to \infty$, the interaction potential approaches the "hard-core" limiting form.   To obtain this, we consider the inverse $(m - 6)$ function; then in Equation 3, the constants are

$$C_m = \left(\frac{m}{m-6}\right)\left(\frac{m}{6}\right)^{\frac{6}{m-6}} D\sigma^m = C\sigma^m$$

$$C_6 = -\left(\frac{m}{m-6}\right)\left(\frac{m}{6}\right)^{\frac{6}{m-6}} D\sigma^6$$

$$C_4 = -\frac{\alpha e^2}{2}$$

The transition probability for this potential is, from Equation 4,

$$P = \frac{4\pi^2 \hbar m (C\sigma^m)^{3/2}\rho^2}{M\epsilon^2} \sqrt{\frac{2\pi m\mu}{2+3m}} \left(\frac{\epsilon}{m+2}\sqrt{\frac{2\mu}{C\sigma^m}}\frac{1}{\hbar}\right)^{\frac{3m+2}{m+2}} \sqrt{\frac{\chi_m}{kT}} \quad (11)$$

$$\times \exp\left[-\left(\frac{2+3m}{2+m}\right)\frac{\chi_m}{kT} - \frac{\Gamma\left(\frac{1}{m}+1\right)\Gamma\left(\frac{2}{3}-\frac{5}{m}\right)}{\Gamma\left(\frac{1}{m}+\frac{3}{2}\right)\Gamma\left(1-\frac{5}{m}\right)}\frac{C_6}{C^{6/m}\sigma^6}\frac{\chi_m^{6/m}}{kT} - \right.$$

$$\frac{\Gamma\left(\frac{1}{m}+1\right)\Gamma\left(\frac{3}{2}-\frac{3}{m}\right)}{\Gamma\left(\frac{1}{m}+\frac{3}{2}\right)\Gamma\left(1-\frac{3}{m}\right)}\frac{C_4}{C^{4/m}\sigma^4}\frac{\chi_m^{4/m}}{kT} +$$

$$\left[\left(\frac{m}{2+3M}\right)\left(\frac{\Gamma\left(\frac{1}{m}+2\right)\Gamma\left(\frac{5}{2}-\frac{5}{m}\right)}{\Gamma\left(\frac{1}{m}+\frac{3}{2}\right)\Gamma\left(1-\frac{5}{m}\right)}\right)^2 - \right.$$

$$\left.\left(\frac{3m-10}{4m}\right)\left(\frac{\Gamma\left(\frac{1}{m}+1\right)\Gamma\left(\frac{3}{2}-\frac{11}{m}\right)}{\Gamma\left(\frac{1}{m}+\frac{3}{2}\right)\Gamma\left(1-\frac{11}{m}\right)}\right)\right]\left(\frac{C_6}{C^{6/m}\sigma^6}\right)^2\frac{\chi_m^{\frac{12}{m}-1}}{kT} + \frac{\epsilon}{2kT}\right]$$

Therefore, when we assume m is very large $(m \gg 12)$, with the aid of the matching expression *(30)* between the exponential range parameter a and the LJ parameter σ,

$$a = \left[\frac{\Gamma\left(\frac{1}{2}+\frac{1}{m}\right)}{\Gamma\left(\frac{1}{m}\right)\sqrt{\pi}}\right]\left(\frac{'C}{\chi_m}\right)^{\frac{1}{m}}\sigma,$$

we obtain

$$\mathbf{P} \sim \frac{16\rho^2\epsilon}{M} \sqrt{\frac{\pi}{3}} \left(\frac{\pi\mu a}{\hbar}\right)^2 \sqrt{\frac{\chi'}{kT}} \tag{12}$$

$$\times \exp\left[-\frac{3\chi'}{kT} + \frac{D}{kT} + \frac{\alpha e^2}{2\sigma^4 kT} + \frac{\epsilon}{2kT}\right]$$

where

$$\chi' = \left(\sqrt{\frac{\mu}{2}} \frac{\pi a\epsilon kT}{\hbar}\right)^{2/3}$$

In the limit $m \to \infty$, the interaction potential behaves as

$$U(r) = \infty \qquad\qquad\qquad r < \sigma$$

$$= -4D\left(\frac{\sigma}{r}\right)^6 - \frac{\alpha e^2}{2\sigma^4}\left(\frac{\sigma}{r}\right)^4 \qquad r > \sigma \tag{13}$$

As Figure 6 shows, the repulsive part is significantly removed from the potential given by Equation 2. Although the leading term $3\chi'/kT$ can be fit identical to $2.714\chi/kT$ of Equation 5 through the matching relation, the sum of D/kT and $\alpha e^2/2 \; \sigma^4 kT$ is quite small compared with that of the second, third, and fourth terms in the exponent of Equation 5.

The attractive energies $4D(\sigma/r)^6$ and $\alpha e^2/2 \; r^4$ have two important effects on the vibrational energy transfer: (a) they "speed up" the approaching collision partners so that the kinetic energy of the relative motion is increased, and (b) they modify the slope of the repulsive part of the interaction potential on which the transition probability depends. By letting $m \to \infty$, we have completely ignored the second effect while we have over-emphasized the first. Note that Equation 12 is identical to an expression we could obtain when the interaction potential is assumed as $U(r) = A \; [\exp \; (-r/a)] - (\alpha e^2/2\sigma^4) - D$. Similarly, if we assume a modified Morse potential of the form

$$U(r) = D[\exp \; (-r/a) - 2 \exp \; (-r/2a)] - \alpha e^2/2\sigma^4,$$

then

$$\mathbf{P} = A \exp\left(-\frac{3\chi'}{kT} + \frac{4\sqrt{D\chi'}}{\pi kT} + \frac{16D}{3\pi^2 kT} + \frac{\alpha e^2}{2\sigma^4 kT} + \frac{\epsilon}{2kT}\right) \tag{14}$$

where A is the same pre-exponential factor given in Equation 12. The polarization energy results in $\alpha e^2/2\sigma^4 kT$ in the exponent, but this is small compared with that in Equation 5. The above analysis would suggest that if we consider the intermolecular potential

$$U(r) = \infty \qquad\qquad\qquad r < r^o$$

$$= -4D\left(\frac{\sigma}{r}\right)^6 - \frac{\alpha e^2}{2\sigma^4}\left(\frac{\sigma}{r}\right)^4 \qquad r > r^o \tag{15}$$

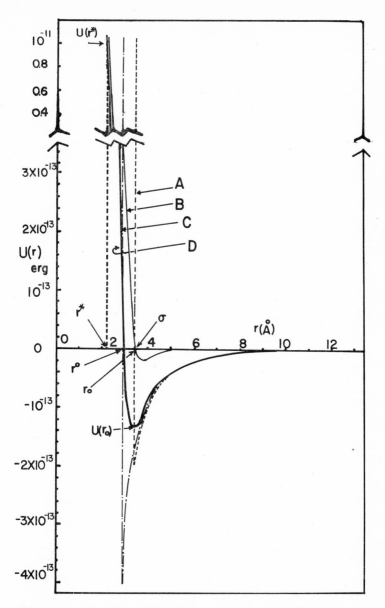

Figure 6. Various potential energy curves for the interaction between O_2^+-O_2: A = U(r) given by Equation 13; B = the inverse (12-6) power potential shown for comparison; C = U(r) given by Equation 15; D = U(r) given by Equation 2. The most probable distance r* and the potential at this distance U(r*) are also shown

where r^o is the radius of the hard-core of the M^+-M collision—i.e., the root of $U(r^o) = 0 = 4D[(\sigma/r^o)^{12} - (\sigma/r^o)^6] - \alpha e^2/2r^{o4}$, then the transition probability is identical to Equation 14, but now σ is replaced by r^o, and a is calculated from the matching relation with r^o. For diatomic and simple polyatomic molecules $0.91 > r^o/\sigma > 0.83$ or $\alpha e^2/2r^{o4}kT$ is larger than $\alpha e^2/2\sigma^4 kT$ by a factor of 1.46 to 2.07. Table IV shows the values of the polarization term in the exponent for the potentials given by Equations 2, 13, and 15 for $O_2{}^+$. When the depth of the potential well D is small compared with kT, the potential assumed by Equation 15 may adequately describe the M^+-M collision process. Since the "hardcore" limiting potentials ignore the effect of attractive energies on the slope of the repulsive part of $U(r)$, they generally give smaller P values compared with the analytical expression given by Equation 5. Takayanagi's result obtained by assuming the polarization energy $\alpha e^2/2R_c{}^4$ with $R_c \simeq 7$ a.u. seriously underestimates the importance of the energy.

Table IV. Calculated Values of the Polarization Energy Term in the Exponent of P

$T,\ °K.$	$0.254 \left(\dfrac{\alpha e^2}{D^{1/3}\sigma^4}\right)\dfrac{\chi^{1/3}}{kT}$	$\dfrac{\alpha e^2}{2\sigma^4\ kT}$	$\dfrac{\alpha e^2}{2r^{o4}\ kT}$
300	5.357	3.206	5.996
400	4.268	2.405	4.498
600	3.098	1.603	2.998
800	2.469	1.202	2.248
1000	2.070	0.962	1.799
1500	1.503	0.641	1.198
3000	0.869	0.320	0.598

As shown in Figure 6 the most probable distance for the vibrational transition is $r^* = 2.223$ A. for $O_2{}^+$-O_2, and the potential energy at this distance is $U(r^*) = 1.06 \times 10^{-11}$ ergs. This distance is significantly small compared with r^o. To justify using the inverse power potentials for the repulsive part of $U(r)$, we first note that the potential at the most probable distance for the vibrational transitions is much larger than the average kinetic energy of the relative motion. For example, in $O_2{}^+$-O_2 $U(r^*)/kT = 25.6$ even at 3000 °K.; this implies that the incident waves which reach this region control the over-all energy transfer process. The incident particles with sufficiently high collision velocities will reach this region, but it is also possible that the incident waves can reach this region by the potential barrier penetration—i.e., the quantum nature of the translational motion is essential in the problem. At high collision velocities the ordinary perturbation methods (such as this one) fails because the probability becomes too large, and exchange of more than one quantum in a single collision becomes increasingly probable. Yet our approach shows that the collision process is essentially controlled by the partners reached at such close proximity. According to the argument of Rapp and Sharp (25), if energetic collisions must control the over-all process, we should have obtained transition probabilities not much different from unity. However, we obtained the probabilities $\ll 1$ even when we evaluated the perturbation integral at $r = r^*$. If we consider the energetic incident particles, then it represents the energetic "tail" portion of the Boltzmann distribution; hence, it is difficult to understand why so few energetic collisions can play such a dominating role. It is then possible to state that this "close-in" region is reached by less energetic waves by the potential barrier penetration. We do not know quantitatively the precise form of $U(r)$ in close proximity, and as far as this aspect is concerned it seems that for now we cannot hope to have any radically improved form. When the repulsive part of the potential function is relatively "soft," most of the incident waves reach the most probable region for energy transfer by the barrier penetration. It is then no longer surprising that the "soft" inverse (12) power potential can still give reasonable results, and the potential barrier penetration is a necessary consequence because at the most probable distance the relative velocity is zero; hence, despite the large masses, the motion is essentially quantum mechanical (large effective wavelength) (2, 33).

Conclusions

This study has made no substantial improvement in the original theory of distorted waves. By evaluating the vibrational transition probability explicitly for the inverse (12-6-4) power potential, however, we were able to study some interesting aspects of the ion-molecule collisions. We summarize them here.

Calculated collision numbers give the "correct" temperature dependence for simple molecules at ordinary temperatures. It appears that the essential discrepancy between theory and experiment is a factor of 5. We interpret this success as strong evidence that the inverse power potentials are appropriate for describing "close-in" collisions when the perturbation integral is evaluated at the most probable distance for the transition r^*. The incident waves reach this region by penetrating the potential barrier. The vibrational relaxation times of the excited N_2^+ and CO^+ are larger than the neutral molecules by 1-2 orders of magnitude while the time constant for O_2^+ is larger than that for O_2 by less than 1 order of magnitude.

It is physically realistic to introduce a "steric" factor larger than unity, but to do so can be fairly arbitrary. In our study, the calculated Z values are consistently smaller than the observed data by a factor of 5; therefore, if a "steric" factor is introduced, it could best be assumed as 5.

The over-all interaction energy $V(x,r)$ between M^+ and M (or between M and M) may be satisfactorily assumed by $U(r) - x \cdot (\partial V/\partial r)_{x=o}$ in the present systems. This is shown by comparing the present formulas with the results for a more realistic energy $V(x,r) = BV(x)U(r)$.

The "hard-core" limiting forms of $U(r)$ do not lead to physically acceptable results. We conclude that this is caused by a complete neglect of the effect of the attractive forces on the slope of the repulsive part in $U(r)$. If the interaction energy is assumed as the sum of a Morse exponential function and the polarization energy evaluated at $r = r^o$, the resulting transition probabilities appear useful for analyzing ion-molecule collisions.

Acknowledgment

The support of the Petroleum Research Fund of the American Chemical Society is gratefully acknowledged.
The author wishes to thank R. D. Burkhart for valuable suggestions.

Literature Cited

(1) Amme, R., Legvold, S., *J. Chem. Phys.* **30,** 163 (1959); **33,** 91 (1960).
(2) Bauer, E., *J. Chem. Phys.* **23,** 1087 (1955).
(3) Blackman, V., *J. Fluid Mechanics* **1,** 61 (1956).
(4) *Chem. Eng. News* **44,** 1A (March 28, 1966).
(5) Clouston, J. G., Gaydon, A. G., Glass, I. I., *Proc. Roy. Soc.* **248A,** 429 (1958).
(6) Cottrell, T. L., Ream, N., *Trans. Faraday Soc.* **51,** 159 (1955).
(7) Cottrell, T. L., McCoubrey, J. C., "Molecular Energy Transfer in Gases," Chap. 5, Butterworths, London, 1961.
(8) *Ibid.*, Table 5.13, p. 90 for CO_2, Table 5.21, p. 97 for H_2O, and Table 5.25, p. 100 for CH_4.
(9) Dickens, P. G., Ripamonti, A., *Trans. Faraday Soc.* **57,** 735 (1961).
(10) Gaydon, A. G., Hurle, J., *Symp. Combust., 8th, Pasadena, Calif.,* **1960,** 309.
(11) Hasted, J. B., "Physics of Atomic Collisions," Chap. 12, 14, Butterworths, London, 1964.
(12) Herzberg, G., "Spectra of Diatomic Molecules," Table 39, D. Van Nostrand Co., New York, 1950.
(13) Herzfeld, K. F., *Discuss. Faraday Soc.* **33,** 22 (1962).
(14) Hirschfelder, J. O., Curtiss, C. F., Bird, R. B., "Molecular Theory of Gases and Liquids," pp. 950, 1111, John Wiley and Sons, New York, 1954.
(15) Huber, P. W., Kantrowitz, A., *J. Chem. Phys.* **15,** 275 (1947).
(16) Knoetzel, H., Knoetzel, L., *Ann. Physik* **2,** 393 (1948)
(17) Lukasik, S. J., Young, J. E., *Ann. Physik.* **27,** 1149 (1957).
(18) McCoubrey, J. C., Milward, R. C., Ubbelohde, A. R., *Trans. Faraday Soc.* **57,** 1472 (1961).
(19) McDaniel, E. W., "Collision Phenomena in Ionized Gases," Chap. 9, John Wiley and Sons, New York, 1964.
(20) Mies, F. G., *J. Chem. Phys.* **40,** 523 (1964).
(21) Millikan, R. C., White, D. R., *J. Chem. Phys.* **39,** 329 (1963).
(22) Moore, C. B., *J. Chem. Phys.* **43,** 2979 (1965).
(23) Nikitin, E. E., *Opt. i Spektroskopiya* **6,** 141 (1959): Eng. transl. *Opt. Spectry. USSR* **6,** 93 (1959).
(24) Partington, J. R., Shilling, W. G., *Phil. Mag.* **6,** 920 (1928); **9,** 1020 (1930).
(25) Rapp, D., Sharp, T. E., *J. Chem. Phys.* **38,** 264 (1963).
(26) Rosen, P., *J. Chem. Phys.* **1,** 319 (1933).
(27) Schwartz, R. N., Slawsky, Z. I., Herzfeld, K. F., *J. Chem. Phys.* **20,** 1591 (1952).
(28) Schwartz, R. N., Herzfeld, K. F., *J. Chem. Phys.* **22,** 767 (1954).
(29) Shin, H., *J. Chem. Phys.* **42,** 1739 (1965).
(30) Shin, H., *J. Chem. Phys.* **41,** 2864 (1964).
(31) Takayanagi, K., *Joint Inst. Lab. Astrophysics Rept.* No. **17,** 1964.
(32) Tal'roze, V. L., Markin, M. I., Larin, I. K., *Discuss. Faraday Soc.* **33,** 257 (1962).
(33) Widom, B., *J. Chem. Phys.* **27,** 940 (1957).
(34) Windsor, M., Davidson, H., Taylor, R., *Symp. Combust., 7th, London,* **1958,** 80.

RECEIVED April 25, 1966.

Stripping Effects in Ion-Molecule Reactions

A. HENGLEIN

Hahn-Meitner-Institut für Kernforschung Berlin, Sektor Strahlenchemie,
Berlin, West Germany

Certain ion-molecule reactions of the types $XH^+ + XH \rightarrow X + XH_2^+$ and $X_2^+ + H_2 \rightarrow XH^+ + H$ occur as "stripping" or "pick-up" processes at high ion energies while an intermediate inelastic collision complex is formed at low energies. These conclusions are drawn from simple discrimination experiments and measuring the velocity spectra of ion-molecule reactions. The transition from the stripping model to the inelastic complex model can sometimes be detected by studying isotope effects. At very high primary ion energies, deviations occur since the product ion is even more forward-scattered than expected. The stripping and elastic reactive collision models allow reactions to occur with relatively high cross-sections at rather high ion energies (>50 e.v.).

The polarization theory predicts a cross-section for collisions:

$$\sigma_c = 2\pi \frac{e}{V_o}\left(\frac{\alpha}{\mu}\right)^{1/2} = \pi e \left(\frac{2\alpha M}{\mu E}\right)^{1/2} \tag{1}$$

which leads to a very close approach between an incident ion and a neutral molecule (α = polarizibility of the molecule; μ = reduced mass; e, M, and V_0 = charge, mass, and velocity of the ion; E = kinetic energy of the ion). The cross-section of a chemical reaction between the colliding ion and the molecule may be written as:

$$\sigma = \eta \cdot \sigma_c \tag{2}$$

where η is a frequency factor (generally smaller than unity). The reaction $Ar^+ + H_2 \rightarrow ArH^+ + H$ is an example for $\eta = 1.0$ since the measured reaction cross-section agreed with the collision cross-section calculated from Equation 1 (*16*). The validity of Equation 1 has often been checked by measuring the ratio i_s/i_p (currents of secondary and primary ion) as a function of the repeller field strength in conventional mass spectrometers. Proportionality between σ and $E^{-1/2}$ has occasionally been observed, such as for the reaction between Ar^+ and H_2 mentioned above.   Deviations from the square root dependence can be expected if η is not constant but depends on E.   Boelrijk and Hamill emphasized that Equation 1 can only be applied if σ_c exceeds the gas kinetic cross-section σ_g (4).   The electrical interaction between the ion and the induced dipole of the molecule can practically be neglected above a critical energy E_g of the ion where σ_c becomes equal to σ_g.   Generally, E_g is smaller than 1.0 e.v.   Only in a few cases, where M/μ is rather large, can Equation 1 still be used to describe the reaction at energies of a few e.v. Several authors have recently measured cross-sections of ion-molecule reactions at higher ion energies and discussed their results with respect to the polarization theory.   However, these discussions seem meaningless since one cannot discuss deviations from a theory which *a priori* is not applicable in this energy range.

Collisions at low ion energies (where Equation 1 can be applied) lead to a short-lived complex between the ion and the molecule—i.e., both collision partners move with the same linear velocity in the direction of the incident ion.   The decay of the complex may be described by the theory of unimolecular rate processes if its excess energy can fluctuate between the various internal degrees of freedom.   For example, the isotope effect in the reaction of Ar^+ with HD may be explained by the properties of

$$Ar^+ + HD \rightarrow (ArHD)^+ \begin{cases} \nearrow ArH^+ + D \quad\quad (3a) \\ \searrow ArD^+ + H \quad\quad (3b) \end{cases}$$

the intermediate $ArHD^+$ complex.   At low Ar^+ ion energies, the intensity ratio ArH^+/ArD^+ is a little smaller than 1.0 (*12, 16*).   This effect is expected because of the higher frequency factor for splitting off an H atom and because of the higher ArD^+ bond strength owing to the difference in the zero point energies of the ions ArH^+ and ArD^+.   An intermediate complex has also been postulated when it was observed that the relative abundancies of the various secondary ions resulting from different paths of decomposition of the complex agreed with the abundancies of the fragments in the mass spectrum of the corresponding molecule (*1, 6*).

Secondary ions resulting from the random decomposition of an ion-molecule complex should have a distinct velocity spectrum—i.e. by measuring the angular and energy distribution of a secondary ion one should be able to recognize certain details of the collision mechanism.   In most of the conventional studies of ion-molecule reactions, the secondary ions were strongly accelerated immediately after their formation.   Velocity spectra could therefore not be observed.   This paper reviews a few experiments which were carried out to determine the velocity spectra of secondary ions.   The energy of the primary ions was always much higher than the energy E_g mentioned above—i.e. the polarization theory certainly was not expected to describe the observed effects.   In fact, the measured velocity spectra indicated the occurrance of "stripping" and "pick up" processes in which no complex in the sense mentioned above is formed as an intermediate.   These studies were confined to the higher energy range because of certain experimental difficulties. It would be interesting to work with primary ion beams at energies below 1 e.v. in order to study the kinematics of reactions which are properly described by the polarization theory and to study the transition from the stripping to the complex model.

Simple Discrimination Experiments

The secondary ion XH_2^+ resulting from the stripping of a proton from the incident ion XH^+ by a molecule XH has very little kinetic energy in

$$XH^+ + XH \rightarrow X + XH_2^+ \qquad (4)$$

the direction of the incident ion (Equation 4). In an ideal stripping reaction no momentum will be transferred between the heavy masses X of the colliding particles. It can be shown readily that the kinetic energy of the secondary ion will amount to:

$$E_s = E \, \frac{m^2}{M(m + M)} \approx E \frac{m^2}{M^2} \qquad (5)$$

where E and M are the kinetic energy and mass of the primary ion, and m is the mass of the transferred proton. However, if an intermediate complex $(X_2H_2)^+$ is formed, the product ion XH_2^+ will move with the component of the kinetic energy in the direction of the primary ion (Equation 6).

$$E_s = E \, \frac{M}{2\,M} \cdot \frac{M + m}{2\,M} \approx \frac{E}{4} \qquad (6)$$

Since $\frac{m^2}{M^2}$ generally is much smaller than $\frac{1}{4}$, the kinetic energies of the product ions XH_2^+ which are produced in a stripping process or via a complex are quite different. The more energetic ions (resulting from complex formation) can be prevented from entering the analyzing section of a mass spectrometer if the ion source is operated according to the method described by Cermak and Herman (5). The electron accelerating voltage between the filament and the ionization chamber is kept below the ionization potential of the gas. The electrons traverse the chamber without causing any ionization and are then further accelerated by an electric field between the ionization chamber and the electron trap. The primary ions are mainly formed before the trap and are accelerated in the direction opposite to the electron beam before entering the ionization chamber. These primary ions are not able to pass the slit system of the mass spectrometer because of a kinetic energy component perpendicular to the direction of analysis. However, secondary ions produced by collisions with gas molecules in the chamber can be extracted if they are formed with negligible amounts of kinetic energy. For example, secondary ions can be detected this way when they are formed by charge transfer in which the transfer of mass, and therefore of kinetic energy, is extremely small. The maximum kinetic energy component of a secondary ion in the direction of the primary ion which will allow analysis amounted to 2.5 e.v. under our conditions. This figure could be calculated from the geometry of the slit system (11).

Figure 1 shows the ion intensity vs. the voltage between the ionization chamber and the electron trap, the voltage between filament and chamber being held constant at 8 volts. The gas was methane, in which the secondary ions CH_5^+ and CH_4^+ are formed by the following processes:

$$CH_4^+ + CH_4 \begin{cases} \longrightarrow CH_3 + CH_5^+ \text{ (H}^+\text{ stripping)} & \text{(7a)} \\ \longrightarrow C_2H_8^+ \longrightarrow CH_5^+ + CH_3 \text{ (complex)} & \text{(7b)} \\ \longrightarrow CH_4 + CH_4^+ \text{ (charge transfer)} & \text{(7c)} \end{cases}$$

Both ions appear at 5 volts between the chamber and trap, which corresponds to a total energy of the bombarding electrons of $5 + 8 = 13.0$ e.v.—i.e., it corresponds to the appearance potential of CH_4^+ from methane. The increase at higher energies of the curve for CH_4^+ is mainly caused by the increase in formation of primary ions between the chamber and trap. The curve of CH_5^+ at first rises with increasing voltage.

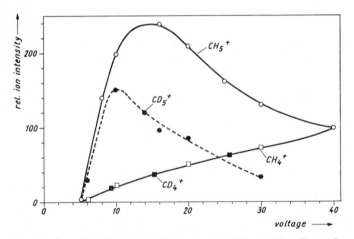

Figure 1. "Ionization efficiency curves" in the Cermak-Herman operation of an ion source. Relative ion intensity normalized at 40 volts for CH_4^+ and CH_5^+. Voltage between filament and ionization chamber constant at 8 volts

However, a maximum is reached at about 15 volts, and a decrease is observed at higher voltages. With increasing voltage, the kinetic energy of the primary ions is also increased. The increase in primary ion current apparently is counterbalanced and finally exceeded by the decrease in the cross-section of the ion molecule reaction. In addition, discrimination of CH_5^+ ions which are formed via a complex becomes more effective. At a potential of 20 volts between trap and chamber, most of the primary ions have kinetic energies around 20 e.v., and a secondary CH_5^+ ion formed via a complex will have $20/4 = 5$ e.v. (Equation 6) perpendicular to the direction of flight through the mass spectrometer.   Since CH_5^+ ions are still observed even at higher voltages, it was supposed that they are at least partly formed in a stripping process.

Figure 1 also shows the results of experiments with deuterated methane.   The curve for CD_4^+ practically is identical with the CH_4^+ curve. However, the decrease in the intensity of CD_5^+ at higher voltages is more pronounced than the decrease for CH_5^+ while nearly the same intensities for both ions are observed at low voltages.   If the protonated molecule is formed via a complex, no significant isotope effect is expected. In the case of stripping, however, strong isotope effects must occur since the mass of the transferred particle appears in Equation 5.   As described in more detail below, the internal energy (and stability) of the product ion strongly depends on the mass of the transferred particle.   The observed isotope effects in Figure 1 indicate the formation of a complex at low primary ion energies and the occurrence of a stripping process at higher energies (*11*).

Velocity Spectra

The experimental arrangement shown in Figure 2 has already been described (*9, 10*).   Primary ions such as Ar^+, N_2^+, or CO^+ are produced by electron impact in a conventional ion source and are accelerated by voltages between 20 and 200 volts.   The ion beam enters the collision chamber which contains hydrogen or deuterium under a pressure of 1–2 μ. The product ions such as ArH^+, N_2H^+ or COH^+ as well as the unreacted primary ions finally enter a Wien velocity filter (crossed electric and magnetic fields) which allows ions of equal linear velocity to reach the collector.   Practically all secondary ions are collected since their deflections from the direction of the incident ions are small because of the large difference in the masses of the collision partners.   The velocity spectrum of the reaction is obtained by scanning the electric field of the Wien filter, automatically registering the ion intensity.   Reaction cross-sections can

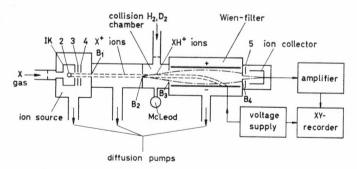

Figure 2.   Schematic presentation of the experimental arrangement for the measurements of velocity spectra

be obtained from the square areas of the bands produced in the spectra by the unreacted primary ions and the product ions.

The velocity spectra of Reactions 8a and 8b are shown in Figure 3.

$$Ar^+ + H_2 \rightarrow ArH^+ + H \tag{8a}$$

$$Ar^+ + D_2 \rightarrow ArD^+ + D \tag{8b}$$

The ion intensity is plotted *vs.* the velocity in units of the velocity V_o of the incident ion. The large peak at V_o is attributed to unreacted primary ions. This band shows a tail towards lower velocities since

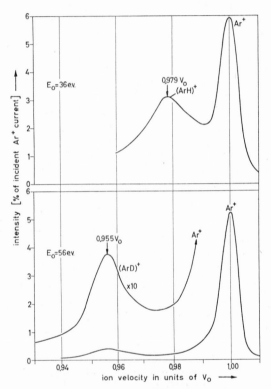

Figure 3. Velocity spectra for the reactions
$Ar^+ + H_2 \rightarrow ArH^+ + H$ *and* $Ar^+ + D_2 \rightarrow$
$ArD^+ + D$

some of the primary ions suffered unreactive collisions. The band of the product ion appears on this background. Table I shows the experimentally determined position of the center of the product ion band and the positions calculated from the "stripping" and "complex" model by using Equations 9 and 10. (It should be noted that "stripping" is not the correct term for reactions of the type $X^+ + H_2 \rightarrow XH^+ + H$ in which an H atom is picked up by the incident ion. By analogy to similar processes in nuclear physics one should use the term "pick-up" reactions.

Table I. Experimental and Theoretical Positions of the Product Ion Bands in the Velocity Spectra of Some Reactions

Reaction	Position of the Center of the Product Ion Band in Units of $V_o{}^a$	Theoretical Position	
		Stripping	Complex
$Ar^+ + H_2 \rightarrow ArH^+ + H$	0.979	0.9756	0.9524
$Ar^+ + D_2 \rightarrow ArD^+ + D$	0.955	0.9524	0.9091
$N_2^+ + H_2 \rightarrow N_2H^+ + H$	0.968	0.9655	0.9333
$N_2^+ + D_2 \rightarrow N_2D^+ + D$	0.939	0.9333	0.8750
$CO^+ + H_2 \rightarrow COH^+ + H$	0.960	0.9655	0.9333
$CO^+ + D_2 \rightarrow COD^+ + D$	0.933	0.9333	0.8750

[a] Primary ion energy: 40 e.v.

The analytical treatment, however, is the same for both types of reactions since it does not matter whether the ion or the molecule is regarded as reference system. We are therefore still using the term "stripping" here in a wider sense.)

According to the ideal stripping model, the incident X^+ ion collides with a quasi-free H atom while the other H atom in the H_2 molecule merely participates as "idle spectator" to the reaction. The conservation of momentum in the system X^+–H requires the secondary ion XH^+ to be formed with the velocity:

$$V = V_o \frac{M}{M + m} \tag{9}$$

in the direction of the primary ion. M and m are the masses of X^+ and of the transferred H atom. If a complex XH_2^+ were formed, it would move with the velocity:

$$V = V_o \frac{M}{M + 2m} \tag{10}$$

in the direction of the primary ion. Both dissociation products of the complex have a velocity component of this size. They may have a second component in different directions if the heat of reaction or the internal energy of the complex more or less appear as kinetic energy of the fragments. If the complex lives longer than one period of rotation, its decay occurs isotropically in the center of mass system. The band of the product ion would be symmetric and be centered at the velocity given by Equation 10. A shorter-lived complex would probably produce an unsymmetric band (which has never been observed).

Comparing the values in Table I shows that the bands of the product ions are located as predicted from the ideal stripping model. We therefore conclude that this model is suitable to describe these ion-molecule reactions at higher energies. It seems from the excellent agreement in Table I that no transfer of momentum to the spectator H atom occurs at all. This would also mean that the product ion moves exactly in the direction of the incoming ion. We found indeed that the divergence of the secondary ion beam must be very small since very thin slits after the collision chamber could be used in the apparatus described in Figure 2

without loss of XH $^+$ intensity.   On the other hand, the Wien filter has
no ideal properties because of magnetic stray fields etc.—i.e. the velocity
spectra are reliable only to a certain degree.   Perhaps therefore the spectator hydrogen atom is not completely "idle" but receives a little momentum, although this effect cannot be remarkable.   Certain deviations
from the ideal stripping model will be discussed below (*see* "band shifts").

The validity of the stripping model can also be checked by measuring
the velocity spectrum of the reactions X $^+$ + HD → XH $^+$ + D (and
XD $^+$ + H).   According to the stripping model, the bands of XH $^+$ and
XD $^+$ should appear at the same positions as the bands of these ions,
when they are produced by the reactions X $^+$ + H$_2$ and X $^+$ + D$_2$, respectively (the mass of the spectative hydrogen atom should not matter at

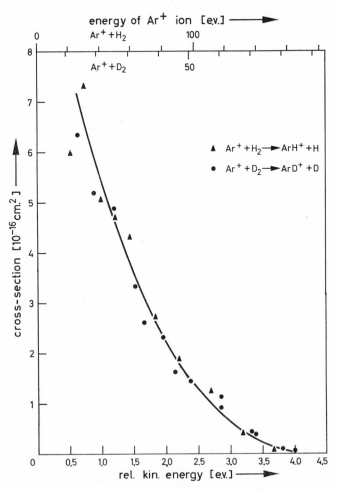

Figure 4.   Cross-sections as functions of the relative
kinetic energy for the reactions of Ar $^+$ with H$_2$ and
D$_2$ (13)

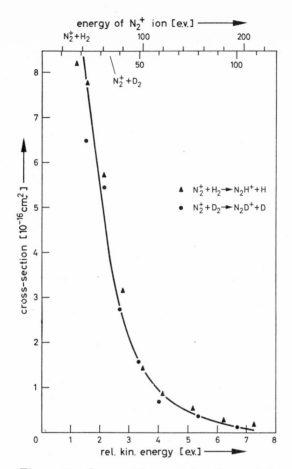

Figure 5.   Cross-sections as functions of the
relative kinetic energy for the reactions of $N_2{}^+$
with H_2 and D_2 (14)

all).   If the complex model is correct, XH^+ and XD^+ should appear at
the same velocity since both ions would result from an intermediate
complex XHD^+.   In all cases the XH^+ and XD^+ bands were located in
the spectra as was expected from the stripping model (8).

Cross-Sections

The cross-sections of the various reactions observed are shown as
functions of the kinetic energies in the center of mass system and in the
laboratory system by Figures 4, 5, and 6.   In all cases, the cross-sections
for reactions between X^+ and H_2 or D_2, respectively, are equal if one
compares them at the same relative kinetic energy.   According to the

stripping model, the relative kinetic energy has to be calculated for $X^+ + H_2$ according to:

$$E_r = E \frac{m_H}{M + m_H} \tag{11}$$

for $X^+ + D_2$ according to:

$$E_r = E \frac{m_D}{M + m_D} \tag{12}$$

That is, if one compares the cross-sections at the same kinetic energy E of the incident ion, the transfer of a H atom always occurs with a larger cross-section than the transfer of a D atom. (The cross-sections at the same relative kinetic energy are equal since the effective radial potential in which the particles move during the collision is the same for H- and D-atom transfer. The effective potential is the sum of the potentials

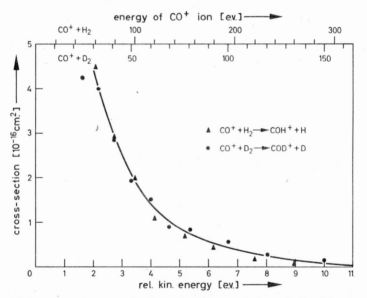

Figure 6. Cross-sections as functions of the relative kinetic energy for the reactions of CO^+ with H_2 and D_2 (14)

caused by the forces between the colliding H atom and primary ion and the centrifugal potential. If differences in the zero point energies are neglected, the potentials between an H or a D atom bonded to another hydrogen atom and the X^+ ion can be assumed to be equal. The centrifugal potential has the same value at constant relative kinetic energy and impact parameter.)

If stripping also occurs in reactions of X^+ ions with HD, then XH^+, and XD^+ should be formed with half the cross-sections as in the reactions $X^+ + H_2$ and $X^+ + D_2$, respectively (at the same kinetic energy E of the

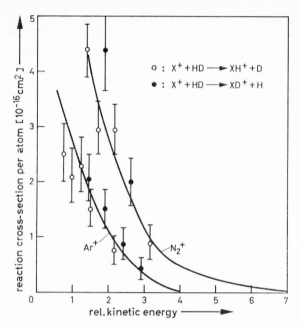

*Figure 7. Cross-sections per H or D atom,
respectively, as a function of the relative kinetic
energy (8)*

incident ion).   Furthermore, XH^+ and XD^+ should be formed with equal
cross-sections from $X^+ + HD$ if one compares the formation of these ions
at the same relative kinetic energy.   This means that E_r must be calculated according to Equation 11 if one considers the formation of ArH^+,
and Equation 12 must be used to calculate E_r for XD^+ formation.   In
other words, the cross-section per hydrogen atom for all reactions between
X^+ and H_2, D_2 or HD must be equal at the same relative kinetic energy
calculated as mentioned above.   Figure 7 shows the dependence of the
cross-section on E_r for all reactions of Ar^+ and N_2^+ ions.   The full lines
were taken from Figures 4 and 5, respectively.   The points in the diagram indicate the measured cross-sections for the reactions of Ar^+ and
N_2^+ with HD.   It can be seen that these points fit the curves as expected
from the stripping model.

Figure 8 presents the results on the various reactions of Ar^+ with
H_2, D_2 and HD in a different form.   The intensity ratio ArH^+/ArD^+ is
plotted as a function of the Ar^+ ion energy.   The dotted line gives the
results obtained by Klein and Friedman (*12*) for the reaction of Ar^+ with
HD.   They found that the ratio ArH^+/ArD^+ is a little smaller than unity
at low Ar^+ energy as expected from the complex model.   With increasing
energy, the ArH^+/ArD^+ ratio slightly increased.   At higher energies,
this ratio is much higher than 1.0 and strongly increases above about 60
e.v.   Theoretically (if the stripping model is ideally fulfilled), the ratio
should become infinite at the critical energy of 94 e.v. for the stripping

of a D atom (*see* below).   Koski and co-workers (2) have, in the mean-
time, published values of the ratio ArH$^+$/ArD$^+$ for the intermediate
range (between about 5 and 20 e.v.) which well fit into Figure 8.

The isotope effects shown by Figures 1 and 8 demonstrate the transition from the stripping or pick-up mechanism to the complex model for
different chemical reactions.   As far as we know this is the first evidence
for such a transition.   It may be emphasized again that this transition
should also be detected in the velocity spectra.   Therefore, it would be
desirable to construct apparatuses which allow one to measure velocity
spectra at ion energies of about 1 e.v.

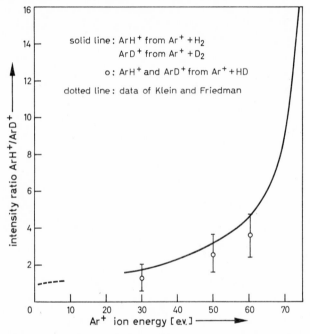

*Figure 8.   The intensity ratio ArH$^+$/ArD$^+$ as a
function of the kinetic energy of the incident Ar$^+$
ion (8)*

The cross-sections at an ion energy of 20 e.v. amount to about 10×10^{-16} sq. cm.   The stripping model is already obeyed at this energy since
the product ion bands appear at the predicted positions in the velocity
spectra.   Cross-sections of this size are comparable to the gas kinetic
collision cross-sections of the molecules or atoms involved.   The time of a
collision is rather short at these high ion energies—i.e. of the order of the
time required for one vibration of an H atom in a loose chemical bond.
Therefore one can hardly expect that a reaction takes place at every
collision.   The rather high reaction cross-sections are only understood if
most of the stripping processes occur in highly excentric collisions.

Energy Considerations

The internal energy, U, of an ion which is formed in a stripping reaction is equal to the sum of the relative kinetic energy (according to Equation 11) plus the heat of the reaction W if W does not appear as

$$U = E \frac{m}{M + m} + W \qquad (13)$$

kinetic energy of the fragments (Equation 13). (W is rather small since most of the reactions listed in Table I are nearly thermoneutral.) The relative kinetic energy appears as vibrational or as rotational excitation of the product ion depending on the eccentricity of the collision. Above a critical energy $E = E_{crit.}$ of the incident ion, U exceeds the dissociation energy of the product ion:

$$E_{crit} = \frac{(D - W)(M + m)}{m} \qquad (14)$$

The reaction cross-section should therefore become zero for $E \geqslant E_c$. By taking $D = 5.0$ e.v. and $W = 0.5$ e.v. for the reactions listed in Table II, the critical energies could be calculated (*13,14*).

Although the curve in Figure 4 is slightly tailing at higher energies, zero cross-sections for the formation of ArH$^+$ and ArD$^+$ may be extrapolated. At about 4 e.v. of relative kinetic energy practically no secondary ions are formed. This corresponds to 164 e.v. of $E_{crit.}$ for ArH$^+$ and 84 e.v. for ArD$^+$. The theoretical values agree fairly well with the experimental results in Table II.

Table II. Theoretical and Experimental Critical Energies for Various Reactions

Reaction	Critical Energy of Incident Ion as Calculated from Equation 14	Experimental Critical Energy[a]
Ar$^+$ + H$_2$ → ArH$^+$ + H	184	164
Ar$^+$ + D$_2$ → ArD$^+$ + D	94	84
N$_2$$^+$ + H$_2$ → N$_2$H$^+$ + H	131	108
N$_2$$^+$ + D$_2$ → N$_2$D$^+$ + D	68	60
CO$^+$ + H$_2$ → COH$^+$ + H	131	120
CO$^+$ + D$_2$ → COD$^+$ + D	68	70

[a] By extrapolation of the steep parts of the curves in Figures 4, 5, and 6 at lower energies.

In the curves in Figure 5 and 6, tailing is much more pronounced. The critical energies obtained by extrapolating the steep parts of the curves agree with the calculated $E_{crit.}$ values (Table II). However, secondary ions are still formed at relative kinetic energies of more than 5 e.v. Although in these ions more than one degree of vibrational freedom is present, it is difficult to believe that N$_2$H$^+$ and COH$^+$ can possess so much internal energy without dissociating immediately. As discussed below, deviations from the stripping model are also observed in the velocity spectra of the reactions of N$_2$$^+$ and CO$^+$ when the relative kinetic energy is higher than a few e.v. These deviations in the spectra indicate that the secondary ions carry less internal energy than anticipated from Equation 13.

Band Shifts (Elastic Collisions with Atom Transfer)

The spectrum in Figure 3 should not change (with respect to the band positions) with increasing energy of the incident ion as long as one is operating in the range where the stripping mechanism is obeyed. However, we observed that the band of the product ion became a little more narrow with increasing energy and was shifted to higher velocities. Figure 9 shows the position of the band center as a function of the primary ion energy for the product ions of N_2^+ and CO^+. The dotted lines give the positions of the bands which are expected from the ideal stripping model (Table I). The shift is less pronounced for the bands of the ions produced by the reaction of Ar^+ with H_2 and D_2 (13,14).

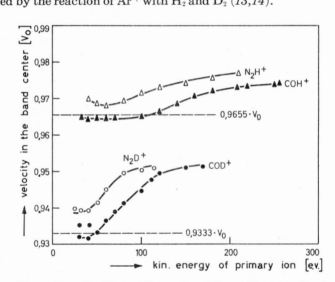

Figure 9. Position of the center of the product ion band as a function of the kinetic energy of the primary ion (14)

Since the secondary ions have more kinetic energy in the forward direction than is expected from the stripping model, some of the energy according to Equation 13 must appear not as internal but as kinetic energy in directed form of the fragments—i.e. the product ion is preferentially scattered into forward (in the center of mass system) while the "spectator" hydrogen atom (which is no longer "idle") moves in backward. This seems to be the first case in which preferential scattering of the product ion resulting from a chemical reaction has been observed. Preferential elastic scattering in the forward direction is a well-known phenomenon when fast-charged particles collide with molecules (Rutherford scattering).

When the product ion moved with a higher kinetic energy than predicted by the stripping model, the collision apparently was more elastic—i.e., less kinetic energy of the incident ion was used for internal excitation of the products. In an ideal "elastic collision with H transfer" the products carry no internal energy at all. If the secondary ion moves forward and the H atom moves backwards, conservation of momentum requires that the primary ion has a velocity:

$$V_{max} \approx \left[1 - \frac{m}{M} (2 - \sqrt{2}) \right] V_o \qquad (15)$$

(if $m \ll M$ and W is neglected). For example, if $M = 28$ and $m = 1$ or 2, V_{max} amounts to 0.979 V_o and 0.958 V_o, respectively. As seen from Figure 9 these values are nearly reached in the cases of N_2H^+ and N_2D^+, respectively.

A final mechanistic explanation for the occurrence of nearly elastic collision with H transfer has not yet been found. In an ideal stripping reaction, the distances between all atoms in the colliding particles must change slowly enough during all phases of the collision to prevent the spectator atom, being pushed away by a repulsive potential. At high energies of the incident ion, the collision may occur in such a short time that the equilibrium distances of the atoms in the whole complex cannot be reached in each phase of the collision. A repulsive potential may now be set up in the last phase and push the spectator atom backward.

Quantum Mechanical Effects

In the discussion of the internal energy U of an ion formed in an ideal stripping process (Equation 13) the quantization of U was not considered. With increasing energy E of the incident ion, the production XH^+ can be formed in higher vibrational levels. If $\epsilon (n + \frac{1}{2})$ denotes the energy of the nth vibrational level, excitation of this level can first occur at the primary ion energy:

$$E_n = \left[\epsilon\left(n + \frac{1}{2}\right) - W \right] \frac{M + m}{m} \qquad (16)$$

when it makes a central collision with the hydrogen atom to be transferred. In more eccentric collisions, part of the relative kinetic energy should appear as rotational energy of the product ion—i.e. more kinetic energy than given by Equation 16 is necessary to excite the nth vibrational level. If the cross-section of the reaction shows a resonance effect at the energies E_n according to Equation 16 (which is the case in many atom or nuclear excitation curves), small discontinuities may be expected in the dependence of σ on E. The conditions under which the curves in Figures 4, 5, and 6 were measured are far too rough to allow the detection of small discontinuities.

If a transition between the stripping mechanism and the model of elastic collisions with atom transfer occurs, product ions in various vibrational levels may be formed at a given primary ion energy, the "spectator" hydrogen atom carrying away the rest of the internal energy U—i.e., the velocity spectrum of the product ion will contain ions of low internal but high kinetic energy in the forward direction as well as ions of high vibrational energy and lower kinetic energy. If resonance for the excitation of vibrational levels exists, the band of the product ion should show a fine structure—i.e., peaks appearing at velocities which differ corresponding to the energy difference ϵ. The background of scattered primary ions is now too high for one to detect any fine structure.

Limits and Application of the Stripping Model

Since the stripping model is suitable for understanding many features of ion-molecule reactions of the type $X^+ + H_2 \rightarrow XH^+ + H$ at high energies, the question may arise whether other types of ion-molecule reactions are also described by this model. The ideal stripping situation in which no momentum is transferred to the rest of a molecule or ion is probably very rare. On the other hand, one can hardly believe that complexes are still formed at higher ion energies, in which all atoms of the colliding particles move with the same velocity for a short time. In other words, it is believed that all kinds of situations between stripping, inelastic complex formation, and elastic collision with chemical reaction will be found. As concluded above, stripping occurs in rather eccentric collisions. In a head-on collision, momentum transfer to the rest of the molecule or ion is much more probable. Stripping appears predominant in certain reactions because of the high cross-sections for eccentric collisions—i.e., there should always be a "background" of rather central collisions which lead to another velocity distribution. Whether stripping is really probable in an eccentric collision is determined by the interaction potentials between the ion and the transferred atom as well as the spectator rest of the molecule. These potentials are different for various reactions and generally not known. Therefore, it is not possible to predict the extent to which ideal stripping may occur.

One of the interesting aspects of the stripping model (and of the elastic reactive collision model) lies in the fact that chemical reactions may occur with relatively high cross-sections at relative kinetic energies which are far higher than the strengths of chemical bonds. This may be of interest to nuclear recoil chemistry where it is generally assumed that hot atoms do not form chemical bonds directly but must first be slowed down to energies of a few e.v. It is also interesting to note that stripping has recently been observed in molecular beam experiments on reactions of alkali atoms with halides (such as $K + Br_2 \rightarrow KBr + Br$) although these reactions occur at room temperature (3, 7, 15).

Literature Cited

(1) Barker, R., Hamill, W. H., Williams, R. R., *J. Phys. Chem.* **63**, 825 (1959).
(2) Berta, M. A., Ellis, B. Y., Koski, W. S., *J. Chem. Phys.*, in press.
(3) Bireley, J. H., Herschbach, D. R., *J. Chem. Phys.* **44**, 1690 (1966).
(4) Boelrijk, N., Hamill, W. H., *J. Am. Chem. Soc.* **84**, 730 (1962).
(5) Cermak, V., Herman, Z., *Nucleonics* **19**, 106 (1961).
(6) Field, F. H., Franklin, J. L., Lampe, F. W., *J. Am. Chem. Soc.* **79**, 2419 (1957).
(7) Grosser, A. E., Bernstein, R. B., *J. Chem. Phys.* **43**, 1140 (1965).
(8) Henglein, A., Lacmann, K., Knoll, B., *J. Chem. Phys.* **43**, 1048 (1965).
(9) Henglein, A., Lacmann, K., Jacobs, G., *Ber. Bunsenges. Physik. Chem.* **69**, 279 (1965).
(10) Henglein, A., Lacmann, K., *Advan. Mass Spectrometry* **3**, 331 (1966).
(11) Henglein, A., Muccini, G. A., *Z. Naturforsch.* **17a**, 452 (1962); **18a**, 753 (1963).
(12) Klein, F. S., Friedman, L., *J. Chem. Phys.* **41**, 1789 (1964).
(13) Lacmann, K., Henglein, A., *Ber. Bunsenges. Physik. Chem.* **69**, 286 (1965).
(14) Lacmann, K., Henglein, A., *Ber. Bunsenges. Physik. Chem.* **69**, 292 (1965).
(15) Minturn, R. E., Datz, S., Becker, R. L., *J. Chem. Phys.* **44**, 1149 (1966).
(16) Stevenson, D. P., Schissler, D. O., *J. Chem. Phys.* **29**, 282 (1958).

RECEIVED May 6, 1966.

6

Isotope Effect in the Reaction of HD⁺ with Rare Gases

M. A. BERTA, B. Y. ELLIS, and W. S. KOSKI

The Johns Hopkins University, Baltimore, Md.

The isotope effects of reactions of HD⁺ ions with He, Ne, Ar, and Kr over an energy range from 3 to 20 e.v. are discussed. The results are interpreted in terms of a stripping model for ion-molecule reactions. The technique of wave vector analysis, which has been successful in nuclear stripping reactions, is used. The method is primarily classical, but it incorporates the vibrational and rotational properties of molecule-ions which may be important. Preliminary calculations indicate that this model is relatively insensitive to the vibrational factors of the molecule-ion but depends strongly on rotational parameters.

The reactions of rare gas ions with HD and the reactions of HD⁺ ions with rare gases have been studied by several investigators (*12, 14, 15*). Stevenson and Schissler studied ion-molecule reactions in a mixture of Ar and HD in the ion source of a conventional mass spectrometer where the average energy of the ions was slightly greater than thermal. They found a value of 0.85 for the ratio ArH⁺/ArD⁺. More recently, Klein and Friedman (*7*) studied this isotope effect in a mass spectrometer where the bombarding ion energy could be varied from essentially zero to 8 e.v. The polarization model for ion-molecule reactions was assumed, and they were able to explain satisfactorily the observed isotope effect which varied from Stevenson and Schissler's value to a value somewhat greater than unity. As two-stage mass spectrometers were introduced into the study of ion-molecule reactions, it became clear that the polarization model was not applicable at higher bombarding ion energies (*4, 5, 8, 9*), and a stripping or spectator mechanism for ion-molecule reactions was proposed. This paper reports on the isotope effect in the reactions of HD⁺ with He, Ne, Ar, and Kr in the energy region of 2–20 e.v. This energy range bridges the region in which the polarization model may be expected to be applicable and the region where the stripping mechanism begins to dominate the process.

80

Results and Discussion

The apparatus and procedure used in this work have been described in detail elsewhere (2, 16), and a schematic diagram of the equipment is included in the article by Lindholm in this volume (10).

In studying ion-molecule reactions such as

$$Ar^+ + HD \rightarrow ArH^+ + D$$

$$\rightarrow ArD^+ + H$$

one finds that at low bombarding energies, the ratio of ArH^+/ArD^+ is not greatly different from unity, and the isotope effects can be explained by the usual vibrational factors that account for chemical isotope effects. As one increases the bombarding energy, the ratio can attain a value much higher than unity, and the effect cannot be accounted for by the same factors that are important at low energies. This is illustrated in Figure 1, where ArH^+/ArD^+ is plotted for various Ar^+ ion energies (2). Note that at 60 e.v. the ratio is about 4 and is rising with energy. This rapid rise in the ratio can be apparently accounted for in the following way.

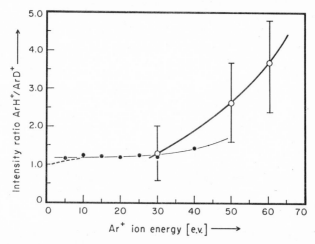

Figure 1. The ratio of the cross-sections of ArH$^+$ to ArD$^+$ as a function of the energy of Ar$^+$ in the reaction Ar$^+$ + HD, (—————) Klein and Friedman (1) ($\substack{\circ \\ \cdot}$)Henglein, Lacmann, and Knoll (5) and (●) this study

Consider the collision of Ar^+ with HD. If one assumes that one of the partners in the diatomic molecule does not participate in the collision but merely acts as a spectator, then conservation of energy and momentum permit the following equation for head-on collisions

$$\frac{p^2}{2M} = \frac{p^2}{2(M + m)} - Q + E_{int} \tag{1}$$

where p is the momentum of the bombarding ion and M is its mass, m is the mass of the struck atom, Q = heat of reaction, and E_{int} is the energy that goes into internal degrees of freedom.   Rearranging and noting that $\dfrac{p^2}{2M}$ is the energy of the bombarding ion, E, we have

$$E = \frac{M + m}{m} (E_{int} - Q) \tag{2}$$

If E_{int} exceeds the dissociation energy, D, the molecule ion, Mm^+, will not form.   In applying such consideration to the Ar^+ reaction with the hydrogen molecule, Henglein $et\ al.$ (5) find that the critical energies are 164 and 84 e.v. in the ArH^+ and ArD^+ cases, respectively.   It is clear, therefore, that if the bombarding energy exceeds 84 e.v., one would expect no ArD^+ formation, and a high ArH^+/ArD^+ ratio would be expected; theoretically, an infinite value is possible.   This interpretation of the $Ar^+ + H_2$ reaction seems to be supported by experimental evidence.   On the other hand, if one attempts to apply this simple approach to reactions of the type $HD^+ + X$, where X is a rare gas, Berta $et\ al.$ (2) have shown that the results do not conform experimentally to expectations.   Their results are summarized in Figure 2.

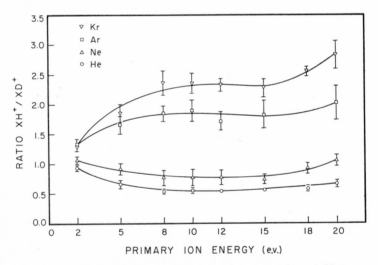

Figure 2.   The ratio of cross-sections for formation of XH^+ to XD^+ as a function of the energy of HD^+ in the reaction $HD^+ + X$, where X is He, Ne, Ar, and Kr

Applying Equation 2 to either the Kr or Ar reaction indicates that one should not expect the formation of ArH^+ or KrH^+ at energies as high as 20 e.v.   In these reactions, product ions exist at much higher energies than one expects from the spectator model, suggesting that the non-colliding partner of the diatomic ion is not solely a spectator.   It apparently participates in the collision, carrying away some of the energy which would normally go into internal degrees of freedom.

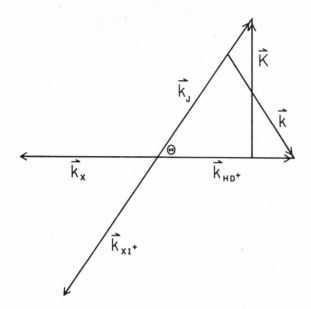

Figure 3. Wave vector diagram for the reaction
$X + HD^+ \rightarrow XI^+ + J$ *where I and J may be H*
or D according to the isotopic product considered

Recent unpublished experiments by Rozett (*13*) indicate that in the reaction $Ar + HD^+$ the isotopic ratio, ArH^+/ArD, continues to increase as one proceeds from 20 to 30 e.v. bombarding energy. In addition (*13*), work on the dissociative reactions such as $HD^+ + Ar \rightarrow Ar + H^+ + D$ shows that the yield of D^+ increases rapidly as one exceeds 20 e.v. ion energy whereas the increase of H^+ yield does not become evident until one reaches roughly twice this energy. These observations appear to be compatible qualitatively with the prediction of the stripping model.

In order to get better insight into the nature of the isotope effect involved in these ion-molecule reactions, we are currently attempting to treat stripping reactions by the technique of wave vector analysis which has been successful in nuclear stripping reactions (*11*). The model is primarily classical, but it incorporates the vibrational and rotational properties of the molecule-ions which may be important. A brief description of the method follows.

Consider the wave vector diagram in Figure 3, where

$$\vec{k}_j = \vec{p}_j/\hbar$$

and $\vec{p}_j$ is the momentum of the jth species. The reaction is:

$$X + HD^+ \rightarrow XI^+ + J$$

where I and J may be H or D according to the isotopic product considered.

$$\vec{k}_{HD^+} = (2\mu_i E/\hbar^2)^{1/2}$$

where

$$\mu_i = \frac{(M_{HD^+})\,(M_X)}{(M_{HD^+} + M_X)}$$

the initial reduced mass, and E is the energy of the bombarding ion.
Conservation of energy requires:

$$k^2_{HD^+}\left[\frac{1}{M_{HD^+}} + \frac{1}{[M_X}\right] + \frac{2Q}{\hbar^2} = k^2_J\left[\frac{1}{M_J} + \frac{1}{M_{XI^+}}\right]$$

where M_J is the mass of the jth species, and Q is the heat of the reaction.
The wave vector of the product J is made up partly by the fraction of the
incident wave vector $\left(\dfrac{M_J}{M_{HD^+}}\right) \vec{k}_{HD^+}$ imparted to it.   Since the wave vector
of J is given by $\vec{k}_J$, the vector difference between $\vec{k}_J$ and $\left(\dfrac{M_J}{M_{HD^+}}\right) \vec{k}_{HD^+}$
must be supplied by the motion of J relative to I.   Thus

$$\vec{K} = \vec{k}_J - \frac{M_J}{M_{HD^+}}\vec{k}_{HD^+}$$

where

$$|\vec{K}| = \left[k_J{}^2 + \left(\frac{M_J}{M_{HD^+}}\right)^2 k_{HD^+}{}^2 - 2\,\frac{M_J}{M_{HD^+}}\,k_{HD^+}\,k_J\,\cos\theta\right]^{1/2}$$

The momentum of I relative to XI$^+$ at the time of reaction can be found
by following a similar path of reasoning and is:

$$\vec{k} = \vec{k}_{HD^+} - \frac{M_X\,\vec{k}_J}{M_{XI^+}}$$

where

$$|\vec{k}| = \left[k_{HD^+}{}^2 + \left(\frac{M_X}{M_{XI^+}}\right)^2 k^2_J - 2\,\frac{M_X}{M_{XI^+}}\,k_{HD^+}\,k_J\,\cos\theta\right]^{1/2}$$

The probability that J has a wave vector $\vec{K}$ relative to I in HD$^+$ is given
by the momentum transform of the wave function for the vibrational
and rotational interactions in HD$^+$.   The probability that I is captured
by X with a wave vector $\vec{k}$ is given by the momentum transform of the
wave function for the rotational and vibrational interactions in XI$^+$.

If $\psi_{HD^+}(\vec{K})$ and $\psi_{XI^+}(\vec{k})$ denote the Fourier transforms of the indicated rotational and vibrational wave functions, the expression for the
differential cross-section is

$$\frac{d\sigma}{d\Omega} \propto |\psi_{HD^+}(\vec{K})|^2\,|\psi_{XI^+}(\vec{k})|^2$$

The expression for the ratio of cross-sections for the HeH$^+$ and HeD$^+$ products complete with the constants of proportionality (3) is given by:

$$\sigma_{\text{HeH}^+}/\sigma_{\text{HeD}^+} =$$

$$\left[\left(\frac{M_{\text{HeH}^+}+M_{\text{H}}}{M_{\text{HeH}^+}+M_{\text{D}}}\right)\left(\frac{M_{\text{D}}M_{\text{HeH}^+}}{M_{\text{HeD}^+}+M_{\text{H}}}\right)\right]^{1/2} \times \frac{\int \left|\psi_{\text{HeD}^+}(\vec{K})\right|^2 \left|\psi_{\text{HeH}^+}(\vec{k})\right|^2 \sin\theta \, d\theta}{\int \left|\psi_{\text{HD}^+}(\vec{K'})\right|^2 \left|\psi_{\text{HeD}^+}(\vec{k'})\right|^2 \sin\theta \, d\theta}$$

where $\vec{K'}$ and $\vec{k'}$ indicate the HeD$^+$ product.

In order to evaluate the above expression, solutions were found for the Schrödinger equation using the Morse potential for rotational quantum number ℓ not equal to zero:

$$V(r) = D\,(1 - e^{-a(r-r_0)})^2 + \ell\,(\ell + 1)\hbar^2/2\mu r_o^2$$

where D is the dissociation energy, r_o is the equilibrium atomic distance of the normal molecule, a is $0.1227\ \omega_e(\mu/D)^{1/2}$, ω_e is the equilibrium vibrational frequency, and μ is reduced mass of the molecule. A constant value of 0.77 was obtained for HeH$^+$/HeD$^+$ ratio in the reaction of He with HD$^+$ ion in the $v = 3$ vibrational state and the $\ell = 0$ rotational state to form HeH$^+$ or HeD$^+$ in the ground states. The energy range covered was 10–20 e.v. The data used in the calculations are given in Table I.

Table I

	HD$^+$	HeH$^+$	HeD$^+$
D, e.v.	2.74[a]	1.931[b]	1.911[c]
Masses	1,2	4,1	4,2
r_o, A.	1.060[a]	1.446[b]	1.446[d]
ω_e, cm.$^{-1}$	1990[a]	3378[b]	2621[d]
$\omega_e X_e$, cm.$^{-1}$	45[a,c]	183[c]	110[c]
	$Q = -0.8$ e.v.		

[a] Calculated from values for H$_2^+$ in Ref. (6).
[b] Data from Anex (1).
[c] $\omega_e X_e = \omega_e^2/4D$.
[d] Isotopic substitution does not alter the force constant or the internuclear distance.

It is clear, after examining the He curve in Figure 2, that agreement between theory and experiment appears to be good for this reaction in the energy range studied. The calculations are being extended to the other rare gases.

Acknowledgment

This work was supported in part by the Directorate of Chemical Sciences, Air Force Office of Scientific Research, under contract AF 49-(638)–1301.

One of us (WSK) is indebted to A. Henglein and Jean H. Futrell for very informative discussions and private communications on matters relating to this research.

Literature Cited

(1) Anex, B., J. Chem. Phys. **38,** 1651 (1963).
(2) Berta, M. A., Koski, W. S., J. Am. Chem. Soc. **86,** 5098 (1964).
(3) Fulton, T., Owen, G. E., Phys. Rev. **108,** 789 (1957).
(4) Henglein, A., Lacmann, K., Jacobs, G., Ber. Bunsenges. Physik. Chem. **69,** 279 (1965).
(5) Henglein, A., Lacmann, K., Knoll, B., J. Chem. Phys. **43,** 1048 (1965).
(6) Herzberg, G., "Spectra of Diatomic Molecules," D. Van Nostrand, Princeton, 1950.
(7) Klein, F. S., Friedman, L., J. Chem. Phys. **41,** 1789 (1964).
(8) Lacmann, K., Henglein, A., Ber. Bunsenges. Physik. Chem. **69,** 286 (1965).
(9) Lacmann, K., Henglein, A., Ibid. **69,** 292 (1965).
(10) Lindholm, E., ADVAN. CHEM. SER. **58,** 1 (1966).
(11) Owen, G. E., Madansky, L., Am. J. Phys. **26,** 260 (1958).
(12) Reuben, B. G., Friedman, L., J. Chem. Phys. **37,** 1636 (1962).
(13) Rozett, R. W., unpublished research.
(14) Stevenson, D. P., Schissler, D. O., J. Chem. Phys. **23,** 1353 (1955).
(15) Stevenson, D. P., Schissler, D. O., J. Chem. Phys. **29,** 282 (1958).
(16) Weiner, E. R., Hertel, G. R., Koski, W. S., J. Am. Chem. Soc. **86,** 788 (1964).

RECEIVED May 10, 1966.

Energy Transfer in Ion-Molecule Reactions

LEWIS FRIEDMAN

Brookhaven National Laboratory, Upton, N. Y. 11973

Experimental energy transfer processes are studied either by investigating the velocity dependence of certain ion-molecule reactions, the distribution of energy in reaction products, or intramolecular isotope effects. Kinetic energy transfer is observed in competitive dissociation reaction channels in HD-rare gas reactions and the similar dissociation process in the methane system yielding $CH_3{}^+$. In some cases the conjectured mechanism, which requires unit reaction efficiency at every ion-molecule collision fails because of the separation of reactant and product potential energy surfaces near possible collision impact parameters. The He^+-O_2 system demonstrates the importance of considering the nature of the interaction potential. Isotopic studies with ^3He and ^4He show that complex formation in He^+-O_2 reactions provides a mechanism for transferring kinetic energy to the neutral He product.

This discussion of ion-molecule reactions is limited to processes involving a chemical change which can be detected by mass analysis of reaction products. Resonant charge transfer between ions and their parent neutral molecules or energy transfer via inelastic collisions will not be included. Emphasis is placed on experimental work done in the Chemistry Department of Brookhaven National Laboratory which has been directed at testing a relatively simple ion-molecule reaction mechanism. For ion-molecule energy transfer studies it is necessary to separate the velocity dependence of the ion-molecule collision cross-section from the velocity or kinetic energy dependence of the ion-molecule reaction cross-section. The mechanism proposed by Gioumousis and Stevenson (G-S) (*8*) is particularly attractive because the collision cross-section is calculated directly from the Langevin (*15*) classical microscopic orbiting cross-section. Gioumousis and Stevenson defined the experimentally observed phenomenological cross-section Q as

$$Q = \frac{I_s}{I_p n l} \tag{1}$$

where I_s is the secondary or product ion current, and I_p is the primary or

reactant ion current observed at the mass spectrometer detector, n is
the concentration of neutral molecules, and l is the reactant ion path
length in the ion source. (This definition applies only to low pressure
reactions where the ratio of I_s/I_p is less than 0.05—i.e., where there is a
trivial depletion of I_p in the reaction.) Using a kinetic analysis and assuming that reaction takes place at every collision, Gioumousis and
Stevenson showed that for ions with a large kinetic energy with respect
to the energy of the neutral reactant molecule, Q is given by

$$Q = 2\pi \left(\frac{e^2\alpha}{\mu}\right)^{1/2} \left(\frac{2m_i}{eEl}\right)^{-1/2} \tag{2}$$

where e is the charge on the ion of mass m_i, μ the reduced mass of the
reacting system, α the polarizability of the molecule, and E is the electric
field in the mass spectrometer ion source. Stevenson and Schissler (23),
in a companion paper to Gioumousis and Stevenson's theoretical study,
demonstrated that Q's obtained experimentally and from Equation 2
were in excellent agreement for the reaction of low energy D_2^+ with D_2
and from the standpoint of data usually obtained in kinetic studies in
good agreement for a number of ion molecule reactions in H_2-rare gas
and H_2-diatomic molecule systems. The Gioumouis and Stevenson model
is somewhat inadequate for higher velocity ions because of the approximation in the Langevin calculation which considers only the ion-induced
dipole interaction in the ion molecule potential energy function. Hamill
and co-workers (1, 14) attempted to account for deviations from the
G-S model in reactions of ions having kinetic energy in excess of a few
e.v. by including a term in the cross-section expression for hard sphere
ion-neutral impacts. This approach, while stimulating, was accepted
with reservations because alternative reaction channels, which were not
measured in the early experiments, could account for the observed deviations from the theoretical model.

Interest at Brookhaven was stirred by the contrast between the
excellent agreement between theory and experiment for the $D_2^+ + D_2$
reaction and the rather poor description provided for the H_2-He and H_2-Ne
systems. The H_2-He system is particularly interesting because of the
relatively few particles involved in the reaction and its potential for accurate theoretical treatment. The reactions of H_2^+ or HD^+ with He
will be among the first to be treated in terms of a theoretically computed
potential energy surface; comparison of experiment and theory in this
system is therefore of prime importance.

Elemental Systems

Some of the problems encountered in the mass spectrometric study
of ion-molecule reactions are illustrated in a review of the H_2-He system
(25). If the spectrometer ion source is used as a reaction chamber, a
mixture of H_2 and He are subjected to electron impact ionization, and both
H_2^+ and He^+ are potential reactant ions. The initial problem is iden-

tifying the reactant ions. Thermochemical considerations suggest that Reaction 3:

$$He^+ + H_2 \rightarrow HeH^+ + H \tag{3}$$

is more probable than Reaction 4

$$H_2^+ + He \rightarrow HeH^+ + H \tag{4}$$

because the latter is endothermic with ground state H_2^+ by approximately 1 e.v. while Reaction 3 is strongly exothermic (8.3 e.v.). Identifying the reactant ion in this system is relatively straightforward because of the marked difference in H_2^+ and He^+ ionization potentials and ionization efficiency curves (Figure 1). The ionization efficiency curve of HeH^+

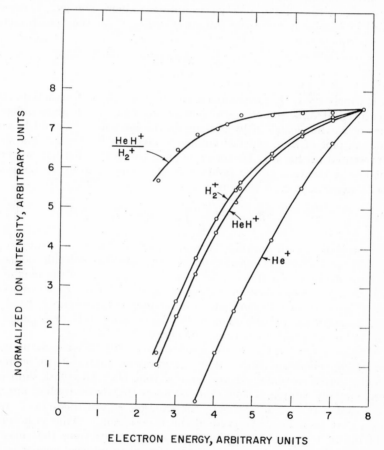

Figure 1. *Normalized ionization efficiency curves for H_2-He mixtures*

The ratio of HeH^+/H_2^+ as a function of electron energy is plotted on the same energy axis. Ion-accelerating voltage = 2500 volts; repeller potential = 3.12 volts; ionizing electron current = 10 μamp.

or its dependence on ionizing electron energy follows that of H_2^+ and falls well below the He^+ curve. The ratio of HeH^+/H_2^+ shows less than a 5% drop for a 50% change in He^+ intensity; hence, only a small fraction of the HeH^+ reaction can proceed via He^+ reactions. However, the HeH^+ curve does not fall exactly on the H_2^+ data but is shifted upward in the linear rise region by approximately 1 e.v. This shift in ionization efficiency curves suggests that reaction of ground state H_2^+ does not occur and that only H_2^+, with approximately 1 e.v. of internal energy produced in the electron impact ionization, reacts with He. For H_2^+ ions with less than a critical amount of kinetic energy, reaction of H_2^+ with less than 1.1 e.v. internal energy is not possible in the isolated collision in the spectrometer ion source.

After identifying the reactant ion, reaction cross-sections were measured as a function of average reactant ion kinetic energy. Q experimental is measured for given values of $(eEl)^{-1/2}$ in the spectrometer, and experimental values of k

$$k = Q_{\text{exp}} \left(\frac{eEl}{2m_i} \right)^{1/2} \qquad (5)$$

are determined. If the G-S model accurately describes the reaction, then k measured at different values of repeller voltage (which gives different values of E, the electric field gradient in the ion source) should be constant. A plot of k vs. repeller voltage is given in Figure 2. The data are presented in this way because k is identical to the thermal rate constant of the reaction or the product of the velocity and the Langevin velocity-dependent cross-section

$$k = 2\pi \left(\frac{e^2\alpha}{\mu} \right)^{1/2} = g\sigma(g) \qquad (6)$$

where g is the reactant ion velocity, and $\sigma(g) = \pi b_o^2$ where b_o is the impact parameter calculated classically for an orbiting ion-molecule collision. The decrease in k as a function of repeller voltage above the maximum in Figure 2 is almost a characteristic of reactions of hydrogen molecule ions. The lower energy data which indicates a kinetic energy threshold for the reaction is not observed in the H_2^+ reactions with H_2 or as generally as the fall-off of k with increasing ion energy.

The maximum value of k is approximately 30% of the value computed using theoretical rather than experimental values of the phenomenological cross-sections. If we assume that only H_2^+ with sufficient internal energy can react, then we must know the distribution of internal energy states in H_2^+ to estimate the fraction of the theoretical cross-section that should be observed in the experiment. (This assumption is not meant to exclude very small cross-section reactions that may be observed in which kinetic energy is transferred to internal energy in the reactive collision. The cross-sections for reaction of internally excited species are assumed to be an order of magnitude or more larger than processes which require direct energy transfer.) The distribution of vibrationally excited H_2^+ produced by Franck-Condon electron impact

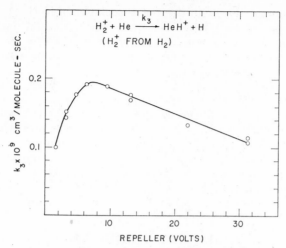

Figure 2. *Rate constant k_3 for production of HEH$^+$ from H_2-He mixtures plotted as a function of repeller voltage*

Values are computed from phenomenological cross-sections using Equation 5.

Table I. Distribution of Excited H_2^+ Produced by Franck-Condon Electron Impact Processes with 50-Volt Ionizing Electrons

ν	% H_2^+
0	8.96
1	16.11
2	17.79
3	15.53
4	12.29
5	9.03
6	6.31
7	4.46
8	3.04
9	2.19
10	1.47
11	0.96
12	0.65
13	0.46
14	0.30
15	0.23
16	0.13
17	0.07
18	0.02

processes can be calculated (2) from the squares of the overlap of the ground state anharmonic oscillator function for H_2 with the respective vibrational wave functions for H_2^+. This calculation is made for electron energies far exceeding the various excited ion threshold of H_2^+ so that excitation to a particular quantum state may be considered independent of electron energy and determined primarily by the vibrational wave function overlap. Results of this calculation are summarized in Table I. If the internal energy threshold for reaction of H_2^+ with He is 1.1 e.v.

(the value computed from the heat of dissociation of HeH^+, 1.68 e.v. (3)), then reactions are permitted from states with quantum number 5 and greater. These states comprise approximately 30% of the total H_2^+ produced by electron impact, in good agreement with the maximum value observed and shown in Figure 2.

The evidence in Figure 2 for a kinetic energy threshold for reaction of excited H_2^+ with He does not support the assumption of a kinetic energy transfer process for the excitation of reactant H_2^+ with $\nu < 5$ in reactive collisions with He. If such processes were probable, a drastic change in the maximum value of Q or k might be expected. The transfer of less than 0.5 e.v. of kinetic to internal energy would add quantum states with $\nu = 3$ and 4 to the inventory of available H_2^+ reactant and increase the maximum value of k by a factor of 2.

Similar results have been obtained for the H_2-Ne system (18) where Reaction 7

$$H_2^+ + Ne \rightarrow NeH^+ + H \tag{7}$$

is endothermic with ground state H_2^+ by 0.6 e.v. and Reaction 8

$$Ne^+ + H_2 \rightarrow NeH^+ + H \tag{8}$$

is exothermic by approximately 6 e.v. In this system, reactions proceed with H_2^+ in quantum states with $\nu \geq 2$, and cross-sections 75% of theoretical are observed if all the H_2^+ measured is assumed to be eligible reactant. A kinetic energy threshold and maximum is observed for the plot of k vs. repeller voltage. Both the He-H_2^+ and Ne-H_2^+ systems were found to be second-order processes at relatively low pressures in the mass spectrometer ion source. However, in the neon systems at higher pressures, a third-order process was found which was second order in neon concentration and first order in hydrogen. The experimental data showing the deviation from second-order processes is presented in Figure 3. The slight upward curvature in the pressure plot was not observed in the lower pressure studies on H_2^+ and He and contributes only a minor fraction of the NeH^+ yield. However, it is possible to resolve the respective contributions of second- and third-order processes and determine the excitation functions of the reactant ion in the third-order process. The results of this study are summarized by the mechanism:

$$Ne^* + H_2 \rightarrow H_2^* + Ne \tag{9}$$

$$H_2^* \rightarrow H_2^{+\prime} + e \tag{10}$$

$$H_2^+ + Ne \rightarrow NeH^{+\prime} + H \tag{11}$$

Ne^* is metastable neon produced by electron impact. Ne^* transfers its excitation to hydrogen molecules. The hydrogen molecules participating in these energy transfer collisions are produced in highly excited preionized states which ionize after a time lag sufficient to permit the initial neon and hydrogen collision partners to separate. The hydrogen ion is formed in the $\nu = 5$ or 6 quantum states and reacts with a second neon

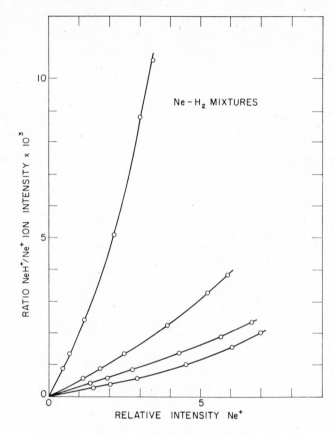

Figure 3.   Plot of NeH$^+$/Ne$^+$ as a function of Ne$^+$
relative intensity at various repeller voltages

atom to give NeH$^+$.   The interesting aspect of this system is that the
plot k *vs.* repeller voltage for the formation of NeH$^+$ by third-order reactions shows no kinetic energy threshold and a somewhat weaker fall-off
in k *vs.* increasing ion kinetic energy (Figure 4).   Here the H$_2$$^+$ reacting
with Ne is excited by several quanta above the reaction energy threshold
in contrast to much of the reacting H$_2$$^+$ in the second-order processes
with electron impact-produced H$_2$$^+$.   These kinetic energy thresholds
violate the assumption that reaction occurs at every ion-molecule collision and suggest that complexes which decompose to give reaction
products exclusively are limited to strongly exothermic reactions.   In
the language of statistical rate theory, nonunit transmission coefficients
can be expected in thermoneutral or slightly exothermic decompositions
of the activated complex.   Evidence from other ion-molecule processes
shows that many exothermic processes have unit transmission coefficients.

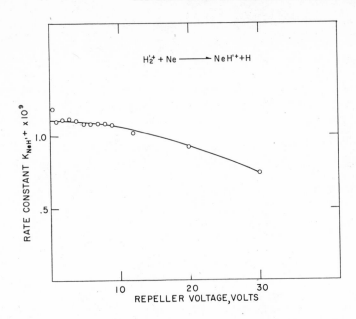

Figure 4. Plot of rate constant $K_{NEH'^+}$ formed in a third-order process as a function of repeller voltage

Table II.   Calculated and Observed Specific Rates of Ion-Molecule Reactions

$k \times 10^9$ cc./molecule-sec.

Reaction Systems	Theory	Experiment
H_2-H_2	2.05	2.02
HD-HD	1.67	1.67
D_2-D_2	1.45	1.44
H_2-He	0.267	0.27
H_2-Ne	0.81	0.77
HD-N_2	1.49	1.47
HD-CO	1.49	1.34
HD-O_2	1.48	1.26
HD-CO_2	1.40	1.29
CH_4-CH_4	1.31	1.3

In spite of the limitations cited above in the low energy reactions of H_2^+ with He and Ne, the G-S model, which assumes reaction at every collision, appears to be useful in studying elemental ion-molecule reactions. The Langevin cross-sections set either an upper limit or good approximation to experimental cross-sections if all reaction channels are considered and the reactant ions, including their energy states, are identified properly. Table II contains a summary of cross-sections measured in this laboratory. The agreement between theory and experiment in Table II constitutes a rather strong argument, but note that the model applies only over a limited range of ion kinetic energies, and the data in Table II are selected maximum values of experimental cross-sections taken from relatively low kinetic energy experiments.

Energy Dependence of Ion-Molecule Reactions

Intramolecular Isotope Effects.   The data in Figure 2 clearly illustrate the failure of the experimental results in following the predicted velocity dependence of the Langevin cross-section.   The remark has been frequently made that in the reactions of complex ions with molecules, hydrocarbon systems etc., experimental cross-sections correlate better with an E^{-1} than $E^{-1/2}$ dependence on reactant ion kinetic energy (*14*, *24*).   This energy dependence of reaction presents a fundamental problem with respect to the nature of the ion-molecule interaction potential.   So far no theory has been proposed which quantitatively predicts the E^{-1} dependence, and under these circumstances interpreting the experiment in these terms is questionable.

Intramolecular isotope effect studies on the systems $HD^+ + He$, $HD^+ + Ne$, $Ar^+ + HD$, and $Kr^+ + HD$ (*12*) suggest that the E^{-1} dependence of reaction cross-section at higher reactant ion kinetic energy may be fortuitous.   In these experiments the velocity dependence of the ratio of XH^+/XD^+ cross-sections was determined.   The experimental results are presented in summary in Figures 5 and 6.   The G-S model makes no predictions concerning these competitive processes. The masses of the respective ions and reduced masses of the respective complex reacting systems are identical for both H and D product ions. Consequently, the intramolecular isotope effect study illuminates those

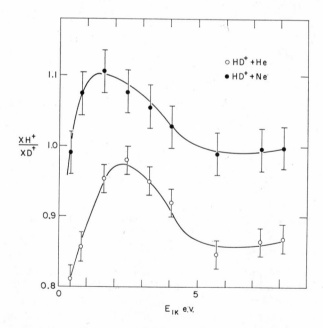

Figure 5.   Ratio of isotopic product ions as a function of average reactant ion kinetic energy; He + HD^+ and Ne + HD^+

aspects of the reaction mechanism which operate after the initial orbiting ion-molecule collision.   There is one mechanism which operates in the initial stage of the collision because of the displacement of center of charge from center of mass in HD^+ or the corresponding displacement of center of polarizability from center of mass if neutral HD reacts.   If linear collision complexes are formed and atom or ion transfer occurs in these complexes—i.e., if a stripping mechanism dominates the ion-molecule reaction process, then the ratio of cross-sections is given by:

$$\frac{\sigma_{XH^+}}{\sigma_{XD^+}} = \left(\frac{r + \Delta r}{r - \Delta r}\right)^2 \tag{12}$$

where r is the radius of the Langevin cross-section, and Δr is the shift of center of charge from center of mass in HD^+ etc.   The kinetic energy dependence of the isotope effect in the stripping reaction comes in via the energy dependence of r or the reaction cross-section.   The isotope effect

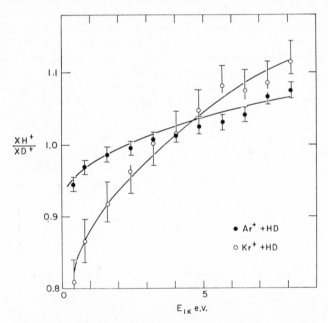

Figure 6.   Ratio of isotopic product ions as a function of average reactant ion kinetic energy; $Ar^+ + HD$ and $Kr^+ + HD$

measured in the experiment must be corrected for all possible orientations of HD^+ and X so that the calculated cross-section is reduced by approximately a factor of 2 from the maximum value estimated for linear complexes.   This displacement isotope effect is minimal for low energy (large cross-section) ion-molecule reactions.   The XH^+/XD^+ ratio is always greater than unity and increases with increasing reactant ion energy.   There is a real upper limit for this isotope effect determined by the minimum value of r practically achieved in ion-molecule collisions without the complete destruction of all product ions.   In the range of energies accessible in most mass spectrometer experiments, XH^+/XD^+ from the displacement isotope effect is less than 2.

Isotope effects which give ratios of XH^+/XD^+ less than unity are perhaps more interesting from the standpoint of energy transfer in reactive collisions.   If a collision complex between an inert gas X and HD^+

$$\begin{array}{c} X \\ / \ \backslash \end{array}$$

is formed with structure $H \quad D^+$, then there will be competitive paths of unimolecular decomposition which in turn depend on the heat of reaction and the magnitude of kinetic to internal energy transfer. The experimental data for the rare gas systems were fitted by the solid lines in Figures 5 and 6 by assuming that both displacement and unimolecular decomposition isotope effects operate in these reaction systems and that 10% of the reactant ion kinetic energy is converted to internal energy in the reactive collisions.   This assumption may seem to run counter to the argument put forth in the study of H_2^+-He and $H_2^+ + Ne$ reactions that internal energy is required for a reactive collision.   But the conflict is eliminated if the distinction between energy transfer in a reactive collision and the necessary condition of sufficient internal energy for a reactive collision is recognized.   (Energy transfer in a reactive collision may take place by the direct excitation of vibration in an impact of a relative high velocity ion with a molecule or the excitation of rotational energy states in the orbiting ion-molecule collision, with rotational energy relaxing into an equilibrium distribution of vibrational and rotational excitation.   This can happen in a potential well on the saddle surface which defines the activated complex or in an impulsive collision as the reactants traverse a convex saddle surface.   The probability of the reactive collision is determined by the approach of the reactants to the saddle surface.   The successful approach requires that the reactants have sufficient energy to surmount the energy barrier determined by the elevation of the saddle surface above the reactant valley.   If more than this energy is available as internal energy in the reactants then for all practical purposes the approach is "down hill."   If the conversion of kinetic to internal energy is required, then the process is "uphill" with a high probability of reflection back onto the valley for many reaction systems. Consequently, processes which require kinetic to internal energy transfer in reactive collisions are expected to have much smaller cross-sections.)   The assumption of kinetic energy transfer was required to account for the maxima in XH^+/XD^+ shown in Figure 5.   These maxima cannot be accounted for by the unimolecular decomposition or displacement isotope effect.   They were explained by considering the effect of kinetic energy transfer on the probability of product ion decomposition. Maxima were not observed in the Ar^+-HD or Kr^+-HD reactions where the fraction of kinetic energy available for conversion into internal energy is considerably smaller than for the He and Ne reactions.   Two other factors militate against the decomposition of ArH^+ and KrH^+.   These reaction products are more strongly bound than HeH^+ and NeH^+, and ArH^+ and KrH^+ are formed by reaction of atomic ions incapable of vibrational excitation, i.e.—$Ar^+ + H_2$. This latter factor makes it possible to decompose approximately 15% of the HeH^+ formed with the transfer of 0.38 e.v. from HD^+ kinetic energy. The zero point energy difference between HeH^+ and HeD^+ requires transfer of 0.43 e.v. to decompose a similar amount of HeD^+. The details of the analysis of the product decomposition isotope effect which gives rise to maxima in the XH^+/XD^+ ratios as a function of HD^+ kinetic energy will not be reviewed here. The important point is that experimental evidence for the decomposition of product ions has been found in the isotopic reactions, and this evidence is found in those reaction systems where the Langevin energy dependence of reaction cross-section is not found experimentally. This correlation suggests that the failure in agreement between experiment and theory arises primarily from the failure to include the products of all reaction channels in the experimental data used to calculate the experimental cross-sections. Thus, the observed fall-off in cross-section with increasing ion kinetic energy for reactions of H_2^+ with H_2, H, or Ne is associated with the competitive or subsequent processes of product decomposition aided by kinetic to internal energy transfer in these reactions.

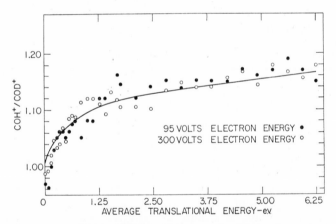

Figure 7. COH^+/COD^+ ratio as a function of reactant ion average translational energy in a CO-HD mixture

Accelerating voltage, 2500 volts and ionizing electron current, 10.5 μamp.   Closed circles are data taken at 95-.e.v. electron energy with data at 200 e.v. given by the open circles.   The smooth curve is the calculated COH^+/COD^+ ratio.

Intramolecular isotope effects were studied in the systems N_2-HD, CO-HD, O_2-HD and CO_2-HD (20). Product decomposition directly associated with rupture of OH or OD bonds was not observed in these reactions. Isotope effects in decomposition processes which gave OH^+ or OD^+ from reactions of O_2^+ with HD and COH^+ or COD^+ from

$CO_2{}^+$-HD reactions were not large enough to shed light on ion-molecule reaction mechanisms. However, the correlation cited above related to energy transfer and product decomposition did hold in these systems. Only minor deviations were observed from the theoretical energy dependence in these ion-molecule reaction cross-sections. Intramolecular isotope effects for the more exothermic processes were almost completely accounted for by the displacement isotope effect. Comparison of calculated and experimental ratios of ABH^+/ABD^+ for CO-HD reactions are given in Figure 7. The N_2H^+/N_2D^+ ratios produced in the least exothermic reaction of the set studied were fitted, assuming that 5% of the kinetic energy of $N_2{}^+$ was converted to internal energy and that competitive unimolecular decomposition and displacement isotope effect occurred. The AB-HD reactions demonstrate the complexity in identifying the energy distributions on reactant ions since both electronic excited states and vibrational distributions must be considered in identifying potential channels of reaction. The available photoionization data and vibronic distributions computed from squares of overlap integrals provide sufficient information to account for the observed reaction cross-sections.

Energy Dependence of Cross-Sections

Reactions of Complex Ions. For reactions of systems containing H_2 or HD the failure to observe an $E^{-1/2}$ dependence of reaction cross-section was probably the result of the failure to include all products of ion-molecule reaction in the calculation of the experimental cross-sections. For reactions of complex molecule ions where electron impact ionization probably produces a distribution of vibrationally excited states, kinetic energy transfer can readily open channels which yield products obscured by primary ionization processes. In such cases an E^{-n} dependence of cross-section may be determined; frequently $n = 1$ has been found.

The methane system is an interesting example of this problem and is probably typical of many hydrocarbon ion-molecule reactions. Figure 8 shows results obtained in several early investigations (*4, 14, 24*) of Reaction 13.

$$CH_4{}^+ + CH_4 \rightarrow CH_5{}^+ + CH_3 \qquad (13)$$

This reaction was considered the only reaction channel because it is the only known channel which is exothermic with ground state $CH_4{}^+$ ions. Reactions yielding $C_2H_5{}^+$ and $C_2H_4{}^+$ have been observed and are the least endothermic of the possible reactions of $CH_4{}^+$ with CH_4. However, ionization efficiency curves establish $CH_3{}^+$ rather than $CH_4{}^+$ as the reactant ion. Reaction 14:

$$CH_4{}^+ + CH_4 \rightarrow CH_3{}^+ + CH_3 + H_2 \qquad (14)$$

requires approximately 1.4 e.v. and is difficult to detect because of the rather large yields of $CH_3{}^+$ produced directly from CH_4 in the electron impact ionization.

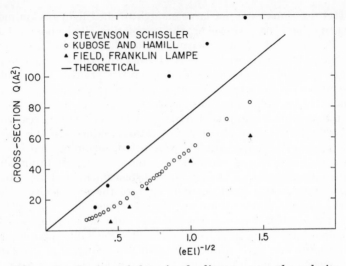

*Figure 8. Review of data in the literature on the velocity
dependence of the reaction* $CH_4^+ + CH_4 \rightarrow CH_5^+ + CH_3$

Solid line gives values calculated for Langevin orbiting cross-sections.

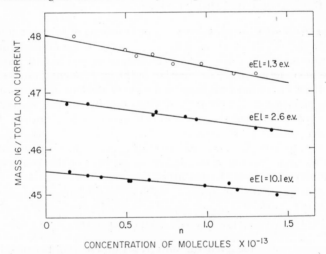

Figure 9. Dependence of the ratio of CH_4^+ *ions to total ions in the methane mass spectrum on the pressure
of methane in the mass spectrometer ion source for
different values of source repeller voltage*

Recently, the CH_4^+-CH_4 reaction has been investigated (9) by
measuring the CH_4^+ disappearance cross-section rather than CH_5^+
formation cross-sections. Results of this work are shown in Figure 9.
Two mechanisms cause a loss of CH_4^+ ions from the total ion yield in the
methane mass spectrum. There are loss processes in the ion source
which generate new ions, CH_5^+, and possibly other products. Other loss

mechanisms are those which destroy CH_4^+ in the mass spectrometer analyzer tube, collision-induced dissociation processes (*18*), or resonant charge transfer with thermal CH_4 molecules, etc. Tube and source processes can be separated by studying the ion repeller or reactant ion energy dependence of total loss processes while holding all other variables constant. Data taken in this type of study are presented in Figure 10 along with a set of independently measured CH_5^+ formation cross-sections. Extrapolating the plot of CH_4^+ loss cross-section *vs.* $(eEl)^{-1/2}$ gives an intercept which measures the contribution of tube losses. Subtracting this component yields loss cross-sections which are in excellent agreement with the solid line in Figure 10, calculated from the Langevin cross-section for the system CH_4^+-CH_4.

The question of which channels account for the difference between the observed CH_5^+ cross-section and the CH_4^+ loss is illuminated by studying the isotopic system CH_4-CD_4. When mixtures of CH_4 and CD_4 were subjected to electron impact, a pressure dependent yield of CH_2D^+ was observed which established the reaction mechanism:

$$CH_4^+ + CH_4 \rightarrow CH_5^+ + CH_3 \tag{15}$$
$$\searrow$$
$$CH_3^+ + H_2$$

Here again there is evidence that vibrationally excited CH_4^+ can react with some kinetic to internal energy transfer and produce ions which

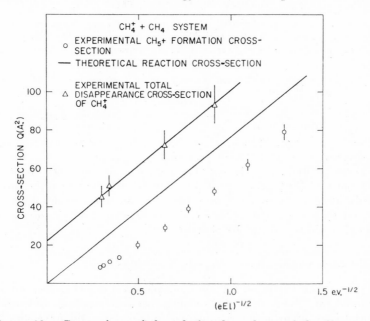

Figure 10. Comparison of the velocity dependence of the disappearance cross-section of CH_4^+, formation cross-section of CH_5^+, and Langevin orbiting collision cross-section, all as a function of reciprocal average kinetic energy of ions in the mass spectrometer source

cannot be formed in isolated collisions of ground state molecule ions and
neutral molecules.   If the ratio of the observed $CH_5{}^+$ cross-section to the
theoretical value for reaction 15 is plotted as a function of energy (Figure
11), this ratio extrapolates back to a value close to unity for reaction of
thermal ions.   The role of internal excitation in $CH_4{}^+$ is demonstrated
in a similar plot for reactions produced from $CH_4{}^+$, ionized by impact of

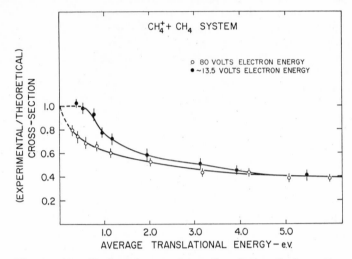

*Figure 11.   Ratio of experimental values of formation
cross-section of $CH_5{}^+$ to calculated Langevin cross-section
for collision of $CH_4{}^+$ with CH_4 as a function of average
ion kinetic energy*

*Data taken for two different internal energy distributions in $CH_4{}^+$
produced by ionization with 13.5- and 80-volt ionizing electrons,
respectively.*

13.5 e.v. electrons.   In this case $CH_4{}^+$ is produced close to the ionization
threshold, and more product $CH_5{}^+$ is observed in low kinetic energy ion-
molecule reactions.   The similarity between reactions of $H_2{}^+$ with He
giving eventually $H^+ + H$ and He and reactions of $CH_4{}^+$ with CH_4
can be noted.   Both processes require kinetic to internal energy transfer
and vibrationally excited reactant ions.   Both processes are accurately
described by the Giomousis-Stevenson model over most of the range of
reactant ion kinetic energy investigated.

Small Cross-Section Ion-Molecule Reactions

A necessary condition for ion-molecule reactions that has not been
considered thus far is that of continuity between reactant and product
potential energy surfaces.   Many reactions of ions and molecules take
place with a transition from one potential energy surface to another.
If no suitable crossings between the respective surfaces exist, then obviously orbiting ion-molecule collisions cannot produce chemical reac-

tions.   A case in point is the He$^+$-H$_2$ system.   Several experimental
studies (*7, 10*) report relatively small cross-sections for Reaction 16.

$$He^+ + H_2 \rightarrow H^+ + H + He \qquad (16)$$

Since the observation made in study of the formation HeH$^+$ indicated
that this product was not formed by reaction of He$^+$ with H$_2$, it had been
assumed that the exothermic heat of reaction of He$^+$ ions with H$_2$ is
probably deposited in the product HeH$^+$ as internal energy, decomposing
the product into H$^+$ and He.   This idea was cited by Light (*16*) in his
phase space theory of ion-molecule reactions to account for the failure to
observe HeH$^+$ from reactions with He$^+$ ions.   The experimental difficulty in the mass spectrometric investigation of this process is that H$^+$
formed by electron impact tends to obscure the ion-molecule–produced
H$^+$ so that a sensitive quantitative cross-section measurement is difficult.

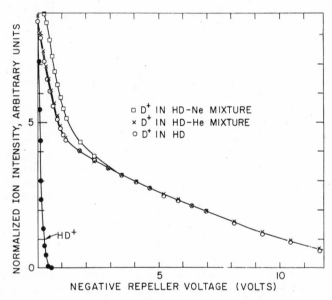

*Figure 12.   Negative repeller study on mixtures of HD
+ He and HD + Ne*

The problems of distinguishing H$^+$ produced from H$_2$ by electron
impact from the product of dissociative charge transfer reactions between
He$^+$ and H$_2$ can be studied by determining the kinetic energy distribution
in the product H$^+$ (*6*).   The reaction He$^+$ + H$_2$ is exothermic by 6.5
e.v. if the products are atoms or atomic ions.   If the reaction is studied
with HD substituted for H$_2$, then the maximum kinetic energy that can
be deposited in the D$^+$ is approximately 2.16 e.v.   On the other hand,
D$^+$ can be produced by electron impact with 5.5 e.v. kinetic energy.   If
a retarding potential is applied at the repeller in the ion-source of a mass
spectrometer, then it is possible to obtain curves related to the kinetic

energy distribution of D^+ produced directly by electron impact on HD and by dissociative charge transfer from He^+ reactions. Data showing the experimentally observed distributions measured this way are shown in Figure 12. First we determined the D^+ ion yield as a function of retarding voltage; then we added He to the ion source and redetermined the D^+ distribution, normalizing the D^+ distributions to the same relative ion intensity well above 2.16 e.v. Since the relative yield of D^+ from HD by electron impact is of the order of 1% of the total ion yield, this technique should sensitively reflect an increment in D^+ produced by relatively low energy He^+-HD reactions. The superposition of the D^+ kinetic energy distributions measured with and without He in the spectrometer ion source allows one to set an upper limit of 0.6 sq. A. for the He^+-H_2 dissociative charge transfer cross-section. This limit is less than 1% of the microscopic Langevin orbiting cross-section. Figure 12 also shows a small reaction cross-section between Ne^+ and HD, which is of the order of 1% of the Langevin cross-section. These results demonstrate an additional limitation on the assumption that exothermic ion-molecule reactions take place at every ion-molecule collision. In the He^+ and Ne^+ dissociative charge transfer processes with H_2, heats of reaction are 6.5 and 3.5 e.v., respectively, and the experimental evidence shows that most low energy ion-molecule collisions are limited to elastic scattering processes. These conclusions were strongly supported by Krauss and Mies (13) who calculated potential energy surfaces for the He^+-H_2 and H_2^+-He systems and demonstrated that indeed there were no crossings within the range of low energy ion-molecule interactions. Whether this phenomenon of separated surfaces is relatively unique and limited to the small molecules He, Ne, and H_2 remains to be seen. The problem of surface crossings should be considered if an exhaustive search for ion-molecule reaction channels indicates small reaction cross-sections.

Dissociative Charge Transfer Reactions

Using a retarding potential in the ion source is particularly useful in studying energy transfer in dissociative charge transfer ion-molecule reactions. The He^+-O_2 system is of particular interest to the atmospheric scientist because of its bearing on the mechanism by which helium escapes the earth's atmosphere. The problem that has challenged many investigators is to establish a mechanism by which He atoms or He^+ ions are given sufficient kinetic energy to escape from the earth's gravitational field (17). Nicolet (22) noted that the estimated rate of escape of helium was similar to the rate of He photoionization. Thus, the primary mechanism of energy input is suggested, but it is clear that the photoionization process does not directly perturb the He kinetic energy distribution. If, on the other hand, He^+ reacted with oxygen, Hansen (11) suggested that Reactions 17 and 18:

$$He^+ + O_2 \rightarrow HeO^+ + O \tag{17}$$

$$HeO^+ + e \rightarrow He + O \tag{18}$$

could occur, and the dissociative recombination process could give products with enough kinetic energy to permit He escape. Fite and co-workers (5) searched for HeO^+ experimentally and did not find it in mass spectrometer studies of afterglow. The possibility of HeO^+ as a transition species in these experiments was not ruled out.

The technique of measuring the O^+ kinetic energy distribution produced by reaction of He^+ and O_2 showed promise for establishing the existence of HeO^+. Experiments with He^3 and He^4 isotopes and O_2 were carried out in the ion source of a mass spectrometer. Retarding potential curves for O^+ in the two systems were determined, and the com-

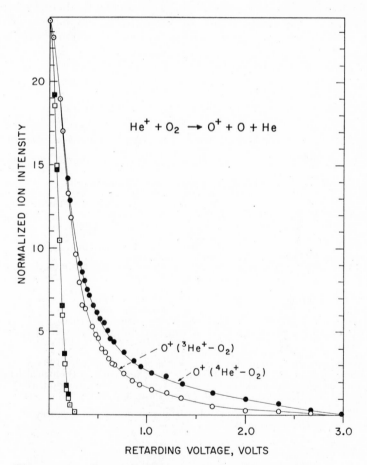

Figure 13. Retarded ion curves for O^+ resulting from $^3He^+$-O_2 and $^4He^+$-O_2 interactions

Normalized ion intensities are plotted as a function of retarding voltage. The unlabeled curve gives the observed kinetic energy distribution for reactant ^3He and ^4He ions (shaded and open squares).

ponent of O^+, produced by electron impact on O_2, was subtracted from both studies. The data obtained from these studies are shown in Figure 13, which shows a significantly smaller average value of kinetic energy deposited in O^+ in reactions of He^3 with O_2. If the reaction mechanism were one of resonant charge transfer followed by dissociation, the He^{+3} and He^{+4} isotopes would deposit almost identical amounts of energy in O_2, which could dissociate into O^+ and O in their respective ground states with 2.93 e.v. kinetic energy in both O^+ and O. The difference between the O^+ kinetic energy distributions obtained with He^{+3} and He^{+4} provides strong evidence for the mechanism which proceeds via HeO^+ with He^3O^+ decomposing and leaving behind a lower velocity O^+. The kinetic energy shift observed in the isotopic reactions and magnitudes of the observed energy distributions which correspond to about 1 e.v. mean kinetic energy also support this conclusion. This mechanism produces He atoms with sufficient kinetic energy to escape the earth's gravitational field.

Literature Cited

(1) Boelrijk, N., Hamill, W. H., *J. Am. Chem. Soc.* **84**, 730 (1962).
(2) Coolidge, A. S., James, H. M., Present, R. D., *J. Chem. Phys.* **4**, 193 (1936).
(3) Evett, A. A., *J. Chem. Phys.* **24**, 150 (1956).
(4) Field, F. H., Franklin, J. L., Lampe, F. W., *J. Am. Chem. Soc.* **79**, 2419 (1957).
(5) Fite, W. L., Smith, A. C. M., Stebbings, R. F., *J. Geophys. Res.* **68**, 3225 (1963).
(6) Friedman, L., Moran, T. F., *J. Chem. Phys.* **42**, 2624 (1965).
(7) Geise, C. F., Maier, W. B., *J. Chem. Phys.* **35**, 1913 (1961).
(8) Gioumousis, G., Stevenson, D. P., *J. Chem. Phys.* **29**, 294 (1958).
(9) Guidoni, A., Friedman, L., *J. Chem. Phys.* in press.
(10) Gustafson, E., Lindholm, E., *Arkiv Fysik* **18**, 219 (1960).
(11) Hanson, W. B., *J. Geophys. Res.* **67**, 183 (1962).
(12) Klein, F. S., Friedman, L., *J. Chem. Phys.* **41**, 1789 (1964).
(13) Krauss, M., Mies, F., private communication.
(14) Kubose, D. A., Hamill, W. H., *J. Am. Chem. Soc.* **85**, 125 (1963).
(15) Langevin, P., *Ann. Chim. Phys.* **5**, 245 (1905).
(16) Light, J. C., *J. Chem. Phys.* **40**, 3221 (1964).
(17) MacDonald, G. J. F., *Rev. Geophysics* **1**, 305 (1963).
(18) Melton, C., Rosenstock, H., *J. Chem. Phys.* **26**, 568 (1957).
(19) Moran, T. F., Friedman, L. *J. Chem. Phys.* **39**, 2491(1963).
(20) Moran, T. F., Friedman, L., *J. Chem. Phys.* **42**, 2391 (1965).
(21) Moran, T. F., Friedman, L., *J. Geophys. Res.* **70**, 4992 (1965).
(22) Nicolet, M., *J. Geophys. Res.* **66**, 2263 (1961).
(23) Stevenson, D. P., Schissler, D. O., *J. Chem. Phys.* **29**, 282 (1958).
(24) Stevenson, D. P., Schissler, D. O., "The Chemical and Biological Effects of Radiation," M. Haissinsky, ed., p. 249, Academic Press, London, 1961.
(25) Von Koch, H., Friedman, L., *J. Chem. Phys.* **38**, 1115 (1963).

RECEIVED April 29, 1966. Research performed under the auspices of the U.S. Atomic Energy Commission.

Effect of Translational Energy on Ion-Molecule Reaction Rates

JEAN H. FUTRELL and FRED P. ABRAMSON

Aerospace Research Laboratories, Wright-Patterson Air Force Base, Ohio 45433

The kinetic energy dependence of ion-molecule reaction rates is reviewed from both experimental and theoretical viewpoints for typical systems. At low energy the theory of Gioumousis and Stevenson is an adequate framework when suitably modified to reflect characteristic properties of a given system. At higher energies it is necessary to invoke orientation effects appropriate to stripping mechanisms to rationalize experimental data. New information on energy dependent isotope effects and multiple dissociation paths for intermediate complexes provide suitable criteria for distinguishing the two fundamental mechanisms and also demonstrate the efficient conversion of translational energy into internal energy. On the basis of these results, certain particularly important areas for future research are suggested.

Ion-molecule reactions are of great interest and importance in all areas of kinetics where ions are involved in the chemistry of the system. Astrophysics, aeronomy, plasmas, and radiation chemistry are examples of such systems in which ion chemistry plays a dominant role. Mass spectrometry provides the technique of choice for studying ion-neutral reactions, and the phenomena of ion-molecule reactions are of great intrinsic interest to mass spectrometry. However, equal emphasis is deservedly placed on measuring reaction rates for application to other systems. Furthermore, the energy dependence of ion-molecule reaction rates is of fundamental importance in assessing the validity of current theories of ion-molecule reaction rates. Both the practical problem of deducing rate parameters valid for other systems and the desire to provide input to theoretical studies of ion-molecule reactions have served as stimuli for the present work.

With these ends in view, one of the principal objectives of research in ion-molecule reactions is to determine the dependence on ion kinetic energy of ion-molecule reaction rates. In the classical measurements of

ion-molecule reaction rates by pressure dependence, the quantity determined is the phenomenological cross-section

$$Q = (nl)^{-1} \ln (1 + I_s/I_p) \qquad (1)$$

where I_s and I_p are the secondary and primary ion currents, n is concentration of molecules, and l the ion path length. Q is also the average over
the ion path length of the microscopic cross-section,—i.e.,

$$Q = l^{-1} \int_o^l \sigma [v_i(x)] dx \qquad (2)$$

where σ is the microscopic cross section and $v_i(x)$ is the ion velocity at
point x.   It is assumed that thermal motion of the molecules is negligible.
For an interaction potential of the form $\phi = -e^2\alpha/2r^4$, where e is the
electronic charge, α the polarizability of the neutral, and r the internuclear
distance, one deduces an $1/v$ dependence for σ.   (Light (36) has developed
a more general equation for the dependence of phenomenological cross-
section on energy which does not assume $\sigma \sim v^{-1}$.)   Only for this case,
therefore, is the specific reaction rate constant, k, equal to Qv.   Thus, a
rate constant measured at moderate field strengths in a conventional mass
spectrometer experiment may be used with confidence for other con-
ditions only if one knows that the v^{-1} [or $E^{-1/2}$] dependence of σ is valid.

Much of the research relevant to establishing the energy dependence
of ion-molecule reaction rates has been done with other goals in mind.
In addition, however, systematic studies of kinetic energy effects have
been undertaken by Hamill (4, 30, 46, 63), by Friedman (29, 47, 49, 67),
by Giese and Maier (14, 15, 16, 17), and more recently by this laboratory
(56, 57).   This review draws together details on various aspects of this
problem and discusses them in light of new experimental information
and theoretical considerations.   No comprehensive review of the literature on this topic is implied since the authors wish to illustrate primarily
their own current thinking on this subject.

Theory

Almost all discussions of ion-molecule reaction rate theory begin
with the model invoked by Gioumousis and Stevenson (18).   This theory
is based on the Langevin model of the orbital dynamics between a point
charge and a shapeless, polarizable molecule at rest.   The interaction
potential is that of a point charge in an induced dipole field existing
between the charged and neutral particles.   By balancing a centrifugal
barrier against the attractive potential, an expression is derived for the
impact parameter for intimate collisions beyond which no bounded orbits
occur.   It is assumed that chemical forces become operative for such intimate collisions, driving the ion-molecule reaction to completion.   The
resulting expression for reaction cross-section is

$$\sigma(E_{tr}) = \pi (2e^2\alpha/E_{tr})^{1/2} \qquad (3)$$

where e is the electronic charge, α the polarizability of the molecule, and E_{tr} the translational energy of the reduced mass of the collision partners in center of mass coordinates.

Obviously, one of the shortcomings of this theory is that it is formulated for point-particles, and for high relative velocities the gas kinetic cross-sections of the collision partners will exceed their Langevin cross-sections. Hamill and co-workers (*4, 30*) have introduced a correction term to the Gioumousis-Stevenson theory which includes such a "hard-core" cross-section. Above E_t, the transition energy above which the gas kinetic cross-section dominates the reaction, this formulation predicts an E^{-1} dependence of cross-section on translational energy instead of the $E^{-1/2}$ dependence computed for low translational energy. A similar E^{-1} dependence at higher relative kinetic energy is deduced from a more elaborate treatment by Light and Horrocks (*35*) of hard-core collisions.

Theard and Hamill (*63*) and Moran and Hamill (*46*) have further elaborated the Gioumousis-Stevenson theory by considering reactions of ions with neutrals having permanent dipoles. In the low energy region where the dipole orients along the ion-neutral vector (i.e., minimum potential energy configuration) an ion-dipole cross-section,

$$\sigma_D = \pi e\mu/E_{tr} \tag{4}$$

where μ is the dipole moment, and the other terms are as defined previously, is added to the Langevin cross-section. At slightly higher energies the ion transit time becomes comparable with rotational periods of the molecule, and at still higher ion velocities the permanent dipole term is averaged out. A more elaborate quantum mechanical treatment which includes rotational energies and both linear and symmetric-top molecules is given by Dugan and Magee (*7*). At still higher energies the gas kinetic cross-section in this formulation again becomes the dominant feature.

A complete description of ion-molecule reaction involves the kinematics of both formation and decomposition of the bimolecular complex [PM$^+$].

$$P^+ + M \rightarrow [PM^+] \rightarrow S^+ + N \tag{5}$$

Various factors involved in both steps have been considered explicitly by Friedman and colleagues (*29, 47, 49, 54, 67*) to rationalize isotope effects in these reactions. Their treatment involves orientation effects, displacement isotope effects, and dissociation isotope effects in order to account for observed results. Stevenson and Schachtschneider (*59*) have also presented a treatment of decomposition isotope effects.

Rosenstock (*55*) pointed out that the initial formulation of the theory failed to consider the effect of angular momentum on the decomposition of the complex. The products of reaction must surmount a potential barrier in order to separate, which is exactly analogous to the potential barrier to complex formation. Such considerations are implicit in the phase space theory of Light and co-workers (*34, 36, 37*). These restrictions limit the population of a given output channel of the reaction complex. To the approximation that resonance effects, charge-dipole, and quadrupole interactions may be ignored, the Langevin cross-section is taken as the cross-section for complex formation. Calculating the probability of a given product then follows from the calculation of the phase space available to all nondissociative vibrational states of a given product channel. Wolf (74) recently extended this treatment to include 10 output channels for selected three-body reactions as a function of kinetic energy. The various reaction paths considered for the complex included scattering, charge transfer, and dissociation as well as ion-molecule reactions.

The phase space theory in its present form suffers from the usual computational difficulties and from the fact it has thus far been developed only for treating three-body processes and a limited number of output channels. Further, to treat dissociation as occurring only through excitation of rotational levels beyond a critical value for bound vibrational states is rather artificial. Nevertheless, it is a useful framework for discussing ion-molecule reaction rates and a powerful incentive for further work.

The approaches discussed so far, with the possible exception of Friedman's displacement isotope effect and of Light and Horrock's collision model, refer only to strong coupling collisions. In these collisions it is assumed that thorough mixing occurs, and all information about initial configuration is lost. For exothermic ion-molecule reactions at low kinetic energy, the long range strongly attractive forces make such strong coupling collisions plausible.

At high impacting ion energy the requirements of the strong coupling model are not fulfilled, and a different reaction mechanism becomes operative. Binding energies of atoms become negligible in this approximation, and a hard-core collision model is appropriate. Light and Horrocks (35) have advanced a model for the generalized stripping reaction

$$\overrightarrow{\{1\}} + \{2, 3\} \rightarrow \{1, 3\} + \overrightarrow{\{2\}} \tag{6}$$

which was discussed earlier. It is anticipated from the molecular dynamics involved that such a reaction is most important when $m_1 \simeq m_2$. An alternative scheme, which may be termed "spectator stripping," was proposed by Henglein, Lacmann, and Jacobs (23) for certain high energy ion-molecule reactions. It may be formulated:

$$\overrightarrow{\{1\}} + \{2, 3\} \rightarrow \{1, \overrightarrow{3}\} + \{2\} \tag{7}$$

in which target atom 3 is considered quasi-free, and atom 2 does not participate in the reaction. Data for N_2^+, H_2 and Ar^+, H_2 have been obtained which support this hypothesis (31, 32). Both stripping models lead to very large kinetic isotope effects, approaching ∞ as a limit.

Experimental Techniques

There are several methods for studying the effects of translational energy on ion-molecule reactions. The first class of experiments uses conventional single stage mass spectrometers. The ion source of such an instrument is shown schematically in Figure 1. The simplest of these techniques involves examining the products of reaction at different repeller potentials—i.e., with different electric field gradients within the source. By varying the voltage on the repeller, the average ion energy may be altered. Friedman and Hamill have used this method extensively (*4, 54*). Because the ions are formed in an electric field and react throughout the distance between the electron beam and the exit slit of the source, however, the energy at which the ions react cannot be determined directly. In fact, such an experiment allows ions to react at any energy between thermal and the calculated exit energy, and the results should be considered as representing some average value between these experimental limits. Because the reaction cross-section normally decreases with energy, these experiments tend to emphasize low energy reactions.

In order to minimize this problem, Ryan (*57, 58*) combined the pulse techniques of Tal'roze (*61*) with a small continuous repeller field. In this operation, a cluster of ions is formed by a short ionizing pulse and is allowed to react under the influence of a small d.c. field for a certain time. The reaction is then quenched by applying a large (80 volts/cm.)

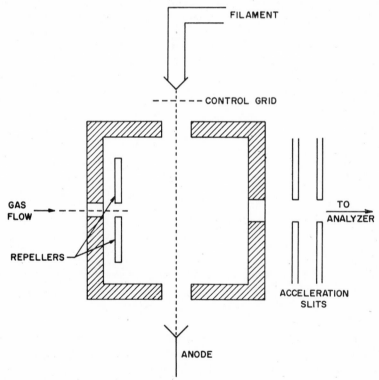

Figure 1.   Schematic diagram of conventional electron impact ion source

repeller pulse superimposed on the d.c. repeller field.   In this way, the energy spread of the ions is caused only by the finite duration of the ionizing pulse and the magnitude of the repeller field.   This nearly monochromatic ion "bunch" is then accelerated by the impressed repeller field and receives an amount of kinetic energy depending upon the distance it has traveled before the reaction is quenched.   By studying a reaction as a function of time, one may observe the effects of translational energy.   A plot of the ratio of product to reactant ion as a function of delay time gives information on the specific rate constant and its energy dependence.   The derivative of this curve is the product of the concentration of the neutral reactant and the rate constant at delay time τ and may be used to deduce k as a function of τ.   The mean energy of the ion bunch is simply related to τ;   hence, k as $f(E)$ is derived easily from these data.

Another modification of a single-stage mass spectrometer was initially devised by Cermak and Herman (5).   In this configuration, the potential between the filament and the block is kept below the ionization potential of the gas.   The potential between the block and anode is then adjusted so that the energy of the electrons is sufficiently high to cause ionization in the anode region and to accelerate those ions back into the source region.   By varying the anode-block potential, the average kinetic energy of the primary ions may be adjusted.   Because of their transverse velocity component, at low repeller fields the observed spectrum will consist entirely of secondary ions.   This method is well suited to studying charge transfer reactions and certain types of ion-molecule reactions. If ion-molecule reactions involve a significant amount of momentum transfer, however, severe discrimination against that product is expected.

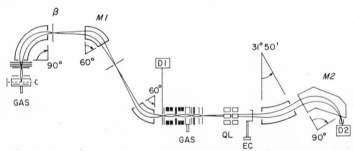

Figure 2.   Schematic of ARL tandem mass spectrometer

QL = *quadrupole lens*, EC = *displaceable electrometer collector*, M1, M2 = *magnetic sectors, and* D1,   D2 = *ion detectors*

Hence, reactions which proceed via complex formation or stripping reactions involving transfer of a relatively massive moiety either are not observed or are registered at grossly distorted intensities.   An additional complication is that elastic or nonreactive scattering collisions may allow a primary ion to be detected as a secondary ion.   Simple charge transfer reactions and proton transfer reactions are therefore the classes of ion-neutral interaction most appropriately studied by this technique.

A considerably more complex method for studying the effects of translational energy involves the use of tandem mass spectrometers. In these experiments the first mass spectrometer serves as the ion gun for a second mass spectrometer which analyzes the reaction products. Because of the physical separation of the ionization region and reaction chamber, several parameters may be varied independently. The reactive ions are generally mass selected and also may be accelerated or decelerated to the kinetic energy desired. The reactant ion-product ion relationship is given directly and unambiguously. The earliest tandem mass spectrometer was built by Lindholm (*38*). Since then several instruments have been constructed to study the effects of translational energy (*11, 15, 28, 33, 64, 65, 68, 73*). Figure 2 shows a new tandem mass spectrometer constructed at our laboratories for studying ion-molecule reactions. This instrument is unique inasmuch as the double focusing feature of the ion gun permits adjustment of the energy spread of the primary ion beam by adjusting the electric sector slit designated β in Figure 2.

In general, the primary beam is extracted from some ionization region, mass selected, and then decelerated or accelerated before passage into the reaction chamber. On most of the smaller instruments (*15, 72*), low (below 10 volts) primary acceleration potentials are used so that the beam may enter the reaction chamber with little if any change in kinetic energy. Such instruments often suffer from inadequate primary ion mass resolution; hence, for gases which have several abundant isotopes it is necessary to use an isotopically enriched gas. In larger machines, primary ion kinetic energy decreases up to 1000-fold by using a strong focussing deceleration lens system. The exact details of these lens systems have been described in other articles (*11, 20*).

The low energy ions leaving the reaction chamber are re-accelerated for conventional mass analysis. Many of these instruments use a pair of quadrupole lenses (*13*) following re-acceleration to increase the intensity of secondary ions. Such a lens system is particularly well adapted to this application because of its large physical size and strong focussing properties.

There are two basic types of tandem machines; transverse and in-line. The transverse instruments (*28, 33, 68, 72, 73*) are designed to discriminate strongly against mass transfer processes and therefore favor collection of the products of charge transfer reactions. Even with this geometry, however, mass transfer products may be observed at low translational energies. It is also possible (*27, 72*) to use higher than normal repeller potentials to extract the primary beam from the reaction chamber along with those secondaries which result from mass transfer reactions. By using the in-line configuration, as in the ARL and Giese designs, the products of mass or momentum transfer processes may be observed more efficiently.

Henglein (23) has constructed a machine for studying stripping reactions which does not fall into any of the above categories. It consists of an ion gun followed by a flight tube which also serves as a reaction chamber. A velocity selector scans the ions which have suffered little or no change in direction, and energy analysis of the secondary ion beam is used to deduce cross-sections and reaction mechanisms in chosen simple cases.

Results and Discussion

Rare-Gas-Hydrogen Reactions. Ion-molecule reactions in the rare gas-hydrogen system are of great interest both theoretically and experimentally. The properties of the reactants and products are well known or may be calculated, and the properties of the intermediate three-body complex pose a tractable theoretical problem. Systematic studies of cross-section energy dependence and isotope effects in these systems have been undertaken by Friedman and co-workers (29, 47, 49, 67), by Koski and co-workers (2, 3), and by Giese and Maier (15, 16).

The experimental data of Friedman show a strong energy dependence of σ on ion velocity for the endothermic reactions,

$$H_2^+ + He \rightarrow HeH^+ + H \tag{8}$$

$$H_2^+ + Ne \rightarrow NeH^+ + H \tag{9}$$

and both reactions appear to exhibit an energy threshold (0.35 e.v. for HeH^+ and 0.18 e.v. for NeH^+). Also in both cases the exothermic complementary reactions

$$He^+ + H_2 \rightarrow HeH^+ + H \tag{10}$$

$$Ne^+ + H_2 \rightarrow NeH^+ + H \tag{11}$$

have negligibly small cross-sections. The energy threshold is considered in detail by Moran and Friedman (47), who suggest that enforced dipole radiation may occur during the lifetime of the collision complex. This translational energy effect has not yet been confirmed in beam experiments (17) perhaps because it is difficult to obtain low energy H_2^+ ions in useful quantities. A striking success of the phase space theory (37) is the rationalization of both the energy threshold and isotope effects in these reactions without recourse to arbitrary parameters.

The argon-hydrogen and krypton-hydrogen systems are distinguished by the fact that the reaction occurs with comparable cross-sections via both hydrogen molecule ion and rare gas ion reactants—namely,

$$Ar^+ + H_2 \rightarrow ArH^+ + H \tag{12}$$

$$H_2^+ + Ar \rightarrow ArH^+ + H \tag{13}$$

for argon. Since new preliminary data are available for this system, it will be discussed in some detail.

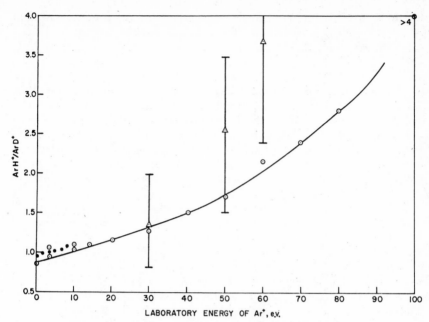

Figure 3. ArH⁺/ArD⁺ as a function of Ar⁺ energy

($\bullet$) *Data of Klein and Friedman (29), ($\triangle$) Data of Henglein, Lacmann, and Knoll (24)*

Our data for the isotope effect in the abstraction reaction, Reaction 12, as a function of Ar^+ energy are plotted in Figure 3, which includes data of Klein and Friedman (*29*) and Henglein, Lacmann and Knoll (*24*) for purposes of comparison. The agreement is considered good in view of the different nature of the experiments involved. Klein and Friedman used a single-stage instrument, and the data should be corrected for the complementary reaction, Reaction 13. Insufficient data are given, however, for use to make the appropriate correction. Henglein *et al.* use a high energy argon beam and energy analysis only of the secondary ions. Our data are obtained with a tandem mass spectrometer described elsewhere (*11*) and agree with data of Berta, Ellis, and Koski (*2*).

The large isotope effect observed at high ion energy is explained by Henglein (*24, 31*) as a "spectator stripping" reaction in which it ultimately becomes bound. The pronounced isotope effect results from the dissociation of product ions when the internal energy deposited in the product exceeds its dissociation energy. By considering conservation of energy and momentum, one may write for the "free atom" or "spectator stripping" model:

$$E_i = E_{Ar^+} \frac{m_i}{m_{Ar^+} + m_i} - \Delta H \qquad (14)$$

where E_i is the energy deposited in the argon hydride ion product,

E_{Ar^+} is the bombarding ion energy, m_i the mass of the target atom, and ΔH is the heat of the reaction. For a stable product to form, it is necessary that $E_i \leq D$ (ArH$^+$), the dissociation energy of the argon hydride ion. Taking D (ArH$^+$) as 3.03 e.v. (48) and $\Delta H = 1.2$ e.v. (29), one can calculate E_{max}(ArD$^+$) = 38 e.v. and E_{max}(ArH$^+$) = 75 e.v. From this model then one would expect a kinetic isotope effect of infinity above 38 e.v. impacting ion energy. Clearly our data do not support the strict application of the stripping theory at high energy since both reactions persist at an energy which is higher than anticipated by these considerations. However, the theory is supported in a qualitative sense, and stripping with participation of the nonreacting partner (not involving complex formation) seems to be the only acceptable way of explaining the large isotope effect which is observed.

At low energies the moderate isotope effects observed agree well with the data of Klein and Friedman (24) who have satisfactorily explained their results as a combination of isotope effects. The separation of center of mass from center of polarizability in HD produces a configuration isotope effect because of the resulting difference in activation energies for XDH$^+$ and XHD$^+$ complexes. A vibrational isotope effect is involved in the decomposition of the triatomic complex because of the differences in zero-point energies of the probable transition states. Finally, an isotope effect in the dissociation of product ions becomes increasingly important with increasing kinetic energy of the reactant ion. A consideration of these effects and a superposition of a stripping model at still higher energies will account for the data in Figure 3.

An attempt to generalize results for this system is further complicated by considering Reaction 13. Data on the isotope effect for both Reactions 12 and 13 are presented in Figure 4 as a function of kinetic energy in center-of-mass coordinates. Qualitatively, the isotope effects are similar, and the results can be rationalized correspondingly. However, the results are rather different quantitatively, and the abstraction and hydron transfer reactions in this system, as noted by Giese and Maier (15), seem to fall into two distinctively different classes. (We suggest the generic term "hydron" to represent any of the isotopic hydrogen nuclei—i.e., H$^+$, D$^+$, T$^+$.) The major difference in initial preparation of the reaction complex at low center-of-mass energies introduced by interchanging the ionic and neutral reactants in the argon-HD system is the vibrational excitation in HD$^+$. The experimental results in Figure 4 are therefore the superposition of reactions of a distribution of vibrationally excited HD$^+$ from $v = 0$ to $v = 10$, $v = 2$ being the most probable transition for ionization of HD by 70 volt electrons (71). The phase space theory of Light (34, 37) explicitly accounts for such factors and is therefore esthetically the most suitable vehicle for rationalizing the observed differences. Detailed calculations are now in progress and will be reported at a later date.

Endothermic Charge Transfer Reactions. One of the most interesting categories in studying the dependence of ion-molecule reactions on translational energy is that involving endothermic charge transfer reactions. In these reactions, the mass spectroscopist can derive dissociation energies within 0.1 e.v. By using the energy of translation of a primary ion to induce vibrational and/or electronic transitions in some neutral particle, the operator has a tool which may be as valuable as photoionization or electron impact in determining molecular properties. In favorable cases this method may well combine the best features of both other methods. Because of the nature of charge exchange, ions with thermal velocities transfer energy in discrete amounts, as in photoionization. As the kinetic energy of the ion of mass m_i is increased, the amount of energy, E_R, which is available for reaction with a neutral particle of mass m_n is related to the laboratory energy, E_L, by

$$E_R = E_L \left(\frac{m_n}{m_n + m_i} \right) \tag{15}$$

The term following E_L is always less than unity so that an adventitious correction to the laboratory energy occurs. This enhances the precision of the E_R measurement. As with electrons, selection rules for ionization and dissociation seem to be relaxed.

Gustafsson and Lindholm (*19*) have shown the effects of translational energy on charge transfer reactions with H_2, N_2, and CO. They observe that endothermic reaction cross-sections increase with increasing kinetic

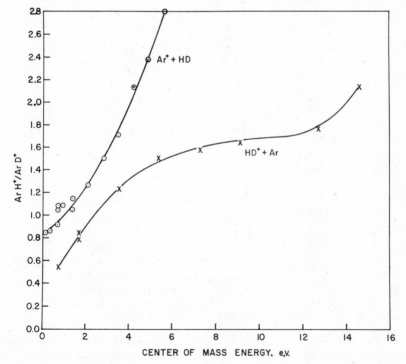

Figure 4. ArH$^+$/ArD$^+$ *from the reactions of Ar$^+$ with HD and HD$^+$ with Ar as a function of energy in the center of mass system*

energy although only five energies were used in their study.   Lavrovskaya
et al. (*33*) briefly examined charge exchange processes of Xe^+ with acetone
and with ethylene.   The first comprehensive study was made by Giese
and Maier (*14*) in 1963, using a tandem in-line mass spectrometer con-
ceptually similar to the ARL instrument and capable of producing low
energy ions.   Figure 5 illustrates typical endothermic charge transfer
reaction cross-sections as a function of translational energy according to
Maier (*41*).   The threshold behavior for

$$Ar^+ + C_2H_2 \rightarrow CH^+ + CH + Ar \qquad (16)$$

occurs because the reaction is $\sim$5 e.v. endothermic and cannot occur until
the kinetic energy of the system—i.e., the barycentric energy—is at least
5 e.v.   The position of the threshold appears to agree well with that value.
Maier has also investigated the reaction of rare gas ions with N_2 and N_2O

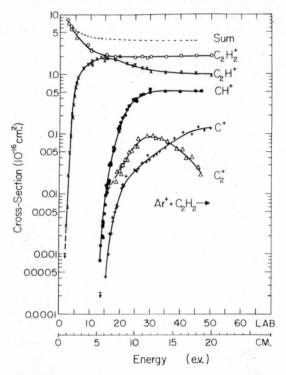

*Figure 5.   Cross-sections for production of $C_2H_2^+$,
C_2H^+, CH^+, C^+, and C_2^+ from the reaction of
Ar^+ with C_2H_2 as a function of Ar^+ kinetic
energy.   (Journal of Chemical Physics)*

(*40*) and with C_2H_2, C_2H_4, and D_2 (*41*).   The experiments on the organic
molecules show that in charge transfer reactions the total energy of the
system must be considered.   Koski and co-workers (*3, 25, 26, 27*)
have also observed several cases of maxima in cross-section with in-

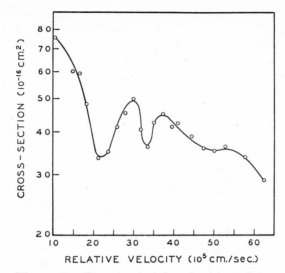

Figure 6. Cross-section for change exchange of HD⁺ with Ar as a function of the relative velocity of the ion. (Journal of the American Chemical Society)

creasing kinetic energy as expected for endothermic charge transfer reactions. Berta and Koski (3) also have observed resonances in the charge transfer reaction

$$HD^+ + Ar \rightarrow Ar^+ + HD \tag{17}$$

Their results, shown in Figure 6, exhibit maxima which approximate the spacing of vibrational levels of H_2^+ in accordance with the Massey criterion (42).

Exothermic Charge Transfer. While endothermic charge transfer reactions may provide new information concerning molecular parameters, most of the work done on charge transfer reactions to date has been concerned with exothermic processes. Many experimenters have studied such reactions, but only a few have varied kinetic energy as a parameter (5, 6, 10, 12, 19, 21, 22, 25, 26, 27, 28, 33, 39, 51, 52, 60, 62, 65, 68, 69, 70, 72, 73). The general features of such an experiment are indicated in Figure 5. For exothermic processes, the cross-sections seem to be relatively independent of translational energy. As kinetic energy increases some endothermic charge transfer reactions appear, and their cross-sections may rise with kinetic energy. Another feature is often apparent in these reactions. At low (<10 e.v.) kinetic energies the exothermic charge transfer cross-sections may rise because of a change in reaction mechanism. At low energies the traditional model of ion-induced dipole complex formation of Gioumousis and Stevenson (G-S) (18) must be partly responsible for forming complexes which lead to charge transfer— i.e., charge transfer represents a possible output channel for ion-molecule reaction centers approaching closer than the critical impact parameter.

As the translational energy of the impacting ion increases, the G-S cross section will rapidly fall off until at energies above ~10 e.v., the electron jump model for the reaction will predominate. That mechanism does not seem to depend strongly on translational energy.

Hertel and Koski (27) have examined the energy dependence of charge transfer reactions between rare gas ions and CH_4 in the region 2–10 e.v. They find that only for He^+ does the cross-section follow the G-S prediction that $\sigma \sim E^{-0.5}$. For the other gases they find larger values for the exponent, some as large as 1.5. These experiments show the general lack of a comprehensive theory capable of describing ion-molecule reactions in general.

Another feature of charge transfer spectra which has been repeatedly observed by Lindholm (6, 19, 51, 52, 68, 73) and others (28, 33, 69, 70) is that the relative amounts of fragment ions resulting from charge transfer are not strongly influenced by kinetic energy. Indeed, some increase in decomposition to smaller fragments is seen, but this is a minor feature and seems similar to the effects of electron energy on cracking patterns at energies well above threshold for all dissociation processes (45).

Experiments at Very Low Energy. Ryan and Futrell (57) have studied the energy dependence of various ion-molecule reactions in the low energy (0–1 e.v.) region using the pulse technique described above and in more detail elsewhere (58). Surprisingly enough this study showed that the energy dependence of a number of condensation type reactions as well as simpler atom transfer reactions could be described adequately by the G-S theory. Specifically, in the low energy region studied, the specific rate constants of the reactions listed in Table I were independent of energy. Therefore, the microscopic cross-sections of these reactions exhibit a $1/E^{1/2}$ dependence on ion kinetic energy. For the competitive reactions of the same ion listed in Table I the implication is that a charge-induced dipole force governs the collision dynamics of the reaction and that the probability of a given output channel is energy invariant for these systems at low ion kinetic energy.

Table I. Reactions for which $\sigma \sim 1/v$ in the Energy Region 0–1 e.v.[a]

$$CH_4^+ + CH_4 \rightarrow CH_5^+ + CH_3$$
$$CH_3^+ + CH_4 \rightarrow C_2H_5^+ + H_2$$
$$CO^+ + H_2 \rightarrow COH^+ + H$$
$$C_2H_3^+ + C_2H_4 \rightarrow C_2H_5^+ + C_2H_2$$
$$C_2H_4^+ + C_2H_4 \rightarrow C_3H_5^+ + CH_3$$
$$C_2H_2^+ + C_2H_2 \rightarrow C_2H_3^+ + C_2H$$
$$C_2H_2^+ + C_2H_2 \rightarrow C_4H_3^+ + H$$
$$C_2H_2^+ + C_2H_2 \rightarrow C_4H_2^+ + H_2$$
$$C_2^+ + C_2H_2 \rightarrow C_4H^+ + H$$

[a] Data of Ryan and Futrell (57).

This paper also reported results for three permanent dipole molecules, HCl, H_2O, and NH_3, which exhibited an energy dependence of the specific rate constant in this energy range. The data for ammonia are typical and are presented in Figure 7. The points are experimental results, and the solid curves are calculated from the theoretical expression:

$$\frac{\Delta I_s}{I_p} = \eta \int_{t_1}^{t_2} g \left[\pi e \left(\frac{2\alpha}{E_{tr}} \right)^{1/2} + \frac{\pi e \mu}{E_{tr}} \right] dt \qquad (18)$$

where η is an efficiency factor determined empirically to be 0.33 to achieve a best fit for this reaction, g is the ion velocity, and the other terms have been defined previously. This equation was a slightly modi- fied form of the equations deduced by Moran and Hamill (46) for reactions involving a point charge interacting with a polarizable permanent dipole molecule at low enough energy for the dipole to orient to the most favorable position. The agreement with experiment is quite satisfactory, and the deviation at low energy (*ca.* 0.08 e.v. ion energy) is expected for any treatment which ignores thermal motion of the reaction pair. Just as for the molecules discussed above, a simple model for the inter-

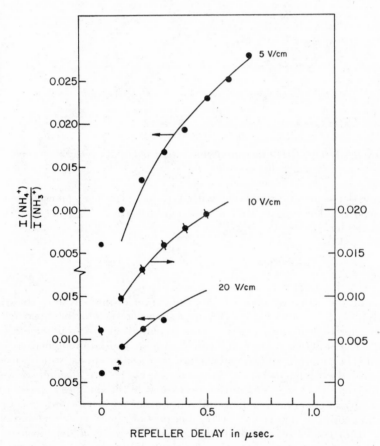

Figure 7. A comparison of the experimental results for the reac- tion producing NH_4^+ in NH_3 with calculated curves. (Journal of Chemical Physics)

action potential adequately accounts for the results in the low kinetic energy region.

Hydrogen. Because hydrogen represents the simplest nonatomic system and because its isotopes are readily available, we have examined some of the ion-molecule reactions of hydrogen as a function of kinetic

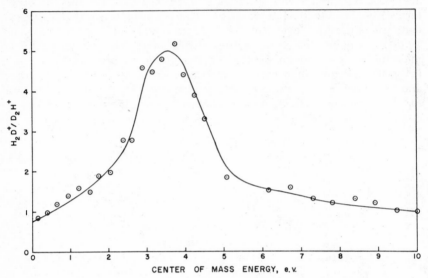

Figure 8. H_2D^+/D_2H^+ *as a function kinetic energy in the center of mass for the reaction of* HD^+ *with HD*

energy. The reaction of HD^+ with HD has also been investigated by Giese (*16*). He reports that at low energies the ratio of H_2D^+/D_2H^+ produced by

$$HD^+ + HD \nearrow \begin{matrix} H_2D^+ + D & (19) \\ \\ D_2H^+ + H & (20) \end{matrix}$$

is about 0.8 while at 0.25 e.v. in the center-of-mass system this ratio is 1.1, and at 3.5 e.v. it is 3.0. Figure 8 shows our results for this reaction, which agree well with Giese. Our explanation for the decrease in HD_2^+/D_2H^+ above 4 e.v. is the conversion of translational energy of the initial HD^+ ion into vibrational excitation of the products, which through normal vibrational isotope effects causes H_2D^{+*} to decompose more readily than D_2H^{+*}. The initial increase at lower energies appears to be caused by an energy dependent difference in the effective volume occupied by the proton or deuteron in HD^+ because of displacement of center of mass from center of charge in the ion and because of displacement of center of mass from the center of polarizability in HD (*29*). Such a mechanism may also operate in the HD^+-rare gas systems. We also observe the production of protons and deuterons at about 4 e.v., which we attribute both to collisional dissociation of the HD^+ and of dissociation of excited H_2D^+ and D_2H^+. The former type of dissociation has been studied in more detail by Vance and Bailey (*65*) using a tandem mass spectrometer of different design.   They find that there is an energy independent cross-section of about 5 sq. A. between 30–100 e.v. for this reaction.   Menendez *et al.* have observed this type of dissociation for H_2^+-Ar collisions (*44*).

The reaction of D_2^+ with HD illustrates several features related to kinetic energy.   The percentage of the secondary reactions as a function of kinetic energy represented by each of several reaction paths is given in Figure 9.   The reactions which describe this system are

$$D_2^+ + HD \rightarrow HD_2^+ + D \tag{21}$$

$$\rightarrow D_3^+ + H \tag{22}$$

$$\rightarrow HD^+ + D_2 \tag{23}$$

$$\rightarrow D^+ + D + HD \tag{24}$$

There are actually two types of reactions which are included in Reaction 21.   One is a deuteron transfer, but there is also an abstraction reaction like Reaction 22 which produces a product at $m/e\,5$.   The irregular nature of the curves in Figure 9 is presumably caused by recurring maxima in the charge transfer cross-section as described by the Massey criterion (*42*). The type of behavior shown in Figure 9 is typical of many ion-molecule reactions inasmuch as the percentage of ion-molecule reactions decreases with respect to charge transfer as the kinetic energy of the incident ion

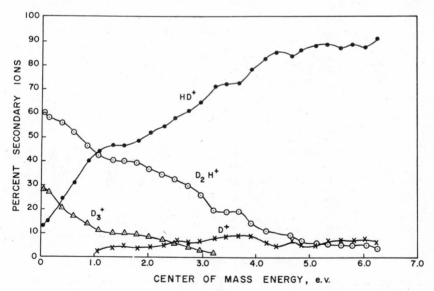

Figure 9.   Percentage of secondary ions from reactions of D_2^+ with HD as a function of kinetic energy in the center of mass

increases.   A similar type of behavior has been demonstrated in many experiments on charge transfer—e.g. the work of von Koch on methane and ethane (*69, 70*).

Methane.   Certain effects of translational energy on reactions of methane have been studied by Henglein and Muccini (*22*) and by the authors.   Henglein and Muccini studied isotope effects in hydron transfer reactions using a single-stage mass spectrometer operating in the method of Cermak and Herman (*5*).   They observed that the ratio of proton transfer to deuteron transfer increased with increasing kinetic energy for several simple compounds.   This effect was explained by differences in vibrational frequency between C-H and C-D bonds which becomes more and more significant as the time of the reaction becomes shorter at higher kinetic energies.   Our data from a tandem mass spectrometer study for the reactions of $CH_2D_2^+$ with CD_4 is compared with the results of Henglein and Muccini for $CH_2D_2^+$ reacting with dideutero-

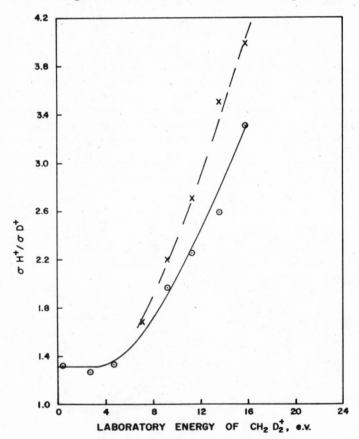

Figure 10.   Isotope effects in hydron transfer from $CH_2D_2^+$ as a function of ion kinetic energy

(×) *Data of Henglein and Muccini (22)*

methane in Figure 10.   At low (<4 e.v.) kinetic energy, there is a region where translational energy has no effect on the ratio of proton to deuteron transfer.   This region is interpreted as one where hydron transfer results from loose complex formation; here differences in vibrational frequency are not determinative because the complex survives for many vibrational periods.   At higher energies a stripping mechanism produces a sharp rise in the isotope effect.   By observing the transition from complex formation to a stripping mechanism we have concluded that collisions which have a lifetime of less than about two vibrations are more adequately described by a stripping mechanism than by the complex model of Gioumousis and Stevenson (*18*).

We also observe other effects of translational energy in methane which are similar to those found in hydrogen.   There is an abstraction reaction for parent ions which also produces a hydronated methane. In studying the reaction

$$CH_4^+ + CD_4 \nearrow^{CH_4H^+ + CH_3 \cdot} _{\searrow CH_4D^+ + CD_3 \cdot}$$

$$\tag{25}$$
$$\tag{26}$$

the D atom abstraction Reaction 26 decreases much faster with increasing kinetic energy than the proton transfer, Reaction 25.   This is an example of translational energy effects on two exothermic processes which are competitive.   Another example is the reaction of CH_2^+ with CH_4.

$$CH_2^+ + CH_4 \rightarrow C_2H_5^+ + H \cdot \tag{27}$$

$$\rightarrow C_2H_4^+ + H_2 \tag{28}$$

$$\rightarrow C_2H_3^+ + H_2 + H \cdot \tag{29}$$

$$\rightarrow C_2H_2^+ + 2H \cdot \tag{30}$$

Reaction 27 is exothermic by 38 kcal./mole, Reaction 28 by 60 kcal./ mole, and Reaction 29 by 16 kcal./mole while $C_2H_3^+$ appears to be somewhat endothermic (*8*).   Table II shows the spectrum of these ions at two different kinetic energies.   The more extensive decomposition at higher impacting ion velocity is clear evidence for the conversion of kinetic energy to internal energy.

Table II also includes the spectrum of ions resulting from reaction of CH_3^+ with CH_4.

$$CH_3^+ + CH_4 \nearrow^{C_2H_5^+ + H_2} _{\searrow C_2H_3^+ + 2H_2}$$

$$\tag{31}$$
$$\tag{32}$$

In this case Reaction 31 is exothermic by 20 kcal./mole while Reaction 32 is endothermic by 36 kcal./mole.   The striking increase in vinyl ion production is a further example of translational energy being converted into vibrational energy.

A somewhat different example of this conversion is observed in the reaction of CHO^+ ions from methanol with CD_4.   Here proton transfer

Table II.   Effects of Kinetic Energy on C_2 Products

Reactant Ion	*Kinetic Energy, e.v.*	% of C_2 Secondary Ions			
		$C_2H_2^+$	$C_2H_3^+$	$C_2H_4^+$	$C_2H_5^+$
CH_3^+	0.3	0	4.1	0	96
	4.2	0	71	0	29
CH_2^+	0.3	11	25	37	27
	4.2	22	69	5	4

is observed along with CD_3^+ and CHD_2^+. The results are shown in Table III. The reaction which produces these last two ions is endothermic by 24 kcal./mole for ground state CHO^+ but proceeds even at very low translational energies, presumably because of vibronic excitation of some CHO^+ ions. As one increases the kinetic energy of CHO^+, both the ratio of CHD_2^+/CD_3^+ and the intensity of those two ions relative to CD_4H^+ increase. These effects are also explained by an increase in the internal energy of the CD_4H^+ with increasing impact velocity. The change in the relative amount of D_2/HD loss is presumably caused by a washing-out of the differences in zero point energy between a C-H and C-D bond at higher vibrational amplitudes. An isotope effect which is caused by the differences in vibrational frequency of the two bonds becomes relatively more important at higher energies in governing the amount of D_2 and HD elimination.

Another reaction of methane which is similar to that in hydrogen and probably of a general nature is a collisionally induced decomposition of the impacting ion. As we increase the energy of the methane parent ion in Reaction 25 to 8 e.v., we see that the m/e 15 ion which is absent at 0.5 e.v. grows to 1.7 times the proton transfer peak (m/e 21) and 5 times the dissociative proton transfer peaks. Such dissociations have been observed previously at kilovolt energies (*9, 43*). We find them to be significant also for polyatomic ions at a few volts kinetic energy.

Hydrocarbon Reactions. Some interesting features of reactions involving olefins and saturated hydrocarbons are shown by investigating the effects of translational energy. The reactions:

$$1\text{-}C_4H_8^+ + \text{cyclo-}C_6H_{12} \nearrow C_6H_{11}^+ + C_4H_9 \quad (33)$$
$$\searrow C_6H_{10}^+ + C_4H_{10} \quad (34)$$

$$\text{cyclo-}C_6H_{12}^+ + 1\text{-}C_4H_8 \nearrow C_6H_{11}^+ + C_4H_9 \quad (35)$$
$$\searrow C_6H_{10}^+ + C_4H_{10} \quad (36)$$

produce identical products from a formally identical intermediate complex. For 1-butene ions at 0.18 e.v. in the center of mass (C.M.) the ratio of H^-/H_2^- transfer was 0.14. At 0.92 e.v. C.M. this ratio had increased to 7.2. For reaction of cyclohexane ions with 1-butene, the analogous $H \cdot /H_2$ transfer ratio was 1.2 at 0.16 e.v. C.M. while it increased to 18 at 1.1 e.v. These trends appear for all reaction of this type which we have studied thus far. A possible explanation for this behavior is that the four-center complex necessary for H_2 or H_2^- transfer reactions cannot compete efficiently at higher kinetic energy because of the relatively longer lifetime necessary for such reactions.

Since the experiments only involve interchanging the ionic and neutral reactants, it is plausible to consider that a similar reaction complex is involved in the respective H, H^- and H_2, H_2^- transfer reactions.

Summary and Conclusions

Our knowledge of the effect of translational energy on ion-molecule reactions is growing rapidly. This growth is based, primarily, on a rapid emergence of research mass spectrometers which are capable of yielding detailed information on these effects. Theory has not maintained this rapid pace although the phase space theory of Light (*34, 37, 50, 74*) represents a significant evolution of previous theoretical considerations. This method should eventually be capable of describing any ion-molecule reaction involving three nuclei in which quantum effects are unimportant. However, the complexities of the kinematics of many-body collisions severely restricts detailed calculations of even diatomic ion-diatomic molecule reactions.

Table III.   Effect of Ion Translational Energy on the Reaction of CHO^+ with CD_4

Ion Energy e.v.	Relative Intensity, Counts/Sec.				CD_4H^+	CHD_2^+
	CHD_2^+	CD_3^+	CD_4^+	CD_4H^+	$\dfrac{CHD_2^+ +}{CD_3^+}$	CD_3^+
0.3	201	244	57	1337	3.00	0.82
1.9	219	228	61	704	1.57	0.96
4.2	242	223	79	453	0.97	1.09

For more complex polyatomic systems, it seems appropriate to suggest certain possibilities for further theory development. At low kinetic energies, the theory of Gioumousis and Stevenson seems to describe adequately the long range attractive force between ions and nonpolar molecules and therefore can adequately estimate the cross-section for complex formation. Now that new experimental methods are elaborating some of the complexities of ion-molecule reactions, it is necessary to account for the various decomposition paths of the complex. For a reaction such as $CH_2^+ + CH_4 \rightarrow [C_2H_6^{+*}] \rightarrow$ products, a statistical treatment for the decomposition of the $(C_2H_6^{+*})$ based on the quasi-equilibrium theory of mass spectra (*66*) should be capable of predicting various reaction probabilities and the variation of those probabilities with internal energy. For reactions which do not involve condensation but only the transfer of small particles—i.e., H^+, $H\cdot$, H_2, H^-, H_2^-, D^+, D_2 transfer reactions etc.—extending the transition state theory (*1, 53*) might adequately explain both isotope effects and the competition between the two- and four-center reactions for these systems. In any case, exact descriptions of reactions in complex systems will not readily be available, and it appears that extension of existing theories of chemical kinetics may be the best means of providing workable approximations for predicting complex ion-molecule reaction pathways.

A significant recent experimental advance is the introduction of tandem mass spectrometers for studying ion-molecule reactions. Examining various isotope effects as a function of translational energy can provide detailed information about reaction mechanisms. Tandem experiments can also observe many of the possible reaction channels for a given collision complex. Such information provides valuable clues to the chemical and physical nature of the intermediates in ion-neutral interactions.

Obviously, experiments designed to measure cross-sections as a function of energy are needed. At present, tandem experiments are not capable of high precision at low energies because one must assume details of collision mechanics and because it is difficult to estimate collection efficiencies in forward scattering geometry (15). The extension of all known techniques to lower energy (64, 65) and the further development of pulse methods (58) offer the possibility for advances in this area.

Molecular beam techniques provide powerful tools for investigating ion-molecule reactions. The angular dependence of cross-sections gives direct insight into the physical nature of the reaction complex. Turner, Fineman and Stebbings (64) have shown that the reaction

$$N_2^+ + D_2 \rightarrow N_2D^+ + D \qquad (37)$$

exhibits a forward glory. Therefore it can probably best be described as a stripping reaction. The lowest energy they used was 7.5 e.v.; it would be interesting to extend their work to lower ion energies to determine if the concept of a long-lived complex is valid for this system. Further experiments of the same type for other systems are obviously of great value and are anticipated. Nonreactive crossed-beam ion-neutral experiments are also important since they provide information on the interaction potential at large internuclear distances. Such information is quite important in the further evolution of ion-molecule reaction rate theory.

Acknowledgment

This manuscript was written during the tenure of a National Academy of Sciences-National Research Council Postdoctoral Fellowship awarded to F. P. Abramson for the academic year 1965–66. The authors also wish to acknowledge helpful discussions with their colleagues at the Aerospace Research Laboratories.

Literature Cited

(1) Benson, S. W., "The Foundations of Chemical Kinetics," McGraw-Hill Publishing Co., New York, 1960.
(2) Berta, M. A., Ellis, B. Y., Koski, W. S., *J. Chem. Phys.*, in press.
(3) Berta, M. A., Koski, W. S., *J. Am. Chem. Soc.* **86,** 5098 (1964).
(4) Boelrijk, N., Hamill, W. H., *J. Am. Chem. Soc.* **84,** 730 (1962).
(5) Cermak, V., Herman, Z., *Nucleonics* **19,** 106 (1961).

(6) Chupka, W. A., Lindholm, E., *Arkiv Fysik* **25**, 349 (1963).
(7) Dugan, J. V., Magee, J. L., *NASA TN-D-3229* (February 1966).
(8) Field, F. H., Franklin, J. L., "Electron Impact Phenomenon," Academic Press, New York, 1957.
(9) Field, F. H., Franklin, J. L., Munson, M. S. B., *J. Am. Chem. Soc.* **85**, 3575 (1963).
(10) Futrell, J. H., Tiernan, T. O., *J. Chem. Phys.* **39**, 2539 (1963).
(11) Futrell, J. H., Miller, C. D., to be published.
(12) Galli, A., Giardini-Guidoni, A., Volpi, G. G., *Nuovo Cimento* **31**, 1145 (1964).
(13) Giese, C. F., *Rev. Sci. Instr.* **30**, 260 (1959).
(14) Giese, C. F., Maier, W. B., *J. Chem. Phys.* **39**, 197 (1963).
(15) Giese, C. F., Maier, W. B., *J. Chem. Phys.* **39**, 739 (1963).
(16) Giese, C. F., *Bull. Am. Phys. Soc.* **9**, 189 (1964).
(17) Giese, C. F., "Advances in Chemical Physics," Interscience Publishers, New York, 1966.
(18) Gioumousis, G., Stevenson, D. P., *J. Chem. Phys.* **29**, 294 (1958).
(19) Gustafsson, E., Lindholm, E., *Arkiv Fysik* **18**, 219 (1960).
(20) Gustafsson, E., Lindholm, E., private communication, cited in "Atomic and Molecular Processes," D. R. Bates, ed., Academic Press, New York, N. Y., 1962, p. 705.
(21) Henglein, A., Muccini, G. A., *Z. Naturforsch.* **17a**, 452 (1962).
(22) Henglein, A., Muccini, G. A., *Z. Naturforsch.* **18a**, 753 (1963).
(23) Henglein, A., Lacmann, K., Jacobs, G., *Ber. Bunsenges. Phys. Chem.* **69**, 279 (1965).
(24) Henglein, A., Lacmann, K., Knoll, B., *J. Chem. Phys.* **43**, 1048 (1965).
(25) Hertel, G. R., Koski, W. S., *J. Am. Soc.* **86**, 1683 (1964).
(26) Hertel, G. R., Koski, W. S., *J. Am. Chem. Soc.* **87**, 404 (1965).
(27) Hertel, G. R., Koski, W. S., *J. Am. Chem. Soc.* **87**, 1686 (1965).
(28) Homer, J. G., Lehrle, R. S., Robb, J. C., Takahasi, M., Thomas, D. W., *Advan. Mass Spectrometry* **2**, 503 (1963).
(29) Klein, F. S., Friedman, L., *J. Chem. Phys.* **41**, 1789 (1964).
(30) Kubose, D. A., Hamill, W. H., *J. Am. Chem. Soc.* **85**, 125 (1963).
(31) Lacmann, K., Henglein, A., *Ber. Bunsenges. Phys. Chem.* **69**, 286 (1965).
(32) Lacmann, K., Henglein, A., *Ber. Bunsenges. Phys. Chem.* **69**, 292 (1965).
(33) Lavrovskaya, G. K., Markin, M. I., Tal'roze, V. L., *Kinetika i Kataliz* **2**, 21 (1961).
(34) Light, J. C., *J. Chem. Phys.* **40**, 3221 (1964).
(35) Light, J. C., Horrocks, J., *Proc. Phys. Soc.* **84**, 527 (1964).
(36) Light, J. C., *J. Chem. Phys.* **41**, 586 (1964).
(37) Light, J. C., Lin, J., *J. Chem. Phys.* **43**, 3209 (1965).
(38) Lindholm, E., *Z. Naturforsch* **9a**, 535 (1954).
(39) Lindholm, E., *Arkiv Fysik* **8**, 433 (1954).
(40) Maier, W. B., *J. Chem. Phys.* **41**, 2174 (1964).
(41) Maier, W. B., *J. Chem. Phys.* **42**, 1790 (1965).
(42) Massey, H. S. W., Burhop, E. H. S., "Electronic and Ionic Impact Phenomenon," p. 478, Oxford University Press, New York, 1952.
(43) Melton, C. E., Rosenstock, H. M., *J. Chem. Phys.* **26**, 568 (1957).
(44) Menendez, M. G., Thomas, B. S., Bailey, T. L., *J. Chem. Phys.* **42**, 802 (1965).
(45) Monahan, J. E., Stanton, H. E., *J. Chem. Phys.* **37**, 2654 (1963).
(46) Moran, T. F., Hamill, W. H., *J. Chem. Phys.* **39**, 1413 (1963).
(47) Moran, T. F., Friedman, L., *J. Chem. Phys.* **39**, 2491 (1963).
(48) Moran, T. F., Friedman, L., *J. Chem. Phys.* **40**, 860 (1964).
(49) Moran, T. F., Friedman, L., *J. Chem. Phys.* **42**, 2391 (1965).
(50) Pechukas, P., Light, J. C., *J. Chem. Phys.* **42**, 3281 (1965).
(51) Pettersson, E., Lindholm, E., *Arkiv Fysik* **24**, 49 (1963).
(52) Pettersson, E., *Arkiv Fysik* **25**, 181 (1963).
(53) Ree, T. S., Taikyue, R., Eyring, H., Fueno, T., *J. Chem. Phys.* **36**, 281 (1962).
(54) Reuben, B. G., Friedman, L., *J. Chem. Phys.* **37**, 1636 (1962).
(55) Rosenstock, H. M., *U.S. At. Energy Rept.* JLI-**605-3-7**, TID-**4500** (1959).
(56) Ryan, K. R., Futrell, J. H., *J. Chem. Phys.* **42**, 824 (1965).
(57) Ryan, K. R., Futrell, J. H., *J. Chem. Phys.* **43**, 3009 (1965).
(58) Ryan, K. R., Futrell, J. H., Miller, C. D., *Rev. Sci. Instr.* **37**, 107 (1966).
(59) Stevenson, D. P., Schachtschneider, J., "Preprints," ACS, Division of Physical Chemistry, Utah, July 7–10, 1963.

(60) Tal'roze, V. L., *Izv. Akad. Nauk. SSR, Ser. Fiz.* **24,** 1006 (1960).
(61) Tal'roze, V. L., Frankevich, E. L., *Zh. Fiz. Khim.* **34,** 2709 (1960).
(62) Tal'roze, V. L., "Proceedings of a Symposium on the Chemical Effects of Nuclear Transformations," Vol. I, 1963, p. 103,
(63) Theard, L. P., Hamill, W. H., *J. Am. Chem. Soc.* **84,** 1134 (1962).
(64) Turner, B. R., Fineman, M. A., Stebbings, R. F., *J. Chem. Phys.* **42,** 4088 (1965).
(65) Vance, D. W., Bailey, T. L., *J. Chem. Phys.* **44,** 486 (1966).
(66) Vestal, M., Wahrhaftig, A. L., Johnston, W. H., *J. Chem. Phys.* **37,** 1276 (1962).
(67) Von Koch, H., Friedman, L., *J. Chem. Phys.* **38,** 1115 (1963).
(68) Von Koch, H., Lindholm, E., *Arkiv Fysik* **19,** 123 (1961).
(69) Von Koch, H., *Arkiv Fysik* **28,** 529 (1965).
(70) Von Koch, H., *Arkiv Fysik* **28,** 559 (1965).
(71) Wacks, M. E., *J. Res. Nat. Bur. Std.* **68A,** 631 (1964).
(72) Weiner, E. R., Hertel, G. R., Koski, W. S., *J. Am. Chem. Soc.* **86,** 788 (1964).
(73) Wilmenious, P., Lindholm, E., *Arkiv Fysik* **21,** 97 (1962).
(74) Wolf, F. A., *J. Chem. Phys.* **44,** 1619 (1966).

RECEIVED May 3, 1966.

9

The Use of High Pressure Mass Spectrometry to Determine the Energy Dependence of Ion-Molecule Reaction Rates

D. J. HYATT, E. A. DODMAN, and M. J. HENCHMAN

Department of Physical Chemistry, The University, Leeds 2, England

A theory is derived to account for the formation, by hydrogen transfer reactions, of high order ions in a high pressure mass spectrometer. The theory is based upon a detailed analysis of the reactive collision kinematics for the various models of complex formation, proton or hydride ion stripping, and hydrogen atom stripping. Application of the theory can yield information on the energy dependence of the rate constant, and if this is known independently, one can choose among the three mechanisms. The theory is applied to hydrogen transfer reactions occurring in deuterated methanols at high source pressures. The rate constants for these reactions increase as the energy decreases, thereby suggesting some alignment of the molecular dipole towards the oncoming ion.

A central problem in studying ion-molecule reactions is the dependence of the microscopic cross-section, σ or the rate constant k upon the relative velocity of the ion and the molecule. Only from reliable, established data on this dependence can one choose among the various theoretical models advanced to account for the kinetics of these processes such as the polarization theory of Gioumousis and Stevenson (10) or the more recent phase-space treatment of Light (26).

It might be thought that such data are best obtained using longitudinal tandem machines, as pioneered by Giese (9), wherein both mass and velocity selection of the primary ion are achieved. Nevertheless, this kind of approach is subject to two considerable constraints. First, space-charge explosion of the primary ion beam sets an effective lower energy limit at 1–3 e.v. on the production of a monoenergetic ion beam at this time; second, the only reactions which can in general be observed are those for which much of the momentum of the primary ion is retained in the secondary ion—for example, hydrogen atom transfer reactions such as Reaction A.

$$N_2^+ + D_2 \rightarrow N_2D^+ + D \tag{A}$$

Attempts to observe the familiar methane reaction:

$$CH_4{}^+ + CH_4 \rightarrow CH_5{}^+ + CH_3 \qquad \text{(B)}$$

using 10 e.v. ions in this kind of machine were unsuccessful (16), suggesting that it is a proton transfer reaction occurring by a stripping mechanism at this energy.

While, with this reservation, longitudinal tandem machines provide the best means to determine the variation of $\sigma(E)$ with E (the ion energy) for energies above ca. 3 e.v., for the important energy range of 0.05–3 e.v. one must use traditional methods where ionization and reaction occur within the same region. This so-called pressure method which has produced so many of the results on ion-molecule reactions in the past decade (37), yields only a phenomenological cross-section Q or an average rate constant $\bar{k}$ such that:

$$Q = \frac{1}{E_e} \int_0^{E_e} \sigma(E)dE \qquad \text{(1)}$$

$$\bar{k} = \frac{1}{v_e} \int_0^{v_e} k(v)dv \qquad \text{(2)}$$

where E_e and v_e are the ion-exit energy and velocity, and each of these is considerably greater than its thermal counterpart. E_e depends on the strength of the repeller field, and traditional repeller studies give data on the variation of Q with E_e. The more fundamental dependence of $\sigma(E)$ upon E lies masked within this although a limited knowledge of the energy dependence of the microscopic cross-section can be obtained from Light's relationship (25) (Equation 3).

$$\sigma(E_e) = Q(E_e) + E_e \cdot \frac{dQ}{dE_e} \qquad \text{(3)}$$

Tal'roze's pulsing technique (38) allows direct determination of the microscopic cross-section or rate constant at thermal energies ($\sim$0.05 e.v.), and the recent exploitation of this method by Futrell (33) and Harrison (36) is a most welcome development. An extension of this (35), involving short pulses and a continuous repeller field, permits measurements of phenomenological cross-sections to much lower values of the ion exit energy E_e than are reliable in the repeller studies. As Futrell has pointed out (33), it is important to consider the self-consistency of the repeller studies and to determine whether or not the conclusions from the repeller studies agree with those obtained using the pulsing technique. Establishing the validity of repeller results— i.e., that they truly represent the variation of Q or $\bar{k}$ with E_e and are not the consequence of instrumental artifacts—is important since they are often used to support fresh concepts or to test new theory. Hamill (23, 39), for example, from a detailed analysis of repeller curves, has derived a theory for the dependence of $\sigma(E)$ upon E. Friedman (28,

42) also has interpreted maxima found in repeller curves of $\bar{k}(E_e)$ against E_e for the reactions:

$$H_2^+ + He \rightarrow HeH^+ + H \tag{C}$$

$$H_2^+ + Ne \rightarrow NeH^+ + H \tag{D}$$

in terms of a kinetic energy threshold at low ion energies and short range repulsive forces at high ion energies.

A wide difference often exists between repeller curves measured for the same reaction on different machines. Rosenstock (*31*) was the first to draw attention to such a conflict between two studies (*1, 5*) on Reaction E.

$$C_2H_2^+ + C_2H_2 \begin{array}{c} \nearrow C_4H_2^+ + H_2 \\ \searrow C_4H_3^+ + H \end{array} \tag{E}$$

Stevenson and Schissler (*37*) have shown the wide divergence which exists between two repeller studies on the methane reaction (B). A similar situation exists for the perdeutero reaction

$$CD_4^+ + CD_4 \rightarrow CD_5^+ + CD_3 \tag{F}$$

where differences also exist for the two repeller studies in the literature (*7, 23*). Discussion of these two methane reactions (B and F) can be extended since Futrell's recent paper (*34*) on his new pulsing technique shows that the rate constant of Reaction B is independent of ion energy up to 0.825 e.v. (the differing rate constants found there for Reaction B at 0 volt/cm. and 10 volts/cm. are apparent, not real (*11*)). (We thank Dr. Harrison for the observation that the ion ejection time must be considered and that this correction yields equal rate constants for the different repeller voltages.) This conclusion is supported by Harrison's work (*13*) where the thermal rate constants for Reactions B and F, k(0.05 e.v.) obtained by the pulsing technique, agree with those obtained by the conventional pressure method for an ion-exit energy of 3.7 e.v., which we call $\bar{k}$ (3.7 e.v.). These results suggest that the energy dependence of these reactions, at least up to about 4 e.v., agrees with the Gioumousis and Stevenson (*10*) model which is based on the simple electrostatic attraction between the ion and the induced dipole. Furthermore they call into question the meaning of the variation of $\bar{k}(E_e)$ for $E_e < 3.7$ e.v. found in the repeller studies. We feel these variations are the consequence of instrumental effects which are not understood since the repeller results are often irreproducible on different machines, and they conflict with the convincing pulsing results outlined above. Therefore, the validity of repeller studies, particularly at low energies, is questionable. At low energies (*7*) the repeller field is comparable to stray fields penetrating through the slits of the ionization chamber, and it no longer defines the residence time of the ions.

Ion-Molecule Reactions Involving Polar Molecules

The interesting results from using pulsing techniques for reactions between ions and nonpolar molecules invite similar speculations about the more complicated reaction between an ion and a polar molecule. Hamill (29, 39) was the first to apply the theory of Gioumousis and Stevenson (10) to this system, realizing that there were two extreme situations: (1) when the polar molecule continued to rotate as the ion approached thereby averaging out the ion-permanent dipole interaction and leaving only the ion-induced dipole interaction, and (2) when the molecule dipole "locks in" to the incoming ion, and the ion-permanent dipole interaction aids the ion-induced dipole interaction. Theoretically, the energy dependence of the microscopic cross-section is then given by:

$$\sigma(E) = \pi e (2\alpha m_1/\mu E)^{1/2} \qquad (4)$$

or by

$$\sigma(E) = \pi e (2\alpha m_1/\mu E)^{1/2} + \pi e \mu_D m_1/\mu E \qquad (5)$$

where e is the electronic charge, α the polarizability of the molecule, m_1 the mass of the ion, μ the reduced mass, and μ_D the dipole moment of the molecule. The corresponding rate constants are then:

$$\bar{k}(E_e) = 2\pi e (\alpha/\mu)^{1/2} \qquad (6)$$

and

$$\bar{k}(E_e) = 2\pi e (\alpha/\mu)^{1/2} + \pi e \mu_D/\mu \cdot (m_1/2E_e)^{1/2} \cdot \ln(E_e/E)_i \qquad (7)$$

where E_i is the initial ion energy. Equation 7 is only applicable for $E_i \ll E_e$.

Early support for the locking-in of the dipole came from the high rate constants found for the reactions of ions with polar molecules. Many of these rate constants are too large owing to incorrect identification of the primary ions; this considerably limits the pressure method at low source pressures. The high pressure studies overcome this by determining the rate constant from the rate of decrease of the primary ion. If locking-in of the dipole does occur, then $\bar{k}(E_e)$ will depend on E_e, the ion exit energy, and will be significantly smaller than the thermal rate constant $k(E = 0.05$ e.v.$)$, measured by the pulsing technique. Conflicting results now exist here. Table I summarizes data from Harrison's laboratory (12, 40, 41) on the hydrogen transfer reactions of the parent ions in water, ammonia, and methanol. There is little difference between the thermal rate constants, $k(E = 0.05$ e.v.$)$, and the rate constants obtained from conventional low pressure measurements, $\bar{k}(E_e = 3.7$ e.v.$)$. These data suggest that there is no alignment of the molecular dipole moment towards the incoming ion in agreement with the predicted energy dependence for a pure ion-induced dipole interaction (10). These reactions have also been studied by Futrell (8, 34) using his new short pulse/continuous repeller technique (35). Even if one allows for the apparent neglect of contributing hydrogen transfer reactions involving fragment ions such as:

$$OH^+ + H_2O \rightarrow H_3O^+ + O \qquad (L)$$

and the corrections suggested by Harrison (*11*), the rate constants of these reactions *do* depend on the ion energy, and the energy dependence agrees qualitatively with predictions of the dipole alignment mechanism.

There is a little information available from repeller studies. In their paper on methanol, Thynne *et al.* (*40*) present, without analysis, data on the variation of the phenomenological cross-sections of Reactions J and K with the ion-exit energy obtained from conventional low pressure measurements. These data can be used to examine the dependence of $\bar{k}(E_e)$ upon E_e via the relation:

$$\bar{k}(E_e) = (E_e/2m_1)^{1/2} \cdot Q(E_e) \qquad (8)$$

for the over-all process:

$$CD_3OH^+ + CD_3OH \rightarrow products \qquad (J + K)$$

When this is done, the dependence of $\bar{k}(E_e)$ upon E_e is even greater than predicted by the dipole-alignment model, and the thermal rate constant predicted from this variation, extrapolated to thermal energies, is more than twice the thermal rate constant found experimentally by using the pulsing technique.

The two pulsing studies disagree—an unfortunate conflict since the technique has seemed so promising. The repeller studies differ from both pulsing results, but are worse from those measured on the same machine; once again their significance is questionable. We report here high pressure results on the methanol reaction that provide independent evidence on the energy dependence of the rate constant.

High Pressure Study of the Methanol Reaction Using Deuterated Methanols

Experimental. High pressure mass spectrometry is now a well established method for investigating ion-molecule reactions, owing largely to an impressive series of papers from Field's laboratory. The Leeds high pressure mass spectrometer used in this study can handle source pressures up to 0.2 torr and has been previously described (*17*). Three refinements have been added to the source. The repeller, which is a rectangular stainless steel plate, is mounted on two different rods made of two thermocouple alloys T_1 and T_2, and this device allows direct monitoring of the gas temperature in the ionization chamber. An additional electrode has been fitted between the filament and the ionization chamber to produce a better defined electron beam. Finally provision has been made to measure the gas pressure directly in the ionization chamber. About 20 1-mm. diameter holes have been bored in the chamber wall to link this with an additional side chamber; this in turn connects with a second gas line, which passes through the vacuum envelope to a McLeod gage. No gas flow occurs in this second line, and it allows direct measurement of the source pressure. Relevant source dimensions are: repeller-ion exit slit = 0.33 cm.; center of electron beam-ion exit slit = 0.10 cm. In a study on methane, the usual semi-log plot for the decrease of the CH_4^+ ion is linear up to a source pressure of 0.15 torr and yields a rate constant of $k = 8.8 \times 10^{-10}$ cc./molecule-sec., in excellent agreement with published values (6).

Results. In the past two years we have undertaken a high pressure examination of the ion-molecule reactions occurring in a series of polar molecules—namely, methylamine, methanol, ethylamine, and ethanol (3). In all cases, the major secondary ion is the (parent + 1) ion and in the first two cases, it is the *only* secondary ion. *All* hydrogenic primary ions undergo the general reaction,

$$RH^+ + M \xrightarrow{H^+} MH^+ + R \qquad \text{(M)}$$

and thus proton transfer is the predominating mode of reaction. Typical results for some of the primary ions in methanol are shown in Figure 1. The semi-log plots are linear, and full details of this work will be published later. Ambiguity concerning the nature of the hydrogen transfer exists only when the primary ion is the parent ion—i.e., RH = M; thus, Reaction I can either involve a proton or a hydrogen atom transfer. If the collision complex is long lived, say $>10^{-12}$ sec., this distinction is meaningless because the identities of the primary ion and the molecule are lost in the complex. If the complex is short lived, the evidence points to its being predominantly a proton transfer process because of (a) the prevalence of proton transfer in reactions involving the hydrogenic fragment ions; (b) the similarity in rates between these reactions and the reaction of the parent ion, and (c) the results from the tandem machines at energies greater than 5 e.v. The fact that reactions such as I are not observed in longitudinal tandem machines (16) but are observed in transverse ones (44) or via the Cermak technique (18) means that they are proton transfer processes occurring by a stripping mechanism in this energy range.

The difference between the ionization potential of methanol (10.9 e.v.) and the appearance potential of CH_2OH^+ (11.9 e.v.) (4) is sufficiently large that, by controlling the electron energy, Reaction I can be studied to the effective exclusion of Reaction N.

$$CH_2OH^+ + CH_3OH \rightarrow CH_3OH_2^+ + CH_2O \qquad \text{(N)}$$

In our experiments studied under these conditions CH_2OH^+/CH_3OH^+ <0.1, and the situation is further enhanced by the rate constant of Reaction N being less than that of Reaction I (Figure 1). Similar experiments were run for CD_3OH (Merck, Sharp and Dohme, Canada, containing <1% CD_2HOH by low voltage analysis) and CH_3OD (Fluka A.G., Switzerland, containing <1% CH_3OH by NMR analysis). In the latter compound, it was first necessary to "deuterate" the mass spectrometer by flushing it with D_2O for three days. Other pertinent operating conditions were: source temperature 180°C., field strength 9.1 volts/cm. corresponding to an ion exit energy of 0.91 e.v. For all three compounds, the rate constant for the disappearance of the parent

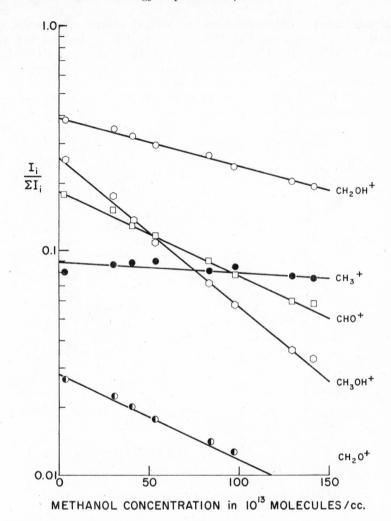

METHANOL CONCENTRATION in 10^{13} MOLECULES/cc.

*Figure 1.   Dependence of relative ion concentrations upon the
ionization chamber concentration of CH_3OH*

ion was the same and equal to 2.0×10^{-9} cc./molecule-sec.   These
values of $\bar{k}(E_e = 0.91$ e.v.) can be compared with the following values
obtained by other workers: CH_3OH, $\bar{k} = 2.45 \times 10^{-9}$ (repeller field 10
volts/cm., but E_e unspecified) (*32*); CD_3OH, $\bar{k}(E_e = 1.5$ e.v.$) = 1.6 \times
10^{-9}$ (obtained from (*40*)).   They agree with the conclusion of Yamamoto
et al. (*45*) that the rate constants for the three compounds are the same.
Our values agree probably fortuitously well with the theoretical prediction
of the aligned-dipole model of $\bar{k}(E_e = 0.91$ e.v.$) = 2.0 \times 10^{-9}$ cc./
molecule sec.

The product ions for this reaction in CD_3OH are $CD_3OH_2{}^+$ and
CD_3OHD^+ (Reactions J and K), according to whether the transferred

hydrogen comes from the hydroxyl or methyl groups. Similarily, for CH_3OD the products are $CH_3OD_2{}^+$ and CH_3ODH^+. In Figure 2, the ratios $CH_3OD_2{}^+/CH_3ODH^+$ from the CH_3OD study and $CD_3OH_2{}^+/CD_3ODH^+$ from the CD_3OH are plotted against the methanol concentration in the ionization chamber. In each the ratio, designated as R, is corrected for ^{13}C isotopic contributions, and both curves represent the results from three different runs.

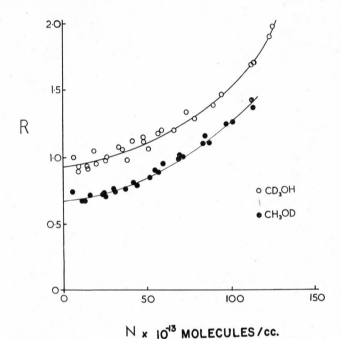

$$N \times 10^{13} \text{ MOLECULES/cc.}$$

Figure 2. Dependence of the ratio R, where $R = CH_3OD_2{}^+/CH_3OHD^+$ for CH_3OD and $R = CD_3OH_2{}^+/CD_3OHD^+$ for CD_3OH, upon the ionization chamber concentration of methanol

The ratio R increases as the source pressure increases. Initially the explanation we offered for this variation invoked a mechanism which depended on the energy of the ion (*14, 15*). From simple electrostatic considerations the collision complex for hydroxyl-hydrogen transfer has a lower potential energy than for the methyl-hydrogen transfer, and the former should be increasingly favored as the ion energy is reduced. Increasing the source pressure increases the proportion of reactive events occurring at low energies and should, on the basis of the model, cause an increase in R. An order-of-magnitude calculation confirms that the observed variation of R should occur in the energy range under consideration, but the crucial test of the model lies in its prediction that the hydrogen transfer should occur almost exclusively from the hydroxyl site at thermal energies. Both laboratories able to measure this using

Table I. Comparison between Rate Constants Measured by the Pulsing Technique and the Pressure Method

Reaction		Thermal Rate Constant $k(E = 0.05\,e.v.)$ $\times\ 10^{10}$ cc./- molecule-sec.	Rate Constant $\bar{k}(E_e = 3.7\,e.v.)$ $\times\ 10^{10}$ cc./- molecule-sec.	Reference
$H_2O^+ + H_2O \rightarrow H_3O^+ + OH$	(G)	4.93	6.04	12
$NH_3^+ + NH_3 \rightarrow NH_4^+ + NH_2$	(H)	5.2	7.7	41
$CH_3OH^+ + CH_3OH \rightarrow$				
$CH_3OH_2^+ + \begin{cases} CH_3O \\ CH_2OH \end{cases}$	(I)	12.2	14.6	40
$CD_3OH^+ + CD_3OH \rightarrow$ $CD_3OH_2^+ + CD_3O$	(J)	5.0	6.3	40
$CD_3OH^+ + CD_3OH \rightarrow$ $CD_3OHD^+ + CD_2OH$	(K)	6.0	8.2	40

the pulsing technique report conclusively that this is not so (8, 40); rather, the relative contributions of methyl- and hydroxyl-hydrogen transfer are insensitive to the ion energy (see Table I).

The explanation for the variation of R with N, the molecular source concentration, lies in reactions of higher order involving transfer of the hydrogen ion from one methanol molecule to another, of the type

$$CH_3OH_2^+ + CH_3OH \rightarrow CH_3OH + CH_3OH_2^+ \qquad (O)$$

and with such a high rate constant that third- and fourth-order ions must be major ions at source pressures as low as 0.05 torr. Such higher order reactions can be detected only by using CD_3OH and CH_3OD. Consider the case of CD_3OH for example. The secondary ion $CD_3OH_2^+$ produced by Reaction J will not change its identity as it reacts further according to Reaction O since only a proton can be transferred. On the other hand, CD_3OHD^+ produced by Reaction K can transfer either a deuteron or a proton. Therefore, as the source pressure is increased, secondary ions react to form tertiaries, which in turn react to form quaternaries; CD_3OHD^+ is progressively transferred into $CD_3OH_2^+$, and the ratio R increases.

Munson (30) has shown that $CH_3OH_2^+$ can undergo reactions other than Reaction O to form $C_2H_7O^+$ ($m/e = 47$), a third-order ion, and the disolvated proton $(CH_3OH)_2H^+$ ($m/e = 65$), a fourth order ion; these in turn will form higher solvated protons. The rate constants of these reactions are sufficiently low, perhaps because they require three-body collisions, that the reactions only become significant at the high pressures possible in Munson's source. Thus, at the highest pressure used in our study (0.05 torr), the ion, $m/e = 65$, is not detectable, and the ion, $m/e = 47$, constitutes only 1% of the total spectrum. Munson's results confirm this once his arbitrary pressure scale has been calibrated from our own data. Thus, these kinds of higher order process are unimportant in the pressure range 0–0.05 torr and cannot be responsible for the variation of R with pressure reported here.

The value of R extrapolated to $N = 0$ gives a value for the relative ease of transfer of a hydroxyl-hydrogen compared with that of a methyl-hydrogen in Reaction I.   This value for CD_3OH is 2.8 and should be compared with the results of other workers—namely, 2.76 (32), 2.61 (45) and 2.28 (40) while the value for CH_3OD is 2.0 to be compared with other results of 2.13 (32) and 2.0 (45).   The ratio of the relative probabilities obtained for CD_3OH and CH_3OD indicates the magnitude of the isotope effect which favors hydrogen transfer over deuterium.   The reasons for this and the preferential transfer of the hydroxyl-hydrogen are not clear. We are reluctant to invoke any kind of energetic argument in such a situation where the reaction is exothermic occurring without activation energy.

Similar studies on partially deuterated methylamines (14, 15) and ethylamines (3) show that this behavior is common for polar molecules. However the variation of R with N in Figure 2 does more than indicate the prevalence of proton transfer processes of the type O.   The shapes of the curves can yield information on the energy dependence of the rate constants of the ion-molecule reactions occurring in the system.   Moreover, if this dependence is known accurately, one can in principle decide if the proton is transferred by a stripping mechanism or via a long lived collision complex.   This problem is of considerable current interest in view of Henglein's finding (19, 20, 21) that hydrogen atom transfer reactions such as A proceed by a pure stripping mechanism at energies above ca. 30 e.v. and in view of the evidence, discussed above, that the same is true for proton and hydride ion transfers at energies above about 10 e.v. The question is: to how low an energy does stripping persist?   This is made more interesting by the recent molecular beam results that several neutral-neutral reactions occur by a stripping mechanism at thermal energies (22, 27).   Yet experimental means of establishing a stripping mechanism for an ion-molecule reaction in the energy range 0.05–5 e.v. have not been devised.   The remainder of this paper constitutes an approach to this problem.

Kinematic Theory of Multiple-Order Reactions Involving Stripping or Complex Formation

Previous theoretical kinetic treatments of the formation of secondary, tertiary and higher order ions in the ionization chamber of a conventional mass spectrometer operating at high pressure, have used either a "steady state" treatment (2, 24) or an ion-beam approach (43).   These theories are essentially phenomenological, and they make no clear assumptions about the nature of the reactive collision.   The model outlined below is a microscopic one, making definite assumptions about the kinematics of the reactive collision.   If the rate constants of the reactions are fixed, the nature of these assumptions definitely affects the amount of reaction occurring.

Formation of Tertiary Ions. Consider primary ions, of initial intensity $I_P{}^o$ reacting with molecules, of concentration N, according to the general scheme

$$P + \text{molecule} \xrightarrow{k_P} S + \text{neutral} \tag{P}$$

$$S + \text{molecule} \xrightarrow{k_S} T + \text{neutral} \tag{Q}$$

where P, S, and T are the primary, secondary, and tertiary ions, and let the rate constants for these reactions, k_P and k_S, be independent of the energy of the ion according to the ion-induced dipole formalism.

The attenuation of the primary ion beam is given by

$$I_P{}^{t_P} = I_P{}^o \exp(-Nk_P t_P) \tag{9}$$

where $I_P{}^{t_P}$ is the intensity of the primary ions after they have travelled for a time t_P. The number of secondary ions formed during this time, namely $I_S{}^{t_P}$, is therefore given by

$$I_S{}^{t_P} = I_P{}^o [1 - \exp(-Nk_P t_P)] \tag{10}$$

and the rate of change of $I_S{}^{t_P}$ with t_P is its differential:

$$dI_S{}^{t_P} = I_P{}^o Nk_P [\exp(-Nk_P t_P)] \cdot dt_P \tag{11}$$

Equation 11, physically, is the number of secondaries formed in the time interval dt_P after the primary ions have travelled for a time t_P and a distance, say x. This group of secondaries can now react to form tertiary ions over a distance $(l-x)$ where l is the ion path length in the ionization chamber. The intensity of this group suffers an exponential decrease similar to that of the primary ions, such that the intensity of the tertiary ions formed from this group, $dI_T{}^{t_P}$, is given by

$$dI_T{}^{t_P} = dI_S{}^{t_P} \cdot [1 - \exp(-Nk_S t_S)] \tag{12}$$

where t_S is the time the unreacting secondary ions in this group take to travel the distance $(l-x)$. Substitution for $dI_S{}^{t_P}$ from Equation 11 into Equation 12 yields:

$$dI_T{}^{t_P} = I_P{}^o Nk_P [\exp(-Nk_P t_P)] \cdot [1 - \exp(-Nk_S t_S)] dt_P \tag{13}$$

The total amount of tertiary ion formed is the integral of this expression from $t_P = 0$ to $t_P = \tau_P$, where τ_P is the residence time for an unreacting primary ion.

To integrate one must know t_S, which of course is a function of t_P, and the form of this function depends upon the mechanism assumed for Reaction P. At this point we restrict Reaction P to a hydrogen transfer reaction in which the transferred species may be either a proton, hydrogen atom, or hydride ion and for which the masses of the primary ion, the molecule, the secondary ion, and the neutral fragment are identical and large compared with the transferred hydrogen. Three situations must be considered where the type of collision is defined by the relationship between v_P and v_S, the velocities of the primary and secondary ions:

(1) immediately prior to and (2) immediately following the reactive collision (*19, 20*). These velocity relationships and the resulting functions for t_S are summarized in Table II for the various possible mechanisms. This treatment assumes that the velocity of the molecule is negligible compared with that of the ion, and that any exothermicity is not released as translational energy.

Table II.   Kinematic Conditions for the Formation of Tertiary Ions by Various Collision Mechanisms

Collision Mechanism	Relation between Velocities of Primary and Secondary Ions	Function for t_S
Stripping (Proton or hydride ion transfer)	$v_S = 0$	$(\tau_P{}^2 - t_P{}^2)^{1/2}$
Complex Formation	$v_S = v_P/2$	$^1/_2[-t_P + (4\tau_P{}^2 - 3t_P{}^2)^{1/2}]$
Stripping (Hydrogen atom transfer)	$v_S = v_P$	$\tau_P - t_P$

For the case where $t_S = \tau_P - t_P$, Equation 13 can be integrated directly to give $I_T{}^{total}$, the total amount of tertiary ion formed. For the other two cases, integration cannot be performed directly, and values of $I_T{}^{total}$ were evaluated numerically on a KDF 9 computer, using a procedure for Simpson's rule. (Numerical evaluation of the directly integrable case provided a check on this procedure.) I_P and I_S are then given by

$$I_P = I_P{}^o \exp(-Nk_P\tau_P) \tag{14}$$

$$I_S = I_P{}^o - I_P - I_T{}^{total} \tag{15}$$

Typical results for these three collision mechanisms are shown in Figure 3 where the relative intensities of the primary, secondary, and tertiary ions are plotted against N, the concentration of molecules in the source. In deriving these curves, the parameters used were: $k_P = 2.0 \times 10^{-9}$ cc./molecule-sec.; $k_S = 1.0 \times 10^{-9}$ cc./molecule-sec.; $\tau_p = 8.5 \times 10^{-7}$ sec., (the residence time of the ion ($m/e = 33$) in a field of strength 9.1 volts/cm. in the Leeds mass spectrometer). In applying this analysis to a system in which the tertiary ion reacts to form quaternary and higher order ions, $I_T{}^{total}$ represents the sum of tertiaries, quaternaries, etc.

Let us compare these results with the predictions of the theory formulated by Lampe *et al.* (*24*) in terms of a "steady-state" concentration of collision complexes. This is a classical macroscopic treatment insofar as it makes no assumptions about the collision dynamics, but its postulate of collision complexes implies that $v_S = v_P/2$ for the system treated above. Thus, its predictions might be expected to coincide with those of the collision-complex model. Figure 3 shows that this is not so; the points calculated from the "steady-state" theory (Ref. *25*, Equation 10) coincide *exactly* with the curve for which $v_S = v_P$. The reason for this is that the "steady-state" treatment assumes a constant time available for reaction irrespective of the number of reactions occurring in any one reaction

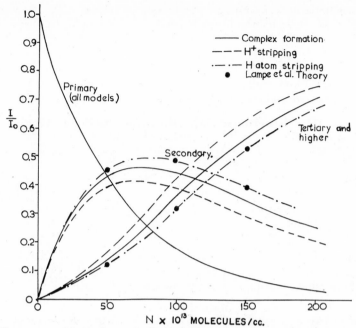

Figure 3. Variation of the relative primary, secondary, and tertiary ion currents with ionization chamber concentration as predicted by the kinematic theory for the three models of complex formation, hydrogen ion, and hydrogen atom stripping. For conditions, see text

sequence; these conditions also apply to our model where $v_S = v_P$. Paradoxically therefore, by assuming the existence of collision complexes and a constant time available for reaction, the "steady-state" theory is shown to contain an internal inconsistency. In most applications the necessary correction is small enough to be of limited importance.

Formation of Quaternary Ions. The treatment outlined above is readily extended by similar reasoning to reactions of the tertiary ions to form quaternary ions.

$$\text{T} + \text{molecule} \xrightarrow{k_T} \text{Q} + \text{neutral} \qquad (R)$$

The expression for the amount of quaternary ions formed, $I_Q{}^{total}$, is here quoted without derivation.

$$I_Q{}^{total} = I_P{}^0 N^2 k_P k_S \int_0^{\tau_P} \exp(-Nk_P t_P) \int_0^{\tau_S{}^{t_P}} \exp(-Nk_S t_S) \cdot$$

$$[1 - \exp(-Nk_T t_T)] \, dt_S \cdot dt_P \qquad (16)$$

Values for $\tau_S{}^{t_P}$ and t_T for the three different models considered above are given in Table III. Once again, the equation for the hydrogen atom stripping mechanism was directly integrated to give $I_Q{}^{total}$, but for the other mechanisms the equation was evaluated numerically. I_P is given by Equation 14, I_S by Equation 15, and I_T by the following expression:

$$I_T = I_T{}^{total} - I_Q{}^{total} \qquad (17)$$

where $I_T{}^{total}$ is derived by integrating Equation 13 in the treatment of the tertiary ion. Plots similar to those in Figure 3 are shown in Figure 4 for the primary, secondary, tertiary, and quaternary ions. The same

Table III. Kinematic Conditions for the Formation of Quaternary Ions by Various Collision Mechanisms

Collision Mechanism	Function for $\tau_S{}^{t_P}$	Function for t_T
Stripping (Proton or hydride ion transfer)	$(\tau_P{}^2 - t_P{}^2)^{1/2}$	$(\tau_P{}^2 - t_P{}^2 - t_S{}^2)^{1/2}$
Complex formation	$1/2[-t_P + (4\tau_P{}^2 - 3t_P{}^2)^{1/2}]$	$1/2[-t_P/2 - t_S + (4\tau_P{}^2 - 3t_P t_S - 3t_S{}^2 - 3.75t_P{}^2)^{1/2}]$
Stripping (Hydrogen atom transfer)	$\tau_P - t_P$	$\tau_P - t_P - t_S$

parameters were used, and k_T was assumed to be equal to k_S. Where quaternary ions react to form higher order ions, the quaternary ion curve represents the sum of quaternaries and higher order ions.

Applying the Kinematic Theory to the Methanol Reactions

The occurrence of multiple-order reactions in the methanol system is shown by the increase of R with N in Figure 2, and the system can be analyzed in terms of the kinematic theory of hydrogen transfer developed above. Consider the situation for CH_3OD for which the following reaction sequence applies.

Secondary Formation

$$CH_3OD^+ + CH_3OD \longrightarrow \begin{array}{l} \rightarrow CH_2OD + CH_3ODH^+ \qquad (S) \\ \rightarrow CH_3O + CH_3OD_2{}^+ \qquad (T) \end{array}$$

Tertiary Formation

$$CH_3ODH^+ + CH_3OD \longrightarrow \begin{array}{l} \rightarrow CH_3OD + CH_3ODH^+ \qquad (U) \\ \rightarrow CH_3OH + CH_3OD_2{}^+ \qquad (V) \end{array}$$

$$CH_3OD_2{}^+ + CH_3OD \rightarrow CH_3OD + CH_3OD_2{}^+ \qquad (W)$$

Formation of quaternary ions from tertiaries proceeds in the same way as that of tertiary ions from secondaries.

At this point several assumptions must be made. The first requires the absence of isotope effects on the rate of Reaction O—i.e., the rate constants of Reactions O, U + V, and W are identical; this is termed k, and the plausibility of the assumption is indicated by the absence of isotope effects on the rate constant of Reaction I. The second assumption requires that in proton transfer reactions like Reaction O, a deuteron is transferred at the same rate as a proton—i.e., the rate constants of Reactions U and V are identical; this is perhaps questionable and will be considered in detail below.   Under these conditions, R, for CH_3OD (the ratio $CH_3OD_2{}^+/CH_3ODH^+$), is given as a function of N, the source concentration, by the expression:

$$R = \frac{(4\alpha + 3)I_Q{}^{total} + (4\alpha + 2)I_T + 4\alpha I_S}{I_Q{}^{total} + 2I_T + 4I_S} \qquad (18)$$

where α, the ratio of the rate constants of reaction T to S is 0.67 (the value of R as $N \to 0$), and I_S, I_T and $I_Q{}^{total}$ are the amount of secondary, tertiary, and quaternary ions at the source pressure N, assuming the production of fifth-order ions is negligible.

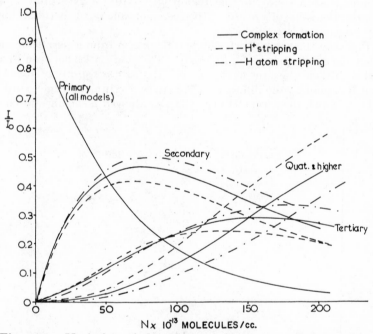

Figure 4.   Variation of the relative primary, secondary, tertiary, and quaternary ion currents with ionization chamber concentration as predicted by the kinematic theory for the three models of complex formation, hydrogen ion, and hydrogen atom stripping. For conditions, see text

The kinematic theory can now be used to determine the appropriate values of I_S, $I_Q{}^{total}$, and I_T (Equations 15, 16, and 17, respectively) for various assumed values of k, the rate constant of Reaction O—a quantity about which nothing is known—and for the various mechanisms. Obviously from the chemistry of the system, Reactions U, V, and W cannot occur by a hydrogen atom transfer mechanism; hence, only two cases need be considered—Reactions S, T, U, V, and W, occurring by either the collision-complex mechanism or the proton stripping mechanism.

Data for the variation of R with N for the system CH_3OD is again shown in Figure 5, but here superimposed on the experimental curve are two pairs of synthetic curves for this variation derived from the theory, for assumed values of k of 0.5×10^{-9} and 1.0×10^{-9} cc./molecule-sec. and for both relevant mechanisms in each case. The upper limit of N is taken as 100×10^{13} molecules/cc. as it is easily shown that at this value and below, the role of fifth-order ions is negligible; furthermore above this, the processes observed by Munson (30) start to compete. Irrespective of the mechanism chosen, the important deduction to be made from Figure 5 is that even though the value for k of 0.5×10^{-9} cc./molecule-sec. gives an approximate fit for the lower range of N, it is unable to account for the region $75 \times 10^{13} < N < 100 \times 10^{13}$. Similarly, the value of k of 1.0×10^{-9} cc./molecule-sec. is better at higher N but hopeless at lower values.

Precisely the same conclusion can be drawn from a parallel analysis of the CD_3OH data shown in Figure 6. The similarities between Figures 5 and 6 provide the best evidence that the rate constants of Reactions U and V cannot be too different. This receives support from a study on CH_2D_2 in which the ratio $CH_2D_3{}^+/CH_3D_2{}^+$ showed no significant change

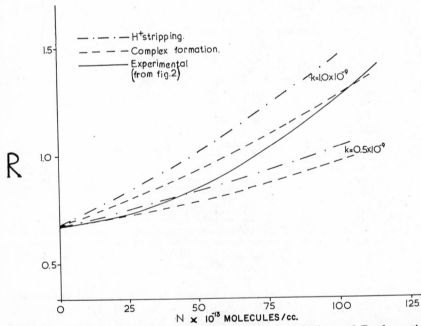

Figure 5. Comparison between the experimental variations of R, the ratio $CH_3OD_2{}^+/CH_3OHD{}^+$, with ionization chamber concentration of CH_3OD and theoretical predictions of the kinematic theory for assumed velocity-independent rate constants of the reaction $CH_3OH_2{}^+ + CH_3OH \rightarrow CH_3OH + CH_3OH_2{}^+$ for both the complex-formation and proton-stripping mechanisms

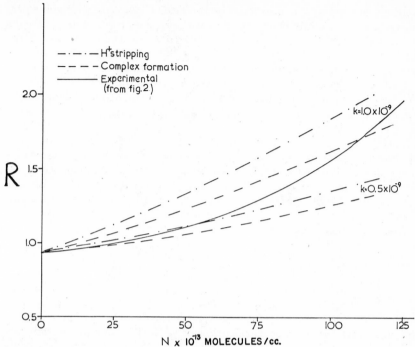

Figure 6. Comparison between the experimental variations of R, the ratio $CD_3OH_2^+/CD_3OHD^+$, with ionization chamber concentration of CD_3OH and theoretical predictions of the kinematic theory for assumed velocity-independent rate constants of the reaction $CH_3OH_2^+ + CH_3OH \rightarrow CH_3OH + CH_3OH_2^+$ for both the complex-formation and proton-stripping mechanisms

in the range $0 < N < 150 \times 10^{13}$ molecules/cc. (3). Even if an isotope effect is assumed and Equation 18 is weighted by factors as high as $\sqrt{2}$, the conclusions stated above still hold—i.e., no theoretical curve, whatever the value of k, can be fitted to the data.

The reason why a lower value of k at low N and a higher value of k at high N provide the best arrangement is not hard to find. The kinematic theory was derived on the assumption that the rate constants were independent of the ion energy. The results of Figure 8 show that this assumption is not valid. High pressure mass spectrometry provides a means of altering the distribution of the ion energies at which reactive events occur (3). As N is increased, more and more reaction occurs early in the ion path at low ion energies, and the low energy events are emphasized. One can conclude from Figures 5 and 6 that one or both of the rate constants of Reactions I and O are energy dependent. The energy dependence of Reaction O would, of course, affect the shape of the curve more than Reaction I. In view of this, the sharp curvature of the experimental lines in Figures 5 and 6 would seem to require that the rate constant of Reaction O is energy dependent. One cannot be dogmatic however about Reaction I. We feel intuitively that if the rate of O is energy dependent, then so must be the rate of I since both involve proton transfer to a methanol molecule with only the proton donor differing in the two cases. It is hardly plausible that one could be energy dependent and the other not. We suggest therefore that these studies provide independent evidence for the validity of the pulsing results of Futrell on the energy dependence of the rate constant of polar molecules and fail to support the findings of Harrison that it is independent of the energy. Since it is energy dependent, alignment of the dipole does occur to some extent.

At this stage nothing can be deduced about the mechanism—i.e., whether the reaction proceeds via complex formation or by proton stripping. Detailed experimental knowledge of the energy dependence of the rate constants is needed, and this is not yet available. Given this and the kinematic theory programmed for an energy dependent rate constant, a decision can in principle be made concerning the importance of stripping processes at these low energies.

Acknowledgments

We owe much to our continued discussions of these problems with A. G. Harrison, to whom we are also indebted for preprints prior to publication. We are grateful to a referee for drawing our attention to Ref. (30) and for seeking clarification of several points which were obviously obscure in the original manuscript. We thank the Petroleum Research Fund for a grant to support both this work and one of us (D.J.H.).

Literature Cited

(1) Barker, R., Hamill, W. H., Williams, Jr., R. R., J. Phys. Chem. 63, 825 (1959).
(2) Derwish, G. A. W., Galli, A., Giardini-Guidoni, A., Volpi, G. G., J. Am. Chem. Soc. 87, 1159 (1965).
(3) Dodman, E. A., Hyatt, D. J., Matus, L., Ogle, C. J., Henchman, M. J., University of Leeds, unpublished results.
(4) Field, F. H., Franklin, J. L., "Electron Impact Phenomena," p. 281, Academic Press, New York, 1957.
(5) Field, F. H., Franklin, J. L., Lampe, F. W., J. Am. Chem. Soc. 79, 2665 (1957).
(6) Field, F. H., Franklin, J. L., Munson, M. S. B., J. Am. Chem. Soc. 85, 3575 (1963).
(7) Franklin, J. L., Field, F. H., Lampe, F. W., Adv. Mass Spectrometry 1, 308. (1959).
(8) Futrell, J. H., Wright-Patterson Air Force Base, Ohio, private communication.
(9) Giese, C. F., Maier, W. B., J. Chem. Phys. 39, 739 (1963).
(10) Gioumousis, G., Stevenson, D. P., J. Chem. Phys. 29, 294 (1958).
(11) Harrison, A. G., University of Toronto, private communication.
(12) Harrison, A. G., Thynne, J. C. J., Trans. Faraday Soc. 62, in press (1966).
(13) Harrison, A. G., Ivko, A., Shannon, T. W., Can. J. Chem. 44, 1351 (1966).
(14) Henchman, M. J., Discuss. Faraday Soc. 39, 63 (1965).
(15) Henchman, M. J., Ogle, C. J., "Abstracts of Papers," 150th Meeting, ACS, September 1965, p. 25V.
(16) Henchman, M. J., Wolfgang, R. L., Yale University, unpublished results.
(17) Henchman, M. J., Otwinowska, H. T., Field, F. H., Advan. Mass Spectrometry 3, 359 (1966).

(18) Henglein, A., Muccini, G. A., Z. Naturforsch. **18a**, 753 (1963).
(19) Henglein, A., Lacmann, K., Jacobs, G., Ber. Bunsenges Physik. Chem. **69**, 279 (1965).
(20) Henglein, A., Lacmann, K., Ber. Bunsenges Physik. Chem. **69**, 286 (1965).
(21) Henglein, A., Lacmann, K., Ber. Bunsenges Physik. Chem. **69**, 292 (1965).
(22) Herschbach, D. R., Advan. Chem. Phys. **10**, 319 (1965).
(23) Kubose, D. A., Hamill, W. H., J. Am. Chem. Soc. **85**, 125 (1963).
(24) Lampe, F. W., Franklin, J. L., Field, F. H., Prog. Reaction Kinetics **1**, 73 (1961).
(25) Light, J. C., J. Chem. Phys. **40**, 3221 (1964).
(26) Light, J. C., Lin, J., J. Chem. Phys. **43**, 3209 (1965).
(27) Minturn, R. E., Datz, S., Becker, R. L., J. Chem. Phys. **44**, 1149 (1966).
(28) Moran, T. F., Friedman, L., J. Chem. Phys. **39**, 2491 (1963).
(29) Moran, T. F., Hamill, W. H., J. Chem. Phys. **39**, 1413 (1963).
(30) Munson, M. S. B., J. Am. Chem. Soc. **87**, 5313 (1965).
(31) Rosenstock, H., et al., AEC Rept. No. JLI-650-3-7, **TID-4500** (October 1959).
(32) Ryan, K. R., Sieck, L. W., Futrell, J. H., J. Chem. Phys. **41**, 111 (1964).
(33) Ryan, K. R., Futrell, J. H., J. Chem. Phys. **42**, 824 (1965).
(34) Ryan, K. R., Futrell, J. H., J. Chem. Phys. **43**, 3009 (1965).
(35) Ryan, K. R., Futrell, J. H., Miller, C. D., Rev. Sci. Instr. **37**, 107 (1966).
(36) Shannon, T. W., Meyer, F., Harrison, A. G., Can. J. Chem. **43**, 159 (1965).
(37) Stevenson, D. P., Schissler, D. O., in "The Chemical and Biological Action of Radiations," Vol. 5, p. 167, M. Haissinsky, ed., Academic Press, London, 1961.
(38) Tal'roze, V. L., Frankevich, E. L., Zh. Fiz. Khim. **34**, 2709 (1960).
(39) Theard, L. P., Hamill, W. H., J. Am. Chem. Soc. **84**, 730 (1962).
(40) Thynne, J. C. J., Amenu-Kpodo, F. K., Harrison, A. G., Can. J. Chem. **44**, in press (1966).
(41) Thynne, J. C. J., Harrison, A. G., Trans. Faraday Soc., **62**, in press (1966).
(42) Von Koch, H., Friedman, L., J. Chem. Phys. **38**, 1115 (1963).
(43) Wexler, S., Jesse, N., J. Am. Chem. Soc. **84**, 3425 (1962).
(44) Wilmenius, P., Lindholm, E., Arkiv. Fysik. **21**, 97 (1962).
(45) Yamamoto, T., Shinozaki, Y., Meshituka, G., Mass Spectroscopy **12**, 93 (1964).

RECEIVED May 9, 1966.

10

Reactions of Thermal Energy Ions by Pulsed Source Mass Spectrometry

A. G. HARRISON and J. J. MYHER

University of Toronto, Toronto, Canada

J. C. J. THYNNE

University of Edinburgh, Edinburgh, Scotland

Pulsed source techniques have been used to study thermal energy ion-molecule reactions. For most of the proton and H atom transfer reactions studied k(thermal)/k(10.5 volts/cm.) is approximately unity in apparent agreement with predictions from the simple ion-induced dipole model. However, the rate constants calculated on this basis are considerably higher than the experimental rate constants indicating reaction channels other than the atom transfer process. Thus, in some cases at least, the relationship of k(thermal) to k(10.5 volts/cm.) may be determined by the variation of the relative importance of the atom transfer process with ion energy rather than by the interaction potential between the ion and the neutral. For most of the condensation ion-molecule reactions studied k(thermal) is considerably greater than k(10.5 volts/cm.).

In mass spectrometric studies of ion-molecule reactions by conventional internal ionization techniques the reactant ions undergo continuous acceleration by the electric field required to withdraw the ions for mass analysis. Consequently, the experimental cross-sections represent an appropriately weighted average for ions with energies ranging from zero to the final exit energy as determined by the electric field strength, E, and the distance of ion travel. Extensive investigations of the dependence of the cross-section on the ion velocity or field strength have been carried out, but frequently they have yielded disagreeing results, particularly at low field strengths. Stevenson and colleagues (*11, 38*) have found an $E^{-1/2}$ dependence for a number of simple systems in agreement with predictions (*11*) from the ion-induced dipole model. On the other hand, Field *et al.* (*6, 8*) have found an E^{-1} dependence while Hamill and co-workers (*29*) have found the energy dependence varies with the final ion exit energy. In part these discrepancies may be caused by instrumental

150

problems such as electronic space charge and discrimination effects which can be expected to become serious at low field strengths.   Some evidence supporting this has been presented recently by Ryan and Futrell (*31*).

More direct observations of the kinetic energy dependence of cross-sections should be possible using external ionization techniques where the reactant ion can be chosen by initial mass analysis and, in principle, its energy more readily controlled.   Several studies using external ionization techniques, both with (*2, 10, 45*) and without (*20, 21, 27, 41*) preliminary mass selection of the reactant ion, have been reported.   However, apparently with these techniques it is not possible to obtain well-defined primary ion beams at energies below 0.5–1 e.v. a region of critical importance both experimentally and theoretically.

Because of these limitations to both the conventional internal ionization and external ionization techniques it has been impossible to obtain accurate kinetic data for the reactions of thermal energy ions.   Such thermal energy data are desirable for applications in such areas as radiation chemistry, discharge and combustion phenomena, and upper atmosphere research.

In 1960 Tal'roze and Frankevich (*39*) first described a pulsed mode of operation of an internal ionization source which permits the study of ion-molecule reactions at energies approaching thermal energies.   In this technique a short pulse of electrons is admitted to a field-free ion source to produce the reactant ions by electron impact.   A known and variable time later, a second voltage pulse is applied to withdraw the ions from the ion source for mass analysis.   In the interval between the two pulses the ions react under essentially thermal conditions, and from variation of the relevant ion currents with the reaction time the thermal rate constants can be estimated.

In the past few years this pulsing technique has been used by several groups, utilizing both magnetic deflection (*16, 31, 37*) and time-of-flight (*12, 13*) instruments, to study ion-molecule reactions at thermal energies. Here we review the results obtained and discuss the applications and limitations of the method, based on our observations and experiences over the past three years.

Design and Operation of Pulsed Source

The construction and operating characteristics of pulsed ion sources used in conjunction with a magnetic deflection instrument have been described previously (*16, 31, 37, 39*); only a brief description need be given here.   Figure 1 shows a schematic diagram of the source used in our laboratory in a 6-inch radius 90° sector-field instrument.   The source is basically of the Nier design, modified by adding an electron beam control plate (plate 2) and by increasing the dimensions of the ionization chamber to reduce ion loss at the walls.

In operation the electron beam is initially arrested by applying a small bias negative with respect to the filament to plate 2.   The pulsed electron beam is then provided by applying a positive pulse to this plate.

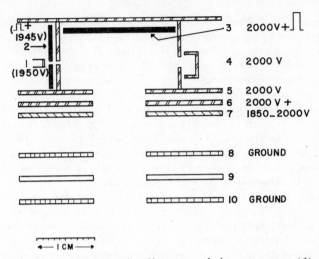

*Figure 1. Schematic diagram of ion source: (1)
filament; (2) electron beam control plate; (3) repeller;
(4) trap; (5) cage; (6) withdrawal plate; (7) focus;
(8, 10) beam-defining plates; (9) beam centering plate*

To prevent withdrawal of the ions thus produced by penetration of the
main accelerating field, either a small positive bias is applied to plate 6 or
alternatively (31) the exit slit from the ionization chamber is covered by
a transparent wire mesh. The ions are withdrawn from the ionization
chamber by a voltage pulse of proper sign applied either to the repeller
plate (plate 3) or to the ion withdrawal plate (plate 6).

The pulsed circuitry of the time-of-flight mass spectrometer is ideally
suited for this type of operation, and both Hand and von Weyssenhoff
(12, 13) and Lampe and Hess (25) have reported experiments using such
an instrument with variable delay between the ionizing and withdrawal
pulses to study secondary processes.

In our experience the most satisfactory criterion for judging the
operation of the pulsed source is the shape of the ion decay curves—i.e.,
the rate at which the ions are lost from the region sampled by the ion
withdrawal pulse. This topic is discussed in detail in the next section.
Typically with our source a bias of 3–5 volts on plate 2 is sufficient to
arrest the electron beam while a positive pulse of 5–10 volts amplitude
and 0.1–1 μsec. duration is applied to produce the pulse of electrons.
The maximum repetition rate is about 2×10^5 pulses sec.$^{-1}$, and in
practice the pulse duration is determined by the sensitivity of the detection system. Higher settings of the bias potential and the pulse amplitude frequently resulted in anomalous features in the ion decay curves,
and these settings are adjusted to give the best decay curves. To ensure
removal of all ions during the withdrawal period, a pulse of at least 1 μsec.
duration is applied to the repeller plate. We found that the recorded ion
current depends on both the duration and amplitude of these pulses, and
in practice they are adjusted to give maximum ion current. These set-

tings as well as the focus plate voltages are mass dependent and are thus readjusted for each mass.

Ion Decay Curves and Discrimination Effects

The usefulness of the pulsed ion source in studying ionic reactions with time as the experimental variable is determined by the rate at which the ions are lost from the volume sampled when the withdrawal pulse is applied. Ions are lost from this volume owing to their thermal kinetic energy (plus any kinetic energy involved in the process of formation) and under the influence of fields arising from surface potentials, space charge, and field penetration. All of these effects will lead to a more rapid loss of the lighter mass ion and hence will lead to discrimination effects which may obscure the changes anticipated from the reaction under study.

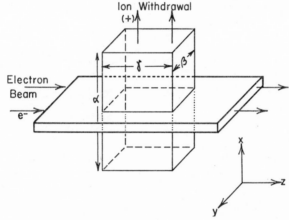

Figure 2. Ion formation and sampling zones

The problem of ion loss can be understood more clearly by referring to Figure 2. The ions are formed initially in a volume defined by the dimensions of the electron beam, which intersects symmetrically the volume sampled by the withdrawal pulse. In our source the dimensions of the electron beam are approximately $x = 0.05$ cm., $y = 0.30$ cm., $z = 1.80$ cm., while for the sampling volume $\alpha = 0.95$ cm., $\beta = 0.15$ cm. $\gamma = 1.0$ cm. Thus, ion loss will occur across the plane at $-\alpha/2$ and by deficit in flow across the planes at $\pm\beta/2$ and $\pm\gamma/2$. The mathematical formulation of the problem has been presented previously (*37*). Figure 3a shows a calculated decay curve for $m/e = 40(\text{Ar}^+)$ compared with two experimental curves. Curve A was obtained by pulsing the repeller plate only while curve B was obtained by pulsing the withdrawal plate (plate 6) 50 volts negative simultaneously with the repeller pulse. In both cases the experimental curves fall off more rapidly than the theoretical curve although the shapes are the same. These results suggest that stray fields may be influencing the rate of ion loss although this more rapid decay may be caused partly by other instrumental factors. With increasing delay time the fraction of the ions in the central region of the sampling volume will tend to decrease while the fraction in peripheral regions will tend to increase.   Applying the repeller pulse will push these peripheral ions out with a greater angle of divergence from the x axis, and these ions will be less efficiently focussed by the ion gun.   The effect of the withdrawal plate pulse is probably to increase the focussing efficiency of the ion gun.   Similar results were obtained using a U-shaped repeller in place of the normal flat repeller.

Typical decay curves for various ionic masses are shown in Figure 3b, where the effect of differing thermal velocity is clearly evident.   Neglect of such decay characteristics can lead to serious discrimination effects.   Note that all the experimental curves have the sigmoid shape

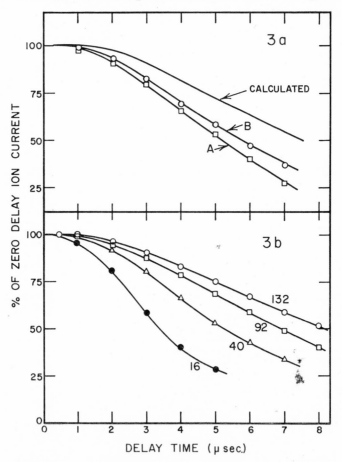

Figure 3.   (a) Comparison of experimental and calculated decay curves; m/e = 40.   (b) Experimental decay curves for various masses

predicted by theory and that the total ion loss in the first part of the delay period is small. Therefore, we have restricted our observations to this time range and, further, have required that the decay curves have this characteristic shape before considering the results reliable.

In addition to the effects discussed above, two further possible sources of discrimination peculiar to ion-molecule reactions must be considered. First, although it is known that most primary ions are formed without kinetic energy, such may not be the case for ions produced by ion molecule reactions. Secondary ions formed in exothermic ion-molecule reactions could retain a considerable fraction of the exothermicity as kinetic energy and diffuse from the sampling region at a rate considerably greater than predicted from the ambient temperature. The limited evidence to date (*40*) indicates that the kinetic energy of the product ions is small, but this may not be true for all types of reactions.

Second, the primary and secondary ions are not formed in the same region and this may lead to different collection efficiencies. In the extreme, primary ions initially formed in the sampling region may diffuse out of the sampling region during the delay period (*32, 39*). If these ions react after leaving the sampling region, the product ion may re-enter the sampling region (assuming the formation process imparts no preferential direction of travel), thus leading to anomalously high secondary ion concentrations. This effect will be serious only if an appreciable fraction of the reactant ions is lost from the sampling region during the delay period.

Identification of Reactant and Product Ions

The variation of ion intensities with reaction time should prove to be a useful approach in identifying reactant and product ions in ion-molecule reactions. The approach has been used little, primarily because most studies have been carried out at relatively low source concentrations where the extent of reaction (and therefore the changes in relative intensities) is small. Some indication of the potential usefulness is shown by ion-molecule reactions in dimethyl ether (*15*). Figure 4 shows the variation of I_{47} $((CH_3)_2OH)^+$, I_{46} $((CH_3)_2O)^+$, and $I_{45}(CH_3OCH_2)^+$ as a function of the delay time at an electron energy where only $(CH_3)_2O^+$ and $CH_3OCH_2^+$ are significant primary ions. The results are expressed as a percentage of the total ionization to allow for ion decay. The increase in $I_{47}/\Sigma I$ clearly shows its secondary character while the decrease in $I_{46}/\Sigma I$ shows that $(CH_3)_2O^+$ is a reactive ion. The constancy of I_{45}/Σ_1 indicates that $CH_3OCH_2^+$ is nonreactive under these conditions.

Similar studies have been carried out (*43*) on the ammonia system in an attempt to detect the reaction:

$$NH_2^+ + NH_3 \rightarrow NH_3^+ + NH_2 \tag{1}$$

The intensity changes observed, while consistent with the occurrence of Reaction 1, were small enough to have originated from discrimination effects. A new instrument is being constructed in our laboratory which

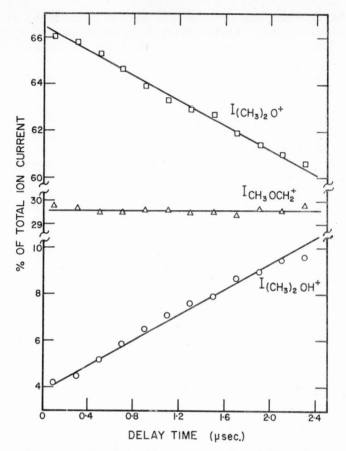

Figure 4.   Ion intensities as a function of delay time,
CH_3OCH_3

should permit operation at considerably higher pressures, thus making the changes caused by chemical reaction much greater compared with ion decay.

Charge Transfer Reactions

It is particularly difficult to study charge transfer reactions by the usual internal ionization method since the secondary ions produced will always coincide with ions produced in primary ionization processes. Indeed these primary ions frequently constitute the major fraction of the total ion current, and the small intensity changes originating from charge transfer reactions are difficult to detect.   For example, Field and Franklin (5) were unable to detect any charge transfer between Xe^+ and CH_4 by the internal ionization method although such reactions have been observed using other techniques (3, 9, 22).

The pulsing mode of operation of the internal ionization source should afford decided advantages for studying charge transfer reactions and should permit one to evaluate the rates at thermal energies. For the charge transfer reaction $A^+ + B \rightarrow B^+ + A$, one should be able to observe increases in the ratio B^+/A^+ with increasing reaction time. However B and A will often differ considerably in mass, and discrimination effects may be much greater than changes owing to charge transfer.

In the only study to date of such reactions by the pulsing method Karachevtsev *et al.* (*24*) have utilized this mass discrimination effect to advantage in studying the reactions of the rare gas ions Ar^+, Kr^+, Xe^+ with CH_4, C_2H_4, and C_2H_6. They deliberately used a long delay (14–20 μsec.) between the ionizing and withdrawal pulses. During this delay period, the lighter mass (and thus higher velocity) hydrocarbon ions formed in the initial impact process are lost preferentially from the sampling region. Hydrocarbon ions formed by charge transfer from the heavier rare gas ions, especially those formed during the latter stages of the delay period, will not be lost, and the hydrocarbon spectrum obtained when the withdrawal pulse is applied shows a considerable enrichment in secondary hydrocarbon ions compared with primary ions. From the variation of this spectrum with rare gas pressure the relative rates of formation of the hydrocarbon fragments were estimated. Table I compares the charge transfer spectrum obtained in this way for $Ar^+ + CH_4$ with spectra obtained by other techniques. The agreement is quite good.

By adding small amounts of H_2 to the gas mixture and observing the rate of formation of ArH^+, they also estimated the following overall rate constants for charge transfer at thermal ion energies.

$$Ar^+ + CH_4 \quad k = 7.5 \times 10^{-9} \text{ cc. molecule}^{-1} \text{ sec.}^{-1}$$

$$Ar^+ + C_2H_4 \quad k = 3.9 \times 10^{-9}$$

$$Ar^+ + C_2H_6 \quad k = 6.3 \times 10^{-9}$$

These rate constants were measured relative to the rate constant for the reaction:

$$Ar^+ + H_2 \rightarrow ArH^+ + H \tag{2}$$

which was taken to have a rate constant of 1.68×10^{-9} cc. molecule^{-1} sec.$^{-1}$ (*38*). Note however, that the rate constant for reaction 2 was not

Table I. Ionic Abundances from Charge Transfer of Ar^+ with CH_4

Ar^+ Energy e.v.	Relative Abundance			Reference
	CH_4^+	CH_3^+	CH_2^+	
Thermal	...	100	21	*24*
0–0.2	19	100	19	*28*
0–2.5	...	100	24	*7*
25	1	100	24	*9*
25	2.3	100	24	*3*
75	2	100	32.8	*23*
500	4	100	23	*26*

measured at thermal energies and further neglects the contribution of the concurrent reaction:

$$H_2{}^+ + Ar \rightarrow ArH^+ + H \tag{3}$$

which has been shown to occur (35). The overall rate constant for the Ar–CH_4 system is appreciably higher than earlier values of 1.1×10^{-9} (7) and 1.9×10^{-9} cc. molecule^{-1} sec.$^{-1}$ (28) obtained using conventional internal ionization techniques.

Proton and Hydrogen Atom Transfer Reactions

Reactions involving a transfer of a proton or a hydrogen atom are an extremely common type of ion-molecule reaction and are particularly suited for study by the pulsed source technique. The secondary ion will usually occur at an m/e ratio where it is not obscured by abundant primary ions, and the product and reactant ions frequently will differ only slightly in mass, thus minimizing discrimination effects.

For the general ion-molecule reaction:

$$P^+ + M \rightarrow S^+ + N \tag{4}$$

studied with reaction time as the experimental variable and assuming the neutral concentration [M] to be constant, the integrated rate expression becomes

$$\ln \left(\frac{[P^+]_0}{[P^+]_t} \right) = k[M]t \tag{5}$$

where $[P^+]_0$ and $[P^+]_t$ represent the concentration of P^+ at time zero and time t. Writing for $[P^+]_0$

$$[P^+]_0 = [P^+]_t + [S^+]_t \tag{6}$$

yields

$$\ln \left(1 + \frac{[S^+]_t}{[P^+]_t} \right) = k[M]t \tag{7}$$

which for $[S^+]/[P^+] << 1$ can be approximated by:

$$[S^+]_t/[P^+]_t = k[M]t \tag{8}$$

In the pulsed system, reaction will take place not only during the delay period but also during the time when the ionizing and withdrawing pulses are being applied. For constant pulse durations and amplitudes the secondary ions produced during these periods can be represented by a constant term added to Equations 7 and 8. Assuming further that the collection efficiencies are the same for both primary and secondary ions, this leads to following equations in terms of the measurable ion currents

$$\ln \left(1 + \frac{I_{S^+}}{I_{P^+}} \right) = k[M]t + C \tag{9}$$

$$\frac{I_{S^+}}{I_{P^+}} = k\,[\mathrm{M}]\,t + \mathrm{C}^1 \qquad (10)$$

where C and C^1 are constants reflecting the reaction occurring during the ionizing and withdrawal pulses, and t represents the delay time between the ionizing and withdrawal pulses. Figure 5 shows the experimental results for several reactions plotted in the form of Equation 10. In all cases satisfactory straight lines are found which agree with predictions. The positive intercepts represent the contributions owing to reactions during the ionizing and withdrawal pulses plus, in some cases, isotope contributions at the m/e ratio of the secondary ion. In several cases an upward curvature is discernible at longer delay times, and this is undoubtedly caused by mass discrimination effects.

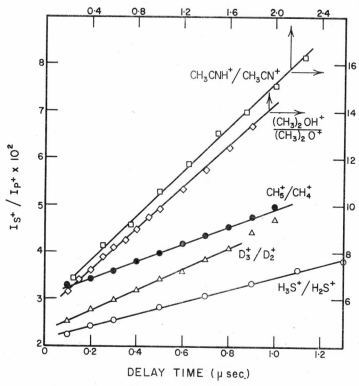

Figure 5. Typical $I_{S}{}^{+}/I_{P}{}^{+}$ vs. delay time plots

In several systems studied the secondary ion is formed by more than one ion-molecule reaction. For example, we have found (*43*) that the $NH_4{}^+$ ion is formed in the ammonia system by the concurrent reactions:

$$NH_3{}^+ + NH_3 \rightarrow NH_4{}^+ + NH_2 \qquad (11)$$

$$NH_2{}^+ + NH_3 \rightarrow NH_4{}^+ + NH \qquad (12)$$

For the two concurrent reactions with low percent reaction the total secondary ion current $I_{NH_4^+}$ after delay time t can be expressed as the sum of two independent contributions:

$$I_{NH_4^+} = [k_{11}I_{NH_3^+}[NH_3] + k_{12}I_{NH_2^+}[NH_3]]t + D \qquad (13)$$

Rearrangement leads to:

$$\frac{I_{NH_4^+}}{I_{NH_3^+}} = \left[k_{11}[NH_3] + k_{12}[NH_3]\frac{I_{NH_2^+}}{I_{NH_3^+}} \right] t + D^1 \qquad (14)$$

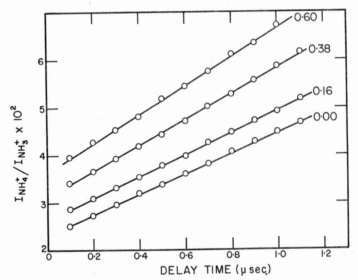

Figure 6. $I_{NH_4^+}/I_{NH_3^+}$ vs. delay time. Figures give $I_{NH_2^+}/I_{NH_3^+}$ ratio.

Equation (14) predicts that for constant $I_{NH_2^+}/I_{NH_3^+}$ the plots of $I_{NH_4^+}/I_{NH_3^+}$ vs. delay time should be linear and with slopes proportional to $I_{NH_{2+}}/I_{NH_3^+}$. Figure 6 shows typical plots of $I_{NH_2^+}/I_{NH_3^+}$ vs. delay time t while Figure 7 shows the slopes of such delay time plots as a function of the ratio $I_{NH_2^+}/I_{NH_3^+}$, this ratio being changed by variation of the electron energy. A good straight line results in agreement with predictions.

Using either of the above approaches we have measured the thermal rate constants for some 40 hydrogen atom and proton transfer reactions. The results are tabulated in Table II where the thermal rate constants are compared with the rate constants obtained at 10.5 volt cm.$^{-1}$ (3.7 e.v. exit energy) either by the usual method of pressure variation or for concurrent reactions by the ratio-plot technique outlined in previous publications (14, 17, 36). The ion source temperature during these measurements was about 310°K. Table II also includes the thermal rate constants measured by others (12, 13, 33, 39) using similar pulsing techniques.

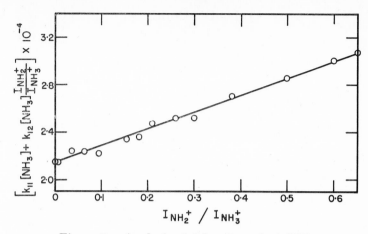

Figure 7. Analysis of delay time plots, NH_3

Table II. Proton and H Atom Transfer Ion-Molecule Reactions

Reaction	Rate Constant $\times 10^{10}$ cc. molecule^{-1} sec.$^{-1}$		k (thermal)	Reference
	Thermal	10.5 volts/cm.	$\dfrac{k(10.5}{\text{volts/cm.})}$	
$H_2^+ + H_2 \to H_3^+ + H$	5.9	13.3	0.44	15
$HD^+ + HD \to H_2D^+ + D$	3.8	8.4	0.45	15
$HD^+ + HD \to HD_2^+ + H$	2.9	6.9	0.42	15
$D_2^+ + D_2 \to D_3^+ + D$	5.8	15.0	0.38	15
$NH_2^+ + NH_3 \to NH_4^+ + NH$	3.4	5.1	0.67	44
$NH_3^+ + NH_3 \to NH_4^+ + NH_2$	5.2	7.7	0.68	44
$OH^+ + H_2O \to H_3O^+ + O$	4.7$_2$	5.9$_1$	0.86	43
$H_2O^+ + H_2O \to H_3O^+ + OH$	4.9$_3$	6.0$_4$	0.82	43
	8.5^a			39
$OD^+ + D_2O \to D_3O^+ + O$	2.2$_5$	2.6$_4$	0.85	43
$D_2O^+ + D_2O \to D_3O^+ + OD$	3.6$_6$	3.5$_4$	1.06	43
$N_2H_3^+ + N_2H_4 \to N_2H_5^+ + N_2H_2$	1.0$_2$	3.8$_3$	0.27	44
$N_2H_4^+ + N_2H_4 \to N_2H_5^+ + N_2H_3$	1.3$_8$	5.5$_2$	0.25	44
$HS^+ + H_2S \to H_3S^+ + S$	3.6	2.6	1.3$_6$	18
$H_2S^+ + H_2S \to H_3S^+ + HS$	2.8	2.1	1.3$_3$	18
$CH_4^+ + CH_4 \to CH_5^+ + CH_3$	6.1$_2$	7.5$_8$	0.81	15
	9.6	10.7	0.90	33
	11.0			39
	11.6			12
$CH_3D^+ + CH_3D \to CH_4D^+ + CH_2D$	4.4$_7$	5.8$_6$	0.76	15
$CH_3D^+ + CH_3D \to CH_3D_2^+ + CH_3$	1.3$_0$	1.7$_3$	0.75	15
$CH_2D_2^+ + CH_2D_2 \to CH_3D_2^+ + CHD_2$	2.7$_0$	4.1$_8$	0.65	15
$CH_2D_2^+ + CH_2D_2 \to CH_2D_3^+ + CH_2D$	2.1$_6$	3.3$_6$	0.65	15
$CHD_3^+ + CHD_3 \to CH_2D_3^+ + CD_3$	1.6$_4$	2.3$_0$	0.71	15
$CHD_3^+ + CHD_3 \to CHD_4^+ + CHD_2$	3.3$_6$	4.9$_0$	0.69	15
$CD_4^+ + CD_4 \to CD_5 + CD_3$	4.7$_1$	6.3$_5$	0.74	15
$CD_4^+ + CO \to CDO^+ + CD_3$	1.9$_6$	5.2$_2$	0.38	15

Table II. Continued

| | | Rate Constant $\times 10^{10}$ cc. molecule^{-1} sec.$^{-1}$ | | k(thermal) |
| | | | 10.5 | k (10.5 |
Reaction		Thermal	volts/cm.	volts/cm.)	Reference
$CO^+ + D_2 \rightarrow CDO^+ + D$		7.16^b			13
$CO^+ + CD_4 \rightarrow CDO^+ + CD_3$		2.6_7	5.5_7	0.48	15
$C_2H_3^+ + C_2H_4 \rightarrow C_2H_5^+ + C_2H_2$		3.5_8	3.6_0	1.0	30
$CH_3OH^+ + CH_3OH \rightarrow$ $CH_3OH_2^+ + ?$		12.2	14.6	0.84	42
$CH_2OH^+ + CH_3OH \rightarrow$ $CH_3OH_2^+ + CH_2O$		9.0	8.3_5	1.1	42
$CD_3OH^+ + CD_3OH \rightarrow$ $CD_3OH_2^+ + CD_3O$		4.9_7	6.3_0	0.79	42
$CD_3OH^+ + CD_3OH \rightarrow$ $CD_3OHD^+ + CD_2OH$		5.9_9	8.2_5	0.73	42
$CD_2OH^+ + CD_3OH \rightarrow$ $CD_3OH_2^+ + CD_2O$		7.1_9	6.6_8	1.0_8	42
$CD_2OH^+ + CD_3OH \rightarrow$ $CD_3OHD^+ + CDOH$		<0.3	0.4_5		42
$(CH_3)_2O^+ + (CH_3)_2O \rightarrow$ $(CH_3)_2OH^+ + CH_3OCH_2$		9.4_9	8.2_4	1.1_5	15
$CH_3OCD_3^+ + CH_3OCD_3 \rightarrow$ $CH_3OCD_3H^+ + CH_2OCD_3$		5.3_6	4.7_6	1.1_3	15
$CH_3OCD_3^+ + CH_3OCD_3 \rightarrow$ $CH_3OCD_3D^+ + CH_3OCD_2$		4.3_9	4.1_3	1.0_7	15
$CH_3CHO^+ + CH_3CHO \rightarrow$ $CH_3CHOH^+ + ?$		12.3	11.2	1.1_0	1
$CHO^+ + CH_3CHO \rightarrow$ $CH_3CHOH^+ + CO$		8.3	13.6	0.61	1
$CD_4^+ + CH_3CHO \rightarrow$ $CH_3CHOD^+ + CD_3$		4.7	9.0	0.52	1
$CH_3CN^+ + CH_3CN \rightarrow$ $CH_3CNH^+ + CH_2CN$		18.7	21.5	0.87	15
$CH_3Cl^+ + CH_3Cl \rightarrow CH_3ClH^+ +$ CH_2Cl		7.3_0	5.1_7	1.4_1	19
$CH_2Cl^+ + CH_3Cl \rightarrow CH_3ClH^+ +$ $CHCl$		1.9_7	1.3_7	1.4_4	19

[a] Measured value neglecting contribution of reaction $OH^+ + H_2O \rightarrow H_3O^+ + O$.
[b] Measured value neglecting contribution of reaction $D_2^+ + CO \rightarrow COD^+ + D$.

As Table II shows, four separate measurements of the thermal rate constants for the reaction:

$$CH_4^+ + CH_4 \rightarrow CH_5^+ + CH_3 \qquad (15)$$

have been made, yielding rate constants between 6.1×10^{-10} and 11.6×10^{-10} cc. molecule^{-1} sec.$^{-1}$ This spread is probably a reasonably true representation of the absolute accuracy of the technique at the present time. One of the major sources of error is undoubtedly the estimation of the source concentration of neutral molecules. Relative values obtained in one laboratory should be somewhat more accurate.

For ion-molecule reactions where the interaction can be attributed to ion-induced dipole forces it has been shown (11) that the rate constant should be independent of ion energy—i.e., the thermal and 10.5 volt cm.$^{-1}$ rate constants should be the same. The third column in Table II shows that for most of the reactions studied the ratio k(thermal)/k(10.5 volts/cm.) is in the range 0.7–1.1. Considering the errors involved this is not significantly different from unity, indicating that most of the reactions agree approximately with the ion-induced dipole model in this energy range. This appears to include a number of reactions where one might expect ion-permanent dipole interactions to be significant. A few noteworthy cases where the ratio of rate constants is not unity are the H_2, HD, D_2, CO–CD_4, and N_2H_4 systems where k(thermal)/k(10.5 volts/cm.) ≤ 0.5 and the H_2S and CH_3Cl systems where the ratio is greater than 1.3. These ratios would appear to be significantly different from unity although the explanation is not apparent at the present time.

In Table III we compare for several reactions the experimental rate constants with rate constants calculated on the basis of ion-induced dipole interactions only from the relation (4):

$$k = 2\pi e(\alpha/\mu)^{1/2} \tag{16}$$

where e is the electronic charge, α is the polarizability of the neutral species, and μ is the reduced mass of the colliding pair. For the self-reactions in CH_3CN, $(CH_3)_2O$, and CH_3OH the experimental rate constants are equal to or greater than the calculated values. This is probably caused by the fact that we have neglected ion-permanent dipole interactions which might be expected to be important for these cases.

Table III. Comparison of Experimental and Theoretical Rate Constants

Reactants	Rate Constant $\times 10^{10}$ cc. molecule^{-1} sec.$^{-1}$		
	Thermal	10.5 volts/cm.	Theory[a]
$H_2^+ + H_2$	5.9	13.3	20.8
$D_2^+ + D_2$	5.8	15.0	14.5
$NH_3^+ + NH_3$	5.2	7.7	10.6
$NH_2^+ + NH_3$	3.4	5.1	10.8
$H_2O^+ + H_2O$	4.9_3	6.0_4	12.2
$OH^+ + H_2O$	4.7_2	5.9_1	12.4
$H_2S^+ + H_2S$	2.8	2.1	10.4
$HS^+ + H_2S$	3.6	2.6	10.5
$CH_4^+ + CH_4$	6.1_2	7.5_8	13.4
$CD_4^+ + CD_4$	4.7_1	6.3_5	11.9
$CD_4^+ + CO$	1.96	5.2_2	9.5
$CO^+ + CD_4$	2.6_7	5.5_7	11.0
$CH_3OH^+ + CH_3OH$	12.2	14.6	10.6
$CH_2OH^+ + CH_3OH$	9.0	8.3_5	10.7
$CH_3CN^+ + CH_3CN$	18.7	21.5	11.0
$(CH_3)_2O^+ + (CH_3)_2O$	9.4_9	8.2_4	11.2
$CH_3Cl^+ + CH_3Cl$	7.3_0	5.1_7	10.1

[a] Calculated on basis of ion-induced dipole interactions only.

For the remaining systems ion-permanent dipole interactions should be negligible. In these systems the experimental rate constants are considerably lower than the calculated values, and this undoubtedly reflects the fact that other reaction channels are available to the collision complex. It might be noted that many of the reactions are of the type:

$$XH^+ + XH \rightarrow XH_2^+ + X \tag{17}$$

where the alternative charge exchange reaction is a resonance process; indeed, Henglein and Muccini (21) have observed charge transfer in addition to Reaction 17 for many of the systems included in Table III.

Since it thus appears that reactions other than the atom transfer process are occurring, one must consider the possibility that the low k(thermal)/k(10.5 volts/cm.) ratios may result from a variation of the relative importance of the atom transfer reaction channel with ion energy. Similarly, in some of the cases where k(thermal) = k(10.5 volts/cm.) the relative importance of the atom transfer process may also change with ion energy. Thus the value of k(thermal)/k(10.5 volts/cm.) does not necessarily provide conclusive evidence for the interaction potential between the ion and the neutral molecules.

Condensation Ion-Molecule Reactions

Condensation reactions are somewhat more difficult to study by the pulsing technique since the secondary ion usually has a considerably higher mass than the primary ion. However, by restricting the total reaction time to 1 μsec. or less, we have found it possible to study this type of reaction under thermal conditions. Preliminary results are presented in Table IV. Many of the product ions in these systems can be formed in more than one reaction, and the details of reaction identification will be presented elsewhere.

Table IV.   Ion-Molecule Reactions in Hydrocarbons

Reaction	Rate Constant $\times 10^{10}$ cc. molecule^{-1} sec.$^{-1}$		k(thermal) $\dfrac{}{k (10.5}$	Reference
	Thermal	10.5 volts/cm.	$\dfrac{k (10.5}{volts/cm.)}$	
$CH_3^+ + CH_4 \rightarrow C_2H_5^+ + H_2$	8.6	6.0	1.4$_4$	34
$CD_3^+ + CD_4 \rightarrow C_2D_5^+ + D_2$	6.1	4.6	1.3$_3$	34
$C_2H_2^+ + CH_4 \rightarrow C_3H_5^+ + H$	1.6$_4$	0.91$_9$	1.79	30
$C_2H_2^+ + C_2H_2 \rightarrow C_4H_3^+ + H$	5.2$_6$	5.0$_2$	1.05	30
$C_2H_2^+ + C_2H_2 \rightarrow C_4H_2^+ + H_2$	2.2$_5$	1.8$_7$	1.20	30
$C_3H_2^+ + C_3H_4$ (allene) $\rightarrow$ $C_4H_3^+ + C_2H_3$	5.4$_8$	3.2$_3$	1.70	30
$C_3H_4^+ + C_3H_4$ (allene) $\rightarrow$ $C_6H_7^+ + H$	3.7$_3$	1.4$_8$	2.52	30
$C_3H_4^+ + C_3H_4$ (propyne) $\rightarrow$ $C_3H_5^+ + C_3H_3$	2.0	2.2	0.91	30
$C_3D_4^+ + C_3D_4$ (propyne) $\rightarrow$ $C_6D_7^+ + D$	4.7$_3$	3.2$_9$	1.44	30

For most of the reactions investigated the ratio k(thermal)/k(10.5 volts/cm.) is considerably above unity. One exception listed in Table IV is the reaction:

$$C_3H_4^+ + C_3H_4 \rightarrow C_3H_5^+ + C_3H_3 \qquad (18)$$

where the ratio is 0.91—i.e., in the same range as found for the simple hydrogen transfer reactions (Table II). Using mixtures of C_3H_4 and C_3D_4 we have found no evidence for isotopic mixing in the product ion, thus indicating that an intimate collision complex is not formed. By contrast, reactions of $C_3H_4^+ + C_3H_4$ producing C_5 and C_6 ions occur with essentially complete scrambling of the hydrogen atoms.

The results in Table IV suggest that the condensation reactions cannot be described adequately by the ion-induced dipole model. In this regard the results agree with conventional studies which have frequently found a higher power inverse dependence of the cross-section on the field strength E for condensation reactions than for hydrogen transfer reactions.

Conclusions

The pulsed source method, despite several limitations, appears to be a very useful technique for studying ion-molecule reactions at thermal energies. Although the studies to have date been limited primarily to simple hydrogen transfer reactions, the technique should also prove useful for studying charge transfer and hydride ion transfer reactions at thermal energies.

In conclusion we would note the modified pulsing technique recently developed by Futrell and colleagues (*32, 33*) for studying ion-molecule reactions at low ion energies. This approach, which is an outgrowth of the pulsing techniques described here, represents a potentially powerful tool for studying ion-molecule reactions not only at thermal energies but also over a range of ion energies not easily accessible by conventional techniques.

Literature Cited

(1) Amenu-Kpodo, F. K., Mater's Thesis, University of Toronto, 1965.
(2) Berta, M. A., Koski, W. S., *J. Am. Chem. Soc.* **86**, 5098 (1964).
(3) Cermak, V., Herman, Z., *Nucleonics* **19**, 106 (1961).
(4) Eliason, M. A., Hirschfelder, J. O., *J. Chem. Phys.* **30**, 1426 (1959).
(5) Field, F. H., Franklin, J. L., *J. Am. Chem. Soc.* **83**, 4509 (1961).
(6) Field, F. H., Franklin, J. L., Lampe, F. W., *J. Am. Chem. Soc.* **79**, 2419, 2665 (1957).
(7) Field, F. H., Head, H. N., Franklin, J. L., *J. Am. Chem. Soc.* **84**, 1118 (1962).
(8) Field, F. H., Lampe, F. W., *J. Am. Chem. Soc.* **80**, 5583 (1958).
(9) Galli, A., Giardini-Guidoni, A., Volpi, G. G., *Nuovo Cimento* **31**, 1145 (1964).
(10) Giese, C. F., Maier, W. B., *J. Chem. Phys.* **35**, 1913 (1961); **39**, 739 (1963).
(11) Gioumousis, G., Stevenson, D. P., *J. Chem. Phys.* **29**, 294 (1958).
(12) Hand, C. W., von Weyssenhoff, H., *Can. J. Chem.* **42**, 195 (1964).
(13) Hand, C. W., von Weyssenhoff, H., *Can. J. Chem.* **42**, 2385 (1964).
(14) Harrison, A. G., *Can. J. Chem.* **41**, 236 (1963).
(15) Harrison, A. G., Ivko, A., Shannon, T. W., *Can. J. Chem.*, **44**, 1351 (1966).
(16) Harrison, A. G., Shannon, T. W., Meyer, F., *Advan. Mass Spectrometry* **3**, 377 (1966).
(17) Harrison, A. G., Tait, J. M. S., *Can. J. Chem.* **40**, 1936 (1962).
(18) Harrison, A. G., Thynne, J. C. J., *Trans. Faraday Soc.*, in press.
(19) Harrison, A. G., Thynne, J. C. J., unpublished results.
(20) Henglein, A., Muccini, G., *Z. Naturforsch.* **17a**, 452 (1962).
(21) Henglein, A., Muccini, G., *Z. Naturforsch.* **18a**, 1753 (1963).
(22) Hertel, G. R., Koski, W. S., *J. Am. Chem. Soc.*, **87**, 1686 (1965).
(23) Homer, J. B., Lehrle, R. S., Robb, J. C., Thomas, D. W., *Advan. Mass Spectrometry* **2**, 503 (1963).
(24) Karachevtsev, G. V., Markin, M. I., Tal'roze, V. L., *Kinetika i Kataliz,* **5**, 377 (1964).
(25) Lampe, F. W., Hess, G. G., *J. Am. Chem. Soc.* **86**, 2952 (1964).
(26) Lindholm, E., *Z. Naturforsch.* **9a**, 535 (1954).

(27) Markin, M. I., Tal'roze, V. L., *Elementarnye Protsessy Khim. Vysokikh Energ. Akad. Nauk SSR, Inst. Khim. Fiz., Tr. Simpoziuma, Moscow*, **1963**, 18, (1965).
(28) Melton, C. E., *J. Chem. Phys.* **33**, 647 (1960).
(29) Moran, T. F., Hamill, W. H., *J. Chem. Phys.* **39**, 1413 (1963); *see* also earlier references cited therein.
(30) Myher, J. J., Harrison, A. G., unpublished results.
(31) Ryan, K. R., Futrell, J. H., *J. Chem. Phys.* **42**, 824 (1965).
(32) Ryan, K. R., Futrell, J. H., *J. Chem. Phys.* **43**, 3009 (1965).
(33) Ryan, K. R., Futrell, J. H., Miller, C. D., *Rev. Sci. Instr.* **37**, 107 (1966).
(34) Shannon, T. W., Ph.D. Thesis, University of Toronto (1965).
(35) Shannon, T. W., Harrison, A. G., *J. Chem. Phys.* **43**, 4201 (1965).
(36) Shannon, T. W., Harrison, A. G., *J. Chem. Phys.* **43**, 4206 (1965).
(37) Shannon, T. W., Meyer, F., Harrison, A. G., *Can. J. Chem.* **43**, 159 (1965).
(38) Stevenson, D. P., Schissler, D. O., *J. Chem. Phys.* **29**, 287 (1958).
(39) Tal'roze, V. L., Frankevich, E. L., *Zh. Fiz. Khim.* **34**, 2709 (1960).
(40) Tal'roze, V. L., Frankevich, E. L., *Tr. Soveshch. po Radiacionnoi Khim., Moscow*, **1957**, 13.
(41) Tal'roze, V. L., Karachevtsev, G. V., *Advan. Mass Spectrometry* **3**, 211 (1966).
(42) Thynne, J. C. J., Amenu-Kpodo, F. K., Harrison, A. G., *Can. J. Chem.*, in press.
(43) Thynne, J. C. J., Harrison, A. G., *Trans. Fraday Soc.*, in press.
(44) Thynne, J. C. J., Harrison, A. G., unpublished results.
(45) Weiner, E. R., Hertel, G. R. Koski, W. S., *J. Am. Chem. Soc.* **86**, 788 (1964).

RECEIVED May 2, 1966.

Chemical Ionization Mass Spectrometry

Paraffin Hydrocarbons

F. H. FIELD, M. S. B. MUNSON, and D. A. BECKER[1]

Esso Research and Engineering Co., Baytown Research and Development Division, Baytown, Tex.

Chemical ionization mass spectra of the normal paraffins studied range from C_8H_{18} to $C_{28}H_{58}$; the branched paraffins contain from nine to 30 carbon atoms. The ion with $m/e = MW - 1$ has a relative intensity of 0.32 $\pm$ 0.05 in the normal paraffins, and ranges from 0.50 to 0.00 in the isoparaffins. The intensities in the high mass end of the chemical ionization spectrum are greater than in corresponding impact mass spectra. Chemical ionization may involve random attack of the reactant ions on the paraffin molecule, followed by localized reactions producing the observed ions. The intensities of the ions with $m/e = MW - 1$ can be semi-quantitatively accounted for in terms of the hydrogen content of the molecule. Olefin ions ($C_nH_{2n}^+$) are formed by an unexplained mechanism in molecules that contain branches larger than methyl.

W e have recently shown (8) in a general way that interesting and potentially useful mass spectra can be generated by chemical ionization techniques. We wish to present here in some detail the results obtained when paraffin hydrocarbons are ionized by the chemical ionization technique using methane as the reactant gas.

In brief, the method consists of introducing small amounts (partial pressures of 10^{-3}–10^{-4} torr) of the substance to be investigated into the ionization chamber of a mass spectrometer which contains a high pressure (1 torr) of methane, the reactant gas. Ionization is effected by electron impact, and because the methane is present in such an overwhelming preponderance, all but a negligibly small amount of the initial ionization occurs in the methane. The methane ions then undergo ion-molecule reactions to produce a set of ions which serve as reactant ions in the chemical ionization process. The important reactant ions formed from

---

[1] Present address: Department of Chemistry, Iowa State University, Ames, Iowa.

methane and their percentage composition at a pressure of 1 torr are
(4): CH_5^+ (48%), $C_2H_5^+$ (40%), and $C_3H_5^+$ (6%). The remaining
ions formed in methane are predominantly $C_2H_4^+$, $C_3H_7^+$, and $C_2H_3^+$.
The reactions producing the major ions are:

$$CH_4^+ + CH_4 \rightarrow CH_5^+ + CH_3 \qquad (1)$$

$$CH_3^+ + CH_4 \rightarrow C_2H_5^+ + H_2 \qquad (2)$$

$$CH_2^+ + 2CH_4 \rightarrow C_3H_5^+ + 2H_2 + H \qquad (3)$$

Thus the reactant ions for chemical ionization formed in the methane
plasma consists of approximately equal amounts of a strong gaseous
Brönsted acid (CH_5^+) and ions which can act either as Lewis acids or
Brönsted acids ($C_2H_5^+ + C_3H_5^+$). These reactant ions will effect the
chemical ionization with an added substance by proton transfer or hydride ion transfer, both of which may be accompanied by fragmentation
of the ion initially formed.

Experimental

The apparatus (Esso chemical physics mass spectrometer) and technique have already been described (8), and only a brief recapitulation will
be given here.   The pressure of methane in the mass spectrometer ionization chamber is maintained at 1.00 ± 0.01 torr.   The paraffins to be
investigated are introduced into the mass spectrometer using the capillary
pipet technique, and the volumes introduced vary from 1 to 10 micro-
liters.   We estimate that these volumes produce a pressure of about
10^{-3} torr in the ionization chamber.   The initial ionization is effected by
electron impact, and the resolved ions are detected using a 10-stage
electron multiplier.   The mass spectrometer is fitted with a probe which
intercepts a small fraction of the unresolved ion current in the analyzer
tube portion of the mass spectrometer.   The probe consists of an appropriate length of 0.015-inch diameter iridium wire, and the current it
intercepts is measured with a Keithley model 415 micromicroammeter.
To enhance the utility of the apparatus for quantitative work, the mass
spectrometer is operated to maintain the current intercepted by the ion
probe constant (±3%) at an arbitrarily selected value (1.5 ± 0.05 ×
10^{-12} amp. for the experiments reported here).   This requires electron
currents on the order of 0.01–0.1 μamp.   The source pressure is measured
by a quartz spiral Bourdon gage, which is attached through a small
tube directly to the source.   Other instrumental conditions are: pressure of methane within the additive reservoir = 4.4 torr;   electron energy = 210 volts;   repeller = 2.0 volts (5.0 volts/cm);   ion accelerating
voltage = 3000 volts.
    For most of the experiments reported here the temperature of the
ionization chamber was 150 °C., but to investigate the effect of temperature on chemical ionization mass spectra, runs were made at ionization
chamber temperatures varying between 216 ° and 131 °C.
    The methane used as reactant gas was Matheson research grade,
which could be used satisfactorily without further purification.   The
paraffin hydrocarbons studied were obtained from the laboratory bank

Table I.   Mass Spectra of n-$C_{18}H_{38}$

Methane Reactant: P_{CH4} = 1.0 torr

m/e	Ion	Chemical Ionization Intensities (Chart Div.) CH$_4$ Only	Chemical Ionization Intensities (Chart Div.) CH$_4$ + 1.8 μ liters n-$C_{18}H_{38}$	Relative Intensities % of Additive Ionization Chem. Ioniz.	Relative Intensities % of Additive Ionization Electron Impact[a]
17	CH_5^+	22,900	22,500		
18		285	290		
19	H_3O^+	6,820	4,960		
27	$C_2H_3^+$	200	235		
28	$C_2H_4^+$	1,840	1,810		
29	$C_2H_5^+$	22,800	22,900		
30		575	560		
31		415	435		
39	$C_3H_3^+$	50	50		
40	$C_3H_4^+$	120	110		
41	$C_3H_5^+$	4,580	4,320		
42		83	82		
43	$C_3H_7^+$	862	750		
44		21	18		
55	$C_4H_7^+$	17	32	1.3	6.7
56	$C_4H_8^+$	3	5	0.2	2.3
57	$C_4H_9^+$	136	166	2.7	29.1
58		5	9	0.1	
59		16	15	~0	
69	$C_5H_9^+$	3	7	0.3	
71	$C_5H_{11}^+$	4	63	5.2	17.6
72			3	0.3	
73		3	3	0	
83	$C_6H_{11}^+$		5	0.4	
85	$C_6H_{13}^+$		50	4.4	11.4
86			4	0.4	
87			3	0.3	
97	$C_7H_{13}^+$		4	0.4	
99	$C_7H_{15}^+$		43	3.8	3.0
100			4	0.4	
111	$C_8H_{15}^+$		2	0.2	
112	$C_8H_{16}^+$		2	0.2	
113	$C_8H_{17}^+$		44	3.9	2.0
114			2	0.2	
127	$C_9H_{19}^+$		39	3.5	1.4
128			3	0.3	
141	$C_{10}H_{21}^+$		42	3.7	1.1
142			3	0.3	
155	$C_{11}H_{23}^+$		36	3.2	0.8
156			4	0.4	
169	$C_{12}H_{25}^+$		31	2.7	0.7
170			5	0.4	
183	$C_{13}H_{27}^+$		28	2.5	0.5
184			3	0.3	
197	$C_{14}H_{29}^+$		25	2.2	0.4
198			3	0.3	
211	$C_{15}H_{31}^+$		15	1.3	0.3
212			1	0.1	
225	$C_{16}H_{33}^+$		14	1.2	0.1
226			2	0.2	
239	$C_{17}H_{35}^+$		36	3.2	0.007
240			4		
253	$C_{18}H_{37}^+$		487	43.1	
254			70	6.2	0.5
255			6	0.5	
ΣI_i		61,900	60,500		
$\Sigma I_{n\text{-}C_{18}H_{38}}$			1,130		

[a] Data taken from Ref. *1.*

of pure compounds, and varied with regard to their original source and degree of purity.   Whenever possible, API standard samples were used.

Results and Discussion

Normal Paraffins.   Table I gives the chemical ionization mass spectrum of *n*-octadecane with methane as the reaction gas and the electron impact mass spectrum of *n*-octadecane for comparison.   These spectra are typical of the spectra obtained for relatively large normal paraffins.   The third column in Table I contains the ion currents for the ions present in methane.   Obviously, small contributions from an additive at $m/e = 17$, 29, and 41 cannot be determined, and normally the mass spectra are reported for ions of m/e greater than 43 or sometimes 57.   When relatively low mass ions are reported, their intensities must be corrected for the ions formed for methane alone.   These mass interferences do not significantly restrict the method since the chemical ionization technique is most useful for higher molecular weight compounds.   The chemical ionization mass spectrum of *n*-octadecane is given in Figure 1, which shows the relative intensities of the various ions formed.   For ease of plotting, only ions with intensity greater than 1% of the total additive ionization are represented.   The spectra of other normal paraffins ranging from C_8H_{18} to $C_{28}H_{58}$ have been measured, and the spectra are all qualitatively similar to that of *n*-octadecane.   They consist almost completely of alkyl ions, and they are represented graphically in Figure 2.   For simplicity of representation, ions resulting from the presence of C^{13} are omitted from Figure 2.

We now consider the spectra of *n*-octadecane in more detail.   The most striking aspect of the chemical ionization mass spectrum of this substance is the large relative intensity of the $C_{18}H_{37}{}^+$ ($m/e = 253$) ion

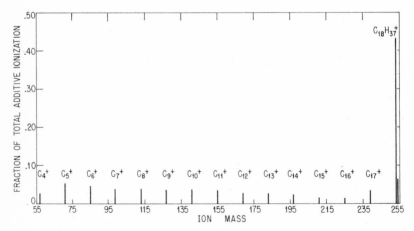

Figure 1.   Chemical ionization mass spectra of n-octadecane

$MW = 254$, reactant $= CH_4$, $P_{CH_4} = 1$ torr

$(I_{rel}$ = 43%). The chemical ionization spectrum exhibits ions at m/e = 254 and 255, but the intensities of these correspond within experimental error to the intensities to be expected for $C^{13}C^{12}{}_{17}H_{33}{}^+$ and $C^{13}{}_1C^{12}{}_{16}H_{33}{}^+$. Thus, no parent ion with formula $C_{18}H_{38}{}^+$ is formed by chemical ionization, and we have shown (8) that none is to be expected (*see* also below). However, we can look upon the ion with m/e = MW − 1 as the chemical ionization equivalent of a parent ion, and Table I shows that the chemical ionization MW − 1 ion has a relative intensity approximately 86 times that of the electron impact parent ion. The chemical ionization spectrum of *n*-octadecane is relatively simple, consisting almost entirely of the alkyl ions at each carbon number, and the variation in intensity is quite small except for the large intensity of the MW − 1 ion. Table I also shows that only a few lower molecular weight alkenyl ions $(C_nH_{2n-1}{}^+)$ of quite small intensities are to be found. Low intensity ions are found also at m/e = 56 and 112.

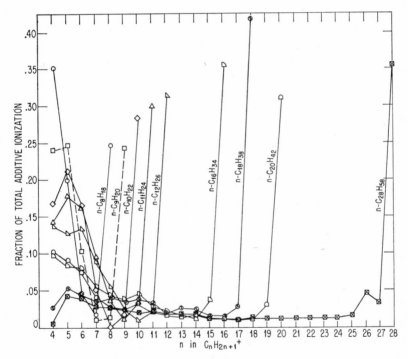

Figure 2.   Chemical ionization mass spectra of normal paraffins

Reactant = CH_4, P_{CH4} = *1 torr*

We have previously shown (8) that the chemical ionization spectra using methane as reactant are generated by the combination of dissociative proton transfer from $CH_5{}^+$ and hydride ion abstraction and alkyl ion displacement by $C_2H_5^+$. We illustrate these reactions with octadecane as follows.

$$CH_5^+ + n\text{-}C_{18}H_{38} \longrightarrow [C_{18}H_{39}^+]^* + CH_4$$

$$\longrightarrow C_{18}H_{37}^+ + H_2$$

$$\longrightarrow C_{18-n}H_{37-2n}^+ + C_nH_{2n+2} \qquad (4)$$

$$C_2H_5^+ + n\text{-}C_{18}H_{38} \longrightarrow [C_{20}H_{43}^+]^*$$

$$\longrightarrow C_{18}H_{37}^+ + C_2H_6$$

$$\longrightarrow C_{18-m}H_{37-2m}^+ + C_{m+2}H_{2m+6} \qquad (5)$$

We have no direct evidence that the transient complexes $(C_{18}H_{39}^+)^*$ and $(C_{20}H_{43}^+)^*$ actually exist, and they are used primarily for convenience in writing the equations. However, transient association complexes do occur in low energy ion-molecule reactions, and their actual existence in this case might be expected.

It is illuminating to examine the energetics of the chemical ionization processes in normal paraffins even though approximate energy values must be used. For n-octadecane we write the following thermochemical relations:

Hydrogen removal

$$n\text{-}C_{18}H_{38} + \begin{cases} CH_5^+ \rightarrow s\text{-}C_{18}H_{37}^+ + CH_4 + H_2 \ \Delta H = -27 \text{ kcal./mole} \qquad (6) \\ C_2H_5^+ \rightarrow s\text{-}C_{18}H_{37}^+ + C_2H_6 \ \Delta H = -25 \text{ kcal./mole} \qquad (7) \end{cases}$$

C-C bond fission

$$n\text{-}C_{18}H_{38} + \begin{cases} CH_5^+ \rightarrow 1\text{-}C_8H_{17}^+ + C_{10}H_{22} + CH_4 \ \Delta H = -12 \text{ kcal./mole} \qquad (8) \\ C_2H_5^+ \rightarrow 1\text{-}C_8H_{17}^+ + C_{12}H_{26} \ \Delta H = 0 \text{ kcal./mole.} \qquad (9) \end{cases}$$

If we assume that rearrangement to form a secondary alkyl ion can occur, the energies for Reactions 8 and 9 become -37 and -25 kcal./mole, respectively. In these and subsequent calculations, the heats of formation of neutral compounds are taken from conventional sources, and heats of formation of ions are taken either from Field and Franklin (5) or are approximated using the group equivalent method of Franklin (6), taking new values for the alkyl ion groups—namely,

$$-CH_2^+ = 235, \quad \diagdown\!\!\overset{+}{C}H\!\!\diagup = 215, \quad -\overset{\diagdown}{\underset{\diagup}{C}}{}^+ = 205 \text{ kcal./mole } (7).$$

The heat of formation CH_5^+ is taken as 229 ± 3 kcal./mole as determined recently in these laboratories (9). In all these energetic considerations we assume that all the energy of the reaction is concentrated in the ionic product species. Thus, the energies written are upper limits to the energies the ionic species actually contain.

Reactions 8 and 9 represent and are typical of all the dissociative ionizations producing the observed fragment alkyl ions. Reaction 9 as given is thermoneutral, but since Reaction 8 is exothermic, we consider that the formation of primary fragment alkyl ions is energetically permitted. The formation of secondary fragment ions would be highly exothermic but requires an ionic rearrangement. Such rearrangements are common in alkyl ions, but the ion which must rearrange in the processes we are considering is a protonated paraffin ion. The tendency toward rearrangement of this kind of ion is not known and may well be different from those in alkyl ions or paraffin molecule-ions. Thus, we tentatively postulate that reaction occurs by bond cleavage without rearrangement.

A possible alternative mechanism for the formation of fragment alkyl ions comes immediately to mind—namely, beta fission of the C_{18} ion formed in Reactions 6 and 7 to form a smaller alkyl ion and an olefin. Thus we write as a typical example:

$$n\text{-}C_{18}H_{38} + CH_5^+ \longrightarrow sec\text{-}C_{18}H_{37}^+ + H_2 + CH_4$$
$$\underset{\longrightarrow}{\big|\ ?} 1\text{-}C_8H_{17}^+ + C_{10}H_{20}$$
$$\Delta H = +18 \text{ kcal./mole.} \quad (10)$$

However, the reaction is endothermic by an appreciable amount, and one must question whether it will occur to any significant extent as an ion-molecule reaction in the ionization chamber of a mass spectrometer. For this reason we are forced to postulate the occurrence of Reactions 8 and 9 to produce the observed alkyl fragment ions. The endothermicity calculated for Reaction 10 results from the fact that we postulate a primary structure for the fragment alkyl ion. Rearrangement to a secondary ion has to be considered as a possibility, as always, but even if it occurs, we believe that the transition state for the formation of the fragment alkyl ion will correspond closely enough to a primary ion structure to make the energy given in Reaction 10 applicable. In this connection Fejes and Emmett (3) suggest that in catalytic processes $n\text{-}C_4H_9^+$ does not isomerize directly to $i\text{-}C_4H_9^+$ but goes instead by an equilibrium process involving olefin loss. Such an equilibrium process is highly improbable under the conditions prevailing in the mass spectrometer ionization chamber.

From Table I or Figure 1 it may be seen that the $n\text{-}C_{18}H_{37}^+$ ion comprises 43% of the total chemical ionization in n-octadecane, and the remainder consists of fragment alkyl ions distributed over a range of carbon numbers. The variation in intensities of the fragment alkyl ions is small and suggests that no strongly specific chemical effects are occurring. A paraffin such as n-octadecane contains no distinguishing feature which would direct the attack of the reactant ions (CH_5^+ and $C_2H_5^+$) to any specific portion of the molecule; thus, to explain the observed spectrum, we postulate as an approximation that the attack by the reactant ion occurs at random along the hydrocarbon chain. Figure 2 shows that the amount of variation in the relative intensity of the MW − 1 ion between the different paraffins is small. Thus, in the range of normal paraffins studied from C_8 to C_{28}, the MW − 1 alkyl ion relative intensity is 0.32 ± 0.05. Clearly the length of the carbon chain has essentially no effect on the tendency for chain breakage to occur, and this seeming lack of interaction between the atoms of the molecule suggests that the ionic reactions occurring tend to be localized at, or in the vicinity of the point of attack of the reactant ion. Furthermore, the ionic species involved in chemical ionization of paraffins are all even electron species wherein the charge must occupy localized orbitals.

Thus we think of the chemical ionization of paraffins as involving a randomly located electrophilic attack of the reactant ion on the paraffin molecule, which is then followed by an essentially localized reaction. The reactions can involve either the C-H electrons or the C-C electrons. In the former case an H^- ion is abstracted (Reactions 6 and 7, for example), and in the latter a kind of alkyl ion displacement (Reactions 8 and 9) occurs. However, the H^- abstraction reaction produces an ion of $m/e = MW - 1$ regardless of the carbon atom from which the abstraction occurs, but the alkyl ion displacement reaction will give fragment alkyl ions of different m/e values. Thus the much larger intensity of the $MW - 1$ alkyl ion is explained. From the relative intensities of the $MW - 1$ ion (about 32%) and the sum of the intensities of the smaller fragment ions (about 68%), we must conclude that the attacking ion effects C-C bond fission about twice as often as C-H fission.

Of course, the postulated mechanism for the chemical ionization reactions is only an oversimplified approximation, as shown by further inspection of Figure 2. For normal paraffins smaller than n-octadecane, the intensities of the C-C fission alkyl ions no longer are approximately equal, but rather the smaller ions are formed in greater abundance. Thus, for n-octane, the butyl ion ($m/e = 57$) is the most intense in the spectrum, and in general the relative intensities of the lower mass fragment ions are larger for the smaller paraffins. This increase in C-C fission fragment ion intensity does not occur significantly at the expense of the $MW - 1$ ion intensity. To a degree this behavior can be rationalized in terms of the mechanism proposed for the chemical ionization process. We have suggested that the relative amount of C-C and C-H bond breaking is determined by localized conditions which are presumably invariant from one CH_2 group to the next along the paraffin chain. It follows then that while the relative intensity of the ion with $m/e = MW - 1$ will be independent of chain length, the relative intensities of each ion formed by C-C fission will become larger as the size of the molecule becomes smaller. Hence, if the fraction of reaction yielding C-C fragmentation is a constant, the relative intensity of a given C-C fission fragment ion will vary inversely with the total number of such fragment ions which can be formed. However, one should still expect that the relative intensities of these fragment ions would not vary with their size, but this is contrary to the observed behavior. We may speculate further that this nonuniformity of intensity results from a somewhat nonrandom attack of the reactant ion on the paraffin molecule. The conditions in the mass spectrometer are such that chemical ionization reactions occur at low relative translational energies of the reactant ion and the neutral

paraffin molecule.   Under these circumstances we think that end effects
will occur, and that these will involve a tendency for the reactant ion to
be unduly attracted toward the center and away from the ends of the
paraffin molecule because the attacking ion will be attracted most
toward the center of mass of the molecule.   For a relatively small molecule like octane this could result in a disproportionately high production
of $C_4H_9^+$ and $C_5H_{11}^+$ ions; in a large molecule such as *n*-octadecane or
n-octacosane, the attraction of the reactant toward the long central
portion of the molecule will be uniform, and the importance of end effects
would be small.

Figure 2 also shows that for the larger normal paraffins the ion with
m/e = MW − 15 has an appreciably larger intensity than the ion with
m/e = MW − 29, MW − 43, etc.   If we might be allowed a flight of
fancy, we might ascribe this slightly higher probability for the removal
of the terminal CH_3 group to an end attack of the reactant ion on the
paraffin molecule—i.e., one colinear with the carbon chain at the end of
the molecule.   This conceivably might have a somewhat higher probability because the mass density (and thus the induced dipole) will
perhaps be somewhat greater along the axis of the molecule.   For most
of the linear paraffins the ion with m/e = MW − 29 is the least intense in
the spectrum, and we can offer no explanation for this behavior.   An
apparent exception is observed in the case of *n*-$C_{28}H_{58}$ (*see* Figure 2), but
we are inclined to think that the relatively large intensity of the $C_{26}H_{53}^+$
ion results from the presence of the small amount of $C_{26}H_{54}$ impurity.

If we compare the chemical ionization spectrum of *n*-octadecane with
its electron impact spectrum (Table I), we note that the chemical ionization MW − 1 ion has a much larger relative intensity than that of the
electron impact parent ion.   Second, the chemical ionization spectrum
is simpler since the electron impact spectrum contains many different
kinds of ions (which are not included in Table I).   Finally, the inde-
pendence of the relative intensity of the chemical ionization MW − 1
ion as a function of molecular size has no analog in electron impact spectra.
As is well known, the relative intensities of the molecule-ions formed by
electron impact decrease monotonically in the normal paraffins as the
molecular weight increases.   Thus, the fraction of the total ionization
contained in the molecule ion in *n*-$C_{10}H_{22}$, *n*-$C_{20}H_{42}$, and *n*-$C_{30}H_{62}$ are
0.031, 0.0067, and 0.0012, respectively.   These values are calculated from
the Tables of Mass Spectral Data (*1*), including in the summation for the
total ionization only ions with mass greater than 54; this gives a more
meaningful comparison with the chemical ionization data.   We do not
understand this decline with molecular size in the stability of the normal
paraffin molecule-ions formed by electron impact, and we cannot really
explain the difference in the tendency toward carbon-carbon bond
fission by electron impact and chemical ionization.   However, three
points of difference between the two processes which may be important
are: (1) ions formed by chemical ionization contain an even number of
electrons, but the molecule-ions formed by electron impact contain an
odd number of electrons; (2) chemical ionization is not a vertical ioniza-

Table II. Alkyl Ion Inten-
Methane Reactant:

Compound No.	Compound	m/e Ion	57 $C_4{}^+$	71 $C_5{}^+$	85 $C_6{}^+$	99 $C_7{}^+$	113 $C_8{}^+$	127 $C_9{}^+$	141 $C_{10}{}^+$	155 $C_{11}{}^+$	169 $C_{12}{}^+$	183 $C_{13}{}^+$	197 $C_{14}{}^+$
	Monosubstituted												
1	2-MeC₁₀		.17	.13	.14	.077	.014	.003	.075	.27			
2	8-n-C₆C₁₅		.041	.042	.034	.021	.018	.016	.015	.011	.011	.010	.053
3	11-n-C₄C₂₂		—	.026	.024	.012	.011	.009	.008	.008	.007	.006	.006
4	11-n-C₅C₂₁		.012	.017	.016	.008	.006	.005	.006	.005	.005	.005	.005
5	9-n-C₈C₂₀		.017	.019	.014	.007	.007	.004	.004	.004	.003	.003	.003
	Disubstituted												
6	2-Me-5-EtC₇		.11	.21	.14	.038	.048	.081	.20				
	Trisubstituted												
7	2,3,6-Me₃C₇		.17	.26	.19	.026	.004	.103	.094				
8	2,4-Me₂-3-i-C₃C₅		.34	.27	.23	.039	0	.013	.019				
9	2,2,5-Me₃C₆		.25	.31	.044	0		.23	.076				
10	2,2,4-Me₃C₇		.32	.19	.17	.036	.004	.12	.057				
11	2,2,6-Me₃C₇		.21	.24	.17	.019	0	.16	.092				
12	3,3,5-Me₃C₇		.13	.44	.14	.015	.048	.095	.045				
	Tetrasubstituted												
13	2,2,3,3-Me₄C₆		.28	.27	.16	.12	.001	.089	.005				
14	2,2,5,5-Me₄C₆		.28	.30	.16	.004	0	.13	.020				
	Pentasubstituted												
15	2,2,4,5,5-Me₅C₆		.36	.14	.29	.088	0	0	.040	.006			
16	2,2,4,6,6-Me₅C₇		.47	.077	.18	.13	.063	0	0	.011	.0015		
	Hexasubstituted												
17	2,6,10,15,19,23-Me₆C₂₄ (squalane)		.011	.024	.022	.026	.051	.048	.042	.038	.038	.052	.043

Table II. Addendum
Names, Molecular Weights, Masses, and Relative Intensities of Minor Ions

Compound	MW	Masses and Relative Intensities
1. 2-Methyldecane	156	$m/e = 56$, .004; $m/e = 97$, .004; $m/e = 112$, .008
2. 8-n-Hexylpentadecane	296	$m/e = 196$, .002
3. 11-n-Butyldocosane	366	$m/e = 69$, .002; $m/e = 70$, .001; $m/e = 83$, .004; $m/e = 97$, .003; $m/e = 111$, .003; $m/e = 125$, .002; $m/e = 139$, .001; $m/e = 153$, .002; $m/e = 210$, .008; $m/e = 224$, .007; $m/e = 308$, .003
4. 11-n-Amylheneicosane	366	$m/e = 69$, .003; $m/e = 70$, .001, $m/e = 83$, .004; $m/e = 97$, .004, $m/e = 111$, .003; $m/e = 125$, .002; $m/e = 139$, .003; $m/e = 153$, .001; $m/e = 167$, .001; $m/e = 181$, .001; $m/e = 195$, .001; $m/e = 224$, .009; $m/e = 237$, .001, $m/e = 251$, .002; $m/e = 294$, .002
5. 9-n-Octyleicosane	394	$m/e = 69$, .004; $m/e = 83$, .004; $m/e = 97$, .004; $m/e = 111$, .003; $m/e = 112$, .001; $m/e = 125$, .004; $m/e = 139$, .001; $m/e = 183$, .003; $m/e = 224$, .001; $m/e = 238$, .003; $m/e = 280$, .005;
6. 2-Methyl-5-ethylheptane	142	$m/e = 69$, .005; $m/e = 70$, .003; $m/e = 83$, .006; $m/e = 97$, .002; $m/e = 98$, .001; $m/e = 111$, .001; $m/e = 112$, .013; $m/e = 125$, .003; $m/e = 139$, .009.
7. 2,3,6-Trimethylheptane	142	$m/e = 69$, .006; $m/e = 70$, .013; $m/e = 83$, .008; $m/e = 97$, .002; $m/e = 98$, .009; $m/e = 111$, .001; $m/e = 125$, .003; $m/e = 139$, .007
8. 2,4-Dimethyl-3-isopropylpentane	142	$m/e = 69$, .003; $m/e = 70$, .006; $m/e = 83$, .008; $m/e = 98$, .010; $m/e = 125$, .002; $m/e = 139$, .003

sities for Branched Paraffins

$P_{CH4} = 1.0$ torr

211 C_{15}^+	225 C_{16}^+	239 C_{17}^+	253 C_{18}^+	267 C_{19}^+	281 C_{20}^+	295 C_{21}^+	309 C_{22}^+	323 C_{23}^+	337 C_{24}^+	351 C_{25}^+	365 C_{26}^+	379 C_{27}^+	393 C_{28}^+	407 C_{29}^+	421 C_{30}^+
.045	.022	.014	.011	.014	.050	.37									
.037	.037	.016	.012	.010	.010	.009	.027	.013	.013	.046	.50				
.005	.038	.016	.010	.009	.008	.022	.013	.011	.015	.047	.53				
.004	.005	.020	.010	.008	.034	.015	.011	.011	.010	.014	.027	.040	.49		

.035	.027	.028	.028	.045	.023	.020	.013	.011	.012	.0081	.0043	.0012	.0012	.042	.12

Table II. Addendum Continued

Names, Molecular Weights, Masses, and Relative Intensities of Minor Ions

Compound	MW	Masses and Relative Intensities
9. 2,2,5-Trimethylhexane	128	$m/e = 56$, .019; $m/e = 69$, .003; $m/e = 70$, .010.
10. 2,2,4-Trimethylheptane	142	$m/e = 56$, .024; $m/e = 69$, .001; $m/e = 83$, .003; $m/e = 84$, .008; $m/e = 125$, .001; $m/e = 139$, .001.
11. 2,2,6-Trimethylheptane	142	$m/e = 56$, .027; $m/e = 83$, .004; $m/e = 84$, .009.
12. 3,3,5-Trimethylheptane	142	$m/e = 69$, .001; $m/e = 70$, .014; $m/e = 83$, .003; $m/e = 112$, .003; $m/e = 125$, .002; $m/e = 139$, .002
13. 2,2,3,3-Tetramethylhexane	142	$m/e = 56$, .002; $m/e = 69$, .005; $m/e = 83$, .005; $m/e = 84$, .024; $m/e = 98$, .001; $m/e = 111$, .002; $m/e = 139$, .002.
14. 2,2,5,5-Tetramethylhexane	142	$m/e = 56$, .039; $m/e = 69$, .004; $m/e = 83$, .004; $m/e = 125$, .001; $m/e = 139$, .001.
15. 2,2,4,5,5-Pentamethylhexane	156	$m/e = 56$, .036; $m/e = 83$, .011.
16. 2,2,4,6,6-Pentamethylheptane	170	$m/e = 56$, .017.
17. 2,6,10,15,19,23-Hexamethyltetracosane (squalane)	422	$m/e = 69$, .002; $m/e = 83$, .002; $m/e = 97$, .007; $m/e = 111$, .006; $m/e = 112$, .002; $m/e = 125$, .004; $m/e = 139$, .004; $m/e = 153$, .002; $m/e = 154$, .001; $m/e = 167$, .001; $m/e = 181$, .002; $m/e = 182$, .004; $m/e = 193$, .002; $m/e = 195$, .002; $m/e = 207$, .002; $m/e = 209$, .001; $m/e = 223$, .002; $m/e = 224$, .001; $m/e = 238$, .003; $m/e = 321$, .001; $m/e = 349$, .001.

tion process; (3) the average energy of the ion formed by electron impact may be appreciably higher than that of the ion formed by chemical ionization. Some preliminary studies in this laboratory with hydrogen as a reactant gas indicate that chemical ionization with this substance produces more fragmentation than methane does; this suggests that the difference in chemical ionization and electron impact spectra results from differences in energy content (energy of H_3^+ is appreciably higher than energies of CH_5^+ or $C_2H_5^+$). Studies using H_3^+ and D_3^+ with light hydrocarbons (C_4 and smaller) have recently been reported by Aquilanti and Volpi (2). In any event, the constancy of the relative intensities of the chemical ionization MW $-$ 1 ions shows that the size of the hydrocarbon alkyl ion is not in itself a predisposing factor toward instability, and in fact the large alkyl carbonium ions are stable. Thus, the chemical ionization results agree with condensed phase reactions such as alkylations of aromatics by large alkyl carbonium ions (synthetic detergent production, for example).

Branched Paraffins. Table II contains the relative ionic intensities obtained for 17 different branched paraffins containing from nine to 30 carbon atoms arranged in order of increasing number of side chain substituents.

We consider first the singly branched paraffins. One can see from Table II that the intensities of the MW $-$ 1 ions are affected little by the presence of a single branch in the molecule. We saw in Figure 1 that the average intensity of the MW $-$ 1 ion in the normal paraffins is 0.32, and Table II shows that for certain larger singly branched paraffins (e.g., 11-n-amylheneicosane) the relative intensity at m/e = MW $-$ 1 becomes as large as 0.53. We have no explanation for this difference. The intensities of these chemical ionization MW $-$ 1 ions are much larger than the intensities of the molecule-ions formed from singly branched paraffins by electron impact, but we shall not belabor the point. It is well known that the presence of branching markedly reduces the stability of the ions formed by electron impact from paraffin hydrocarbons, but we shall show that branching has a much smaller effect on the stabilities of the ions formed by chemical ionization. Thus, chemical ionization mass spectrometry will be much more useful for the qualitative identification and the quantitative analysis of the branched paraffin hydrocarbons than electron impact mass spectrometry. The relative utility of chemical ionization and field ionization mass spectrometry cannot be compared at present.

It is of interest to compare the relative intensities of all the alkyl ions formed from a singly branched paraffin with the intensities of the corresponding ions formed from normal paraffins. Table III lists the ratios of the relative intensities of the several alkyl ions formed from 2-methyldecane (compound 1, Table II) and normal undecane. Within the limits of accuracy and detail with which we are concerned, the intensities of all the ions except the $C_{10}H_{21}^+$ (m/e = 141) are the same. The low value of the ratio for m/e = 127 may be ascribed to a greater possible experimental error because of the low intensities which exist for this ion in both compounds. The intensity of $m/e = 141$ is significantly greater in the branched compound than in the normal compound, and closer examination of the spectra of all the singly branched compounds indicates that greater intensity exists for ions formed by the removal of a carbon branch. Thus, for example, in 9-n-octyleicosane (compound 5, Table II), the $C_{20}{}^+$ ion at $m/e = 281$ formed by removing one of the octyl group is three times as intense as the alkyl ions with slightly larger or slightly smaller numbers of carbon atoms. This enhanced intensity is also found for branch point ions in electron impact mass spectra.

Table III. Intensity Ratios in 2-MeC$_{10}$ and n-C$_{11}$

m/e	Ion	$I_{2\mathrm{MeC}_{10}}/I_{n\text{-}C_{11}}$	
155	$C_{11}H_{23}{}^+$	$.27/.30 =$	.90
141	$C_{10}H_{21}{}^+$	$.075/.020 =$	3.8
127	$C_9H_{19}{}^+$	$.003/.008 =$	.38
113	$C_8H_{17}{}^+$	$.041/.042 =$	1.0
99	$C_7H_{15}{}^+$	$.077/.093 =$	.83
85	$C_6H_{13}{}^+$	$.14/.15 =$	.93
71	$C_5H_{11}{}^+$	$.13/.15 =$	.87
57	$C_4H_9{}^+$	$.17/.12 =$	1.42

The larger intensities generated in the chemical ionization spectra can be thought of as resulting from either or both of two phenomena. We have postulated that the chemical ionization occurs from a localized reaction of the reactant ion, which may attack either the electrons in the C-H bonds or those in the C-C bonds in the near vicinity of the point of attack. If the attack is at a branch point, the relative numbers of C-C bonds are greater than found along a straight chain, and one may expect that the attack at C-C electrons will be enhanced. In addition, we can show that certain MW − 1 ions formed from branched paraffins can undergo an exothermic beta fission at the branch point, which comprises an additional mode of forming the branched point ion. The direct attack of the reactant at the branch with attendant C-C fission may be illustrated by the formation of the $C_{10}{}^+$ ion ($m/e = 141$) from 2-methyldecane:

$$
\begin{aligned}
CH_5{}^+ &\longrightarrow \text{/\\/\\/\\} + 2CH_4 \quad \Delta H = -39 \text{ kcal./mole} \\
C_2H_5{}^+ &\longrightarrow \text{/\\/\\/\\} + C_3H_8 \quad \Delta H = -24 \text{ kcal./mole}
\end{aligned}
\tag{11}
$$

This reaction exemplifies the important process of methyl removal, which becomes even more significant in the case of multiply branched paraffins. The rather large exothermicity of Reaction 11 results from the fact that a secondary carbonium ion is formed. The beta fission process can be illustrated using reactions in 8-n-hexylpentadecane (compound 2) as an example. Table II shows that the ions formed by C-C fission at a branch point ($C_{14}{}^+$, $m/e = 197$ and $C_{15}{}^+$, $m/e = 211$) have intensities appreciably larger than the other alkyl ions in the same region of the mass spectrum.   The beta fission process which contributes to the enhanced intensity can be written as follows:

C_6

/\/\/\/\/\/\/\   (Compound No. 2) $+ CH_5^+ \rightarrow$

$$/\/\/\/\langle\overset{C_6}{\underset{H}{C^+}}\rangle/\/\/\ + H_2 + CH_4$$

$$\downarrow$$

$$/\/\/\underset{H}{\overset{+}{C}}-C_6 + CH_2 = CHC_5H_{11} \qquad (12)$$

$(C_{14}H_{29}^+, m/e = 197)$ $\Delta H = -6$ kcal./mole

Note that in contrast with normal paraffins (Equation 10), beta fission at the branch point is exothermic, and the reaction is energetically allowed.   A similar exothermic reaction can be written using $C_2H_5^+$ as the reactant ion, and two other reactions equivalent to Reaction 12 can be written—namely, those with the charge in the initially formed C_{21}^+ ion on the other two branches of the molecule.   One of these other reactions will also produce a C_{14}^+ ion, but the other will produce a C_{15}^+ ion.

In proceeding to a consideration of the chemical ionization mass spectra of more highly branched paraffins, it will be most convenient to consider separately the several different classes of alkyl ions found in the spectra—i.e., MW $- 1^+$, MW $- 15^+$, MW $- 29^+$, etc.   We can see from Table II that a considerable amount of variation in the relative intensity of the MW $- 1$ ions (always the highest mass ion for which an intensity is given in the table) occurs.   However, we shall show that the observed MW $- 1$ intensities can be approximately accounted for in terms of the concept of localized electrophilic attack by the reactant ion.   First, however, we must consider the energetics of two processes which may be important in generating the spectra of branched paraffins. One of these is the abstraction of a primary hydrogen by the reactant ion.   As a typical example we may write

/\/\/\/ $+$

$$\begin{cases} CH_5^+ \xrightarrow{?} /\/\/\/ + H_2 + CH_4 \quad \Delta H = -2 \text{ kcal./mole} \\ \\ C_2H_5^+ \xrightarrow{?} /\/\/\/\underset{CH_2^+}{} + C_2H_6 \qquad \Delta H = 0 \text{ kcal./mole} \end{cases} \qquad (13)$$

Thus, the process of hydride ion abstraction from a primary position is approximately thermoneutral, and hence we must conclude that it is an energetically allowed process, although possibly with a relatively small reaction rate.   A process competing with primary H^- abstraction (Reaction 13) is methide ion abstraction (Reaction 11, loss of CH_4 from the

MW + 1 ion), and this reaction is 35–40 kcal./mole exothermic. We might expect that the rate for this reaction would be appreciably greater than the rate for primary H⁻ abstraction, and we consequently postulate that primary H⁻ abstraction to yield MW − 1 ions will not occur to any significant extent. The other process we must consider is a simple extension of Reaction 12—namely, beta fission at a branch point. However, we now wish to consider the case where the branch point is a quaternary carbon. As a typical example:

$$
\begin{aligned}
&\text{(isooctyl)} + CH_5{}^+ \longrightarrow \text{(ion)} + H_2 + CH_4 \\
&\qquad\qquad\qquad\qquad\downarrow \\
&\qquad tert = C_4H_9{}^+ + CH_2 = CHC_3H_7
\end{aligned}
\tag{14}
$$

$$\Delta H = -18 \text{ kcal./mole}$$

The corresponding reaction using $C_2H_5{}^+$ as the reactant ion is exothermic by 16 kcal./mole; thus, beta fission to form a tertiary carbonium ion is energetically allowed, and the energy release is large enough for one to think that the reaction rate will be reasonably large.

Since ions with m/e = MW − 1 are formed by removing a hydrogen from a parent hydrocarbon molecule (presumably by a localized reaction), it is reasonable to postulate that the intensity of the MW − 1 ion formed from a given paraffin hydrocarbon will depend on the number of hydrogens that can be removed. In the light of the above energetic considerations, we will assume that primary hydrogens cannot be removed and that the removal of hydrogens on carbon atoms beta to a branch point produces MW − 1 ions which are not collectable as such, but which rapidly decompose by way of beta C-C fission. Nonprimary hydrogens which are not beta to a branch point will be designated as "available" hydrogens. From our results on the chemical ionization mass spectra of normal paraffins, the attack of the reactant ion on a given CH_2 group in the paraffin chain resulted in the formation of MW − 1 ions on the average 32% of the time. We will assume that this figure also applies to the available hydrogens in isoparaffins, and thus the following equation applies:

$$I_i = (0.32)(N_i/N_n) \tag{15}$$

where I_i = relative intensity of MW − 1 ion in isoparaffin, i, N_i = number of available hydrogens in isoparaffin, i, and N_n = number of available hydrogens in the normal paraffin with the same number of carbon atoms as contained in the isoparaffin i.

The MW − 1 intensities calculated using Equation 15 are tabulated in Table IV along with the observed intensities for comparison. The agreement between the calculated and observed values varies from compound to compound, but by and large the trends in the calculated values tend to parallel those in the observed values. We think that the agreement is good enough to constitute evidence indicating the approxi-

mate validity of the postulates that we have made concerning the ionization and dissociation. Furthermore, a reasonable rationalization can
be given for most of the discrepancies found in Table IV. We have calculated the intensities assuming that the alkyl carbonium ions formed
by the initial H⁻ abstraction either remained in or invariably decomposed
from the structure initially formed. Clearly this is an oversimplification
since the existence of 1-2 shifts in carbonium ions has been demonstrated
by years of experience with alkylation, cracking, and other condensed-
phase carbonium ion reactions; in addition we will see that certain ions
formed by chemical ionization in the gas phase necessarily require the
existence of carbonium ion isomerizations. We will assume that 1-2
hydride shifts can occur, but with the proviso that an ion of lower energy
is formed—i.e., a shift converting a secondary to a tertiary carbonium
ion will be allowed, but not the converse. The effect that this might
have on the intensities of the MW − 1 ions can be illustrated with a
few examples. In compound 6 (Table IV) the calculated value of 0.12
is obtained assuming that removal of hydrogens from the two starred
carbons will invariably lead to decomposition of the MW − 1 ion. With
this assumption the calculated value is appreciably lower than that actually observed, but it is quite possible that energetically allowed 1-2 H⁻
shifts from either of the tertiary carbons next to starred carbons can occur.
The charge in the ions thus produced are not beta to a branch point, and
the MW − 1 ion will not decompose. One should expect the observed
value to be larger than the calculated value given in Table IV. A similar
argument applies to compounds 7 and 9 (Table IV). In compounds 8,
11, 13, 14, 15, and 17 no energetically favored 1-2 hydride shift can occur,
and for these substances the agreement between observed and calculated
intensities is excellent.

For compound 10, 12, and 16 the observed intensities are less than
the calculated intensities, and a tertiary starred carbon is found adjacent
to one or two secondary nonstarred carbons. Hydrogens on the secondary nonstarred carbons would be available hydrogens, but the ion formed
at these carbons could be converted by an energetically favorable 1-2 H⁻
shift to an ion with the charge on a starred carbon. Beta fission decomposition of this ion would lead to a lower intensity than the calculated
value shown. The rearrangements and beta fission decompositions are
competitive rate processes, and consequently it does not seem possible
to make our considerations more quantitative. Nonetheless, the fact
that we can rationalize both positive and negative deviations between
calculated and observed values and also comprehend instances of agreement between the two values gives us more confidence in the validity of
our postulates about the processes occurring in the chemical ionization
mass spectra.

We now consider the ions with $m/e = $ MW $- 15$. Table II shows
that for compounds containing one or more methyl branches (compounds
1, 6–17), the intensity of the MW − 15 ion ranges from approximately
0.01 of the total ionization for 2,2,4,6,6-Me$_5$C$_7$ (compound 16) to 0.23%
for 2,2,5-Me$_3$C$_6$ (compound 9). For 2-methyldecane (compound 1) the

Table IV. Calculated and Experimental MW − 1 Intensities

Compound Number	Compound*	Available Hydrogens	I_i(calc.)	I_i(obs.)
		6	0.12	0.20
7		3	0.061	0.094
8		1	0.020	0.019
9		3	0.023	0.076
10		4	0.080	0.057
11		5	0.099	0.092
12		6	0.12	0.045
13		0	0.00	0.005
14		0	0.00	0.02
15		0	0.00	0.006
16		4	0.064	0.0015
17		26	0.15	0.12

* Asterisks represent C-atoms beta to a branch.

intensity of MW − 15 is 0.75, and for nine of the 13 compounds with methyl branches the intensity of MW − 15 is equal to or greater than this value. There is no consistent relationship discernible between the intensity of MW − 15 and the number of methyl groups. The intensities of MW − 15 from 2,4-Me$_2$-3-i-PrC$_5$ (compound 8), 2,2,4,5,5-Me$_5$C$_6$ (compound 15), 2,2,4,6,6-Me$_5$C$_7$ (compound 16), and squalane (compound 17) are lower, ranging from 0.01 to 0.04. For the first and third of these compounds the low MW − 15 intensity can be explained on the basis that the removal of any of the methyls present produces a carbonium ion which can undergo beta fission.   However, this is also true for 2,2,4-Me$_3$C$_7$ (compound 10) and 3,3,5-Me$_3$C$_7$ (compound 12), but these give MW $-$ 15 ions with relative intensities of 0.12 and 0.095, respectively. We conclude from our results that the presence of methyl branches in a molecule generally gives MW $-$ 15 intensities appreciably higher than those found in compounds lacking methyl branches, but exceptions exist. It would appear that factors are involved in methyl loss processes which we do not understand.

In the normal paraffins the intensities of MW $-$ 29 ions tended to be rather small, on the order of 0.01–0.02 of the total additive ionization.   For two of the branched paraffins studied—namely, 2-Me-5-EtC$_7$ (compound 6) and 3,3,5-Me$_3$C$_7$ (compound 12) ethyl branches are present—i.e., the structure is such that removal of an ethyl group would produce a secondary or tertiary carbonium ion.   Table II shows that for these compounds the MW $-$ 29 ion has an intensity of about 0.05 of the additive ionization.   For the remaining branched compounds, the intensity of this ion is quite small, and for most of the compounds the ion is absent.   For almost all of the substances for which the ion is absent completely from the spectra, the structures are such that the MW $-$ 29 ion cannot be formed by a straightforward process in which only one bond is broken.   Since the MW $-$ 29 ion cannot be formed by a beta fission process (the ion undergoing the fission process would have to be a primary ion), the presence of MW $-$ 29 ion with significant intensity in the spectrum of a paraffin hydrocarbon strongly indicates the presence of an ethyl branch.

The intensity of the MW $-$ 43 ion in the chemical ionization mass spectra of normal paraffins in the C$_{10}$–C$_{12}$ range is about 0.04 of the total additive ionization.   Considering the C$_9$-C$_{12}$ branched compounds listed in Table II, those compounds which can form the MW $-$ 43 ion by a

Table V.   Intensities of MW $-$ 43 Ions for Selected Compounds

Compound Number	Compound	I_{MW-43}
11		0.019
12		0.015
13		0.12
14		0.004
15		0.000
16		0.000

single bond fission exhibit intensities for this ion on the order of 0.02–0.04, which is not remarkable. Table V gives the intensities of the MW − 43 ions for compounds for which this ion is of interest. In compound 11, a primary MW − 43 ion can be formed directly by single bond fission at one end of the molecule, and the intensity of 0.019 observed is compatible with the structure of the molecule. However, in compound 12 the MW − 43 ion cannot be formed directly by single bond fission, but the observed intensity is approximately equal to that observed in compound 11. It is most reasonable to explain the formation of MW − 43 ion in compound 12 in terms of a rearrangement process:

$$\text{(16)}$$

$$\Delta H = -6 \text{ kcal./mole}$$

By contrast in compounds 14, 15, and 16, from which MW − 43 also cannot be formed by single bond fission, the intensities of MW − 43 are negligibly small. For these we find that no feasible rearrangement process such as Equation 16 can be written. Thus for compound 14, for example,

$$\text{(17)}$$

The rearranged ion formed in Equation 17 cannot lose three carbons by beta fission process, and thus the MW − 43 intensity will be zero or negligible. The structure of compound 13 is such that the molecule may be looked upon as having a propyl side chain, and thus a tertiary MW − 43 ion can be formed either by direct single bond breaking or by a beta fission process. Consequently it is not surprising to find that the intensity of MW − 43 is 0.12, significantly higher than the MW − 43 intensity observed in the straight chain paraffin. It is clear from these considerations that the intensity of the MW − 43 ion is not a highly reliable guide to the presence in the molecule of a propyl branch. A quite strong MW − 43 intensity such as is observed in compound 13 probably may be taken as good evidence for propyl branch, but smaller intensities can be the result of rearrangement processes. We should point out that the spectra observed for both the normal and the branched paraffins are such that the spectra generally give evidence for the presence of side chains which are relatively short compared with the length of the main chain in the molecule.   Thus as we saw earlier, the spectrum of 9-n-octyleicosane shows evidence for the presence of the octyl side chain, but sufficient decomposition producing MW $-$ 43 or MW $-$ 57 ions occurs in n-decane so that it is difficult or impossible to identify the presence of a propyl or butyl branch in a decane.

We are unable to offer a detailed, coherent explanation for the intensities of ions smaller than MW $-$ 43 for the C_9-C_{12} isoparaffins. For normal decane the intensities of the C_4, C_5, and C_6 alkyl ions are about 0.20, and the corresponding ions from many of the C_9-C_{12} isoparaffins have about this intensity.   Four ions which cannot be produced from their parent molecules without rearrangement of the carbon skeleton are observed to be formed with high intensity.   These are $C_6H_{13}^+$ ($I = 0.23$), $C_5H_{11}^+$ ($I = 0.27$), and $C_4H_9^+$ ($I = 0.34$) from 2,4-dimethyl-3-isopropylpentane (compound 8) and $C_5H_{11}^+$ ($I = 0.27$) from 2,2,3,3-tetramethylhexane (compound 13).   One can write mechanisms involving a series of 1-2 hydride and alkide shifts which will produce these ions, but most of these are so outrageously complicated that we prefer simply to say that factors which we do not understand are operating. The intensities of the $m/e = 57$ ($C_4H_9^+$) ion tend to be disproportionately high when $tert$-butyl structures are found at one end, and especially at both ends, of the molecule. Thus $I_{57} = 0.47$ in 2,2,4,6,6-pentamethylheptane (compound 16), and this can be attributed to the consequences of direct attack plus beta fission processes occurring from charges on the central part of the main carbon chain (sometimes involving 1-2 hydride shifts).   Obviously, the explanation of the observed high butyl ion intensity in a molecule like this is the same as the explanation for the observed low MW $-$ 1 intensity.   When the quaternary carbon in the isoparaffin is two carbon atoms removed from the end of the chain, a large $m/e = 71$ ($C_5H_{11}^+$) ion is formed.   This ion has an intensity of 0.44 in 3,3,5-trimethylheptane (compound 12), and this surprisingly large intensity for a molecule containing only one quaternary carbon may be ascribed to the combined effects of direct bond cleavage at the center of the molecule and a beta fission of the C-C bond to form the $tert$-amyl ion.

The addendum to Table II lists ions other than alkyl which are found in the spectra of the isoparaffins investigated.   These consist of alkenyl ions ($C_nH_{2n-1}^+$) and olefin ions ($C_nH_{2n}^+$).   The intensities of the alkenyl ions are uniformly small, on the order of 0.001–0.005, and they are observed more often at the lower mass numbers.   Thus, the spectrum of 11-n-butyldocosane, MW $= 366$, contains alkenyl ions with masses lying between 69 and 153 but none higher.   In the case of the highly branched decanes in Table II, alkenyl ions are observed up to $m/e = 139$ ($C_{10}H_{19}^+$), but by and large the alkenyl ions tend to be concentrated in the lower end of the chemical ionization mass spectra.   The intensities and distributions of the alkenyl ions found in the spectra of normal paraffins are largely the same as those found in the isoparaffins. If any difference exists, it is that for the normal paraffins the alkenyl ions tend to be even more concentrated in the lower mass end of the spectra. We can write an exothermic reaction producing alkenyl ions from paraffin hydrocarbons—i.e.,

$$n\text{-}C_{10}H_{22} + CH_5^+ \rightarrow C_6H_{11}^+ + CH_4 + C_4H_{10} + H_2 \qquad (18)$$

$$\Delta H = -24 \text{ kcal./mole.}$$

In addition it is possible that alkenyl ions are formed by loss of H_2 from an alkyl ion by an approximately thermoneutral reaction.

The olefin ions found in the spectra of isoparaffins are very interesting and constitute an unexplained problem. They are not found in the spectra of normal paraffins, and they appear in isoparaffin spectra almost exclusively at mass numbers corresponding to fission of side chains, with the possible exception of methyl side chains. Table VI gives the mass numbers and intensities of the olefin ions observed in the several isoparaffins. We also give postulated structures for the olefin ions. Often the structures are just guesses which are given merely to show an approximate relationship between a possible structure of the olefin ion and the parent molecule. The formation of olefin ions from 2-methyldecane is slightly anomalous when compared with olefin ion formation from the other compounds in Table VI. However, for the remaining compounds, a fairly consistent behavior is observed—namely, structures involving side chains greater than methyl give rise to the appearance of olefin ions with intensities of approximately 1–4% of the total ionization. For some compounds the olefin ionization is distributed between several ions corresponding to different ways of decomposition at a branch point. Thus, in compound 3 in Table VI we seen about equal intensities of olefin ions at $m/e = 210$ and $m/e = 224$ corresponding to loss of a C_{11} branch or a C_{10} branch, respectively. The presence of a quaternary carbon in the molecule generally gives rise to the appearance of olefin ions with strong intensities—i.e., about 2% of the total ionization. Hence, the presence of a terminal *tert*-butyl structure in the molecule always appears to result in the formation of the olefin ion $m/e = 56$, which is almost surely isobutylene ion. Although an exception exists (compound 16), molecules having a *tert*-butyl group at both ends seem to have approximately twice the intensity at $m/e = 56$ of compounds having the group at only one end. Compound 12, which contains a quaternary carbon at the 3-position, forms a fairly intense $C_5H_{10}^+$ ($m/e = 70$) ion. On the basis of our results, it appears that the formation of an olefin ion in the spectrum of a paraffin can be used to detect the presence of a side chain (other than methyl). Of course, some olefin ions are formed which do not actually correspond to branch points (such as $m/e = 56$ in compound 1 and $m/e = 70$ in compound 8), but usually the intensities of such ions are small. Thus we would consider that the presence of $m/e = 56$ ion with intensities of 1–2% of the total ionization in the mass spectrum of an unknown paraffin constitutes strong evidence that a terminal *tert*-butyl group was present.

Table VI. Olefin Ion Formation

Compound Number	Compound	Ions	Mass	Intensity
1	[branched alkane structure]	[branched alkene] $^+$	56	0.004
		[alkene structure] $^+$	112	0.008
2	$C_7-\overset{H}{\underset{C_6}{C}}-C_7$	$C_7CH{=}CHC_5^+$	196	0.022
3	$C_{10}-\overset{H}{\underset{C_4}{C}}-C_{11}$	$C_3CH{=}CHC_{10}^+$	210	0.008
		$C_4CH{=}CHC_{10}^+$	224	0.007
4	$C_{10}\overset{H}{\underset{C_5}{C}}C_{10}$	$C_5CH{=}CHC_9^+$	224	0.009
5	$C_8-\overset{H}{\underset{C_8}{C}}-C_{11}$	$C_8CH{=}CHC_7^+$	238	0.003
		$C_8CH{=}CHC_{10}^+$	280	0.005
6	[branched alkane structure]	[alkene] $^+$	70	0.003
		[alkene] $^+$	98	0.001
		[alkene] $^+$	112	0.013
7	[branched alkane structure]	[alkene] $^+$	70	0.013
		[alkene] $^+$	98	0.009
8	[branched alkane structure]	$C_5H_{10}^+$	70	0.006
		[alkene] $^+$	98	0.010
9	[branched alkane structure]	[branched alkene] $^+$	56	0.019
		[branched alkene] $^+$	70	0.010
10	[branched alkane structure]	[branched alkene] $^+$	56	0.024
		[alkene] $^+$	84	0.008
11	[branched alkane structure]	[branched alkene] $^+$	56	0.027
		[alkene] $^+$	84	0.009

Table VI. Continued

Compound Number	Compound	Ions	Mass	Intensity
12	[structure]	[structure]$^+$	70	0.014
		[structure]$^+$	112	0.003
13	[structure]	[structure]$^+$	84	0.024
14	[structure]	[structure]$^+$	56	0.039
15	[structure]	[structure]$^+$	56	0.036
16	[structure]	[structure]$^+$	56	0.017
17	Squalane	$C_8H_{16}{}^+$	112	0.002
		$C_{13}H_{26}{}^+$	182	0.004

In view of the potential practical importance of this phenomenon, it is particularly unfortunate that we are unable to rationalize its occurrence using the energetic criterion which is generally so successful. Thus we write as a typical reaction forming an olefin ion

$$[structure] + CH_5{}^+ \rightarrow [structure]\ ^+ + C_5H_{11}\cdot\ ([structure]) + CH_4 + H_2 \qquad (19)$$

$$\Delta H = +35 \text{ kcal./mole}$$

If the energetic criterion is applicable, we must conclude from the large endothermicity that Reaction 19 does not occur, but then we are at a loss to explain the formation of the $C_4H_8{}^+$ ion. We can write reasonable mechanistic schemes for the olefin formation which rationalize the data and fail only with respect to the energetic criterion. Thus, we can write for the $C_4H_8{}^+$ ion formed from a paraffin with a *tert*-butyl end structure

$$[structure] + CH_5 \rightarrow CH_3\overset{\displaystyle CH_3}{\underset{\displaystyle CH_3}{C}} \underset{\displaystyle H}{\overset{H_2C{-}H}{\left[\cdot\ C\right]} } {-}CH_2CH(CH_3)_2 + CH_4 + H_2$$

$$(20)$$

$$\underset{\displaystyle \cdot C(CH_3)_2}{\overset{\displaystyle CH_2{}^+}{|}} + \cdot CH_2CH_2CH(CH_3)_2$$

$$(i - C_4H_8{}^+)$$

In effect we postulate that the olefin ion is formed by a 1-3 hydride ion shift accompanied by a beta homolytic bond fission.   The fact that olefin ions are formed only at branch points (except methyl branch points) could be explained on an energetic basis if it were not for the contrary fact that the over-all energetics are highly unfavorable.   Thus in Reaction 20 we see that a disubstituted olefin ion is formed, and this will be true for any branch other than a methyl branch.   Thus:

$$+ \ CH_5^+ \ \rightarrow \qquad + \ H_2 \ + \ CH_4 \tag{21}$$

$$\downarrow$$

$$+ \ C_2H_5\cdot$$
$$m/e = 112 \, (C_8H_{16}^+)$$

In a straight chain hydrocarbon, however, an alpha olefin ion is formed:

$$+ \ CH_5^+ \ \rightarrow \qquad + \ H_2 \ + \ CH_4 \tag{22}$$

$$\downarrow$$

$$+ \ n\text{-}C_4H_9$$
$$m/e = 84 \, (C_6H_{12}^+)$$

It can easily be shown that if the reaction occurs at a single methyl branch, an alpha olefin will be formed in this case also.   From the values given by Field and Franklin (5) the energies for alpha olefin ions are 10–15 kcal./mole higher than those for olefin ions with more extensive alkyl substitution.   As suggested above, it is tempting to think that this energy difference constitutes the driving force for the formation of olefin ions with branch chain paraffins, but the over-all endothermicity constitutes a strong contraindication.

Thus we have no convincing explanation for the formation of the olefin ions.   It is possible that their formation involves the mechanisms written in Equations 19–21 despite the strong endothermicity; in this case we must begin to question the general applicability of the energetic criterion for the occurrence of ion-molecule reactions (at least in the high pressure region).   In our experience, another instance where an ion-molecule reaction occurs vigorously, despite the fact that it is quite endothermic is

$$CH_2^+ \ + \ CH_4 \ \rightarrow \ C_2H_3^+ \ + \ H_2 \ + \ H \tag{23}$$

$$\Delta H \ = \ +19 \ \text{kcal./mole.}$$

We are inclined to think that this anomaly and the possible anomaly with olefin ion formation does not invalidate the energetic criterion, and indeed we have used it extensively throughout this paper; however, we feel that a somewhat greater degree of uncertainty occurs with its use now than previously.

Temperature Effects. The chemical ionization spectra of three paraffins (*n*-decane, 2,2,3,3-tetramethylhexane (compound 13), and 2,2,5,5-tetramethylhexane (compound 14) have been determined at several different temperatures of the mass spectrometer ionization chamber, and the relative intensities obtained for the MW − 1 ions are give in Table VII. The relative intensities decrease for all three compounds as the temperature increases, in accordance with the behavior found for the chemical ionization spectrum of ethyl-β-chloropropionate

Table VII. MW − 1 Intensities at Several Ionization Chamber Temperatures

$T\,^{\circ}C.$	I_{MW-1}		
	n-$C_{10}H_{22}$	$2233\ Me_4C_6$	$2255\ Me_4C_6$
131	0.38	0.0044	0.030
147	0.33	0.0030	0.018
173	0.25	0.0014	0.0069
195	0.14	0	0.0021
216	0.14	0	0.0020

(*10*) and for electron impact mass spectra (*6*). In an attempt to understand the phenomenon better, we treated the intensities of the ions from *n*-decane and 2,2,5,5-tetramethylhexane using the methods of first-order kinetics; we assumed that the decreases in the intensities resulted from first-order thermal decompositions of the MW − 1 ions. We found that the "rate constant" for *n*-decane is approximately one-third as large as that for 2,2,5,5-tetramethylhexane, but the temperature coefficient and thus the "activation energy" is the same for the two compounds (3 kcal./mole). We do not understand this behavior and particularly the equality of the activation energies. It seems quite possible that the effect of temperature on the chemical ionization mass spectra may be instrumental in origin, and as such it would not provide any information concerning the chemistry and physics of the reactions involved in generating chemical ionization mass spectra. However, it obviously may be considerably important in practical applications of chemical ionization mass spectrometry.

Acknowledgment

We wish to thank W. C. Gieger for valuable help in making these experiments.

Literature Cited

(1) API Project 44, "Catalog of Mass Spectral Data," Texas A & M University, College Station, Tex., 1963.   Table No. 1007, n-$C_{18}H_{38}$; Table No. 109, n-$C_{10}H_{22}$; Table No. 705, n-$C_{20}H_{42}$; Table No. 1316, n-$C_{30}H_{62}$.
(2) Aquilanti, V., Volpi, G. G., J. Chem. Phys. 44, 2307, 3574 (1966).
(3) P. Fejes, P. H. Emmett, J. Catalysis 5, 193 (1966).
(4) F. H. Field, M. S. B. Munson, J. Am. Chem. Soc. 87, 3289 (1965).
(5) F. H. Field, J. L. Franklin, "Electron Impact Phenomena," Academic Press, New York, 1957.
(6) J. L. Franklin, J. Chem. Phys. 21, 2029 (1953).
(7) J. L. Franklin, private communication.
(8) M. S. B. Munson, F. H. Field, J. Am. Chem. Soc. 88, 2621 (1966).
(9) M. S. B. Munson, F. H. Field, J. Am. Chem. Soc. 87, 3294 (1965).
(10) M. S. B. Munson, F. H. Field, J. Am. Chem. Soc. in press.

RECEIVED May 2, 1966.

High Pressure Mass Spectrometry
with a m.e.v. Proton Beam

Ethylene, Acetylene, and Methane

S. WEXLER, ASSA LIFSHITZ,[1] and A. QUATTROCHI

Argonne National Laboratory, Argonne, Ill.

*A portable mass spectrometer coupled to a 3-m.e.v. Van de
Graaff proton generator has been used to study consecutive ion-
molecule reactions in methane, ethylene, and acetylene at
source pressures up to 1.3 torr. Extensive ionic polymerization occurs in C_2H_4 and C_2H_2 through long chains of very rapid
consecutive and competitive ion-molecule reactions. Reaction
cross-sections were determined for primary and secondary
ions in each gas. Results from the proton bombardment
generally agree with previous investigations in which a beam
of electrons 0.2–0.3 cm. from the exit slit or uncollimated alpha
particles served as the ionizing medium. Since the results from
all techniques agree, experimental observations are not unduly
influenced by difficulties inherent in the different procedures.*

The primary excitation and ionization of gases in "high pressure"
mass spectrometry has previously been accomplished by either a
beam of electrons from a heated filament external to the source chamber
(3, 7, 9, 12, 27, 35, 36, 38), a glow discharge (21), or uncollimated alpha or
beta particles and secondary electrons from radioactive deposits placed
within or adjacent to the source (1, 19, 33, 34). All these methods suffer
from various deficiencies. Although, for example, a beam of electrons can
be made sufficiently intense, the beam is greatly attenuated and scattered
by the high pressure of gas in the source chamber. In addition, mass
discrimination within the source chamber may be caused by the magnetic
field used to collimate the electron beam, and distortion of the electron
beam by the repeller field may give an unreliable value for the mean distance between the plane of ionization and the exit slit of the source. On
the other hand, results of experiments using active sources are often diffi-

[1] Permanent address: Department of Inorganic Chemistry, Hebrew University, Jerusalem, Israel.

cult to interpret because of the lack of collimation and the production of energetic electrons by the α's and β's at the surfaces of the chamber.

To overcome the limitations imposed by the techniques used thus far, we have developed a new technique for studying ion-molecule reactions in the gas phase at relatively high pressures. A specially designed portable mass spectrometer was connected to a Van de Graaff electrostatic generator, and a collimated 2-m.e.v. proton beam, which enters and leaves the source chamber through thin nickel windows, served as the ionization source for the gas. By such an arrangement one can obtain a relatively intense radiation source that consists of a well collimated beam of high energy heavy particles which are little scattered and attenuated by the gas molecules. Although the initial studies reported here are on methane, acetylene, and ethylene at pressures higher than 1 torr, we expect this new approach to permit experiments at far higher pressures. However, even at 1 torr pressure an ion would encounter roughly 90 molecules within the 1-cm. path length between plane of ionization and exit slit of the source chamber. Consequently, the conditions of such experiments as will be described become more like the steady-state conditions of conventional radiolysis studies. Slow reactions should now be noticed, but small concentrations of impurities should affect the observations more than previously. In addition to the intrinsic advantages listed above, this new approach allows us to check previous results obtained under rather narrow and similar conditions (e.g., of electron beam intensity, mean ion path length, and source temperature), by an experimental arrangement in which these parameters are quite different.

Experimental

The portable mass spectrometer, equipped with casters and jacks for movement into position and alignment with the proton beam of the 3 m.e.v. Van de Graaff generator, has been described in previous studies on interactions of high energy ions with molecules (40). However, extensive modifications of the source chamber and detector section were necessary to adapt the instrument to experiments on gases at high pressures. A sketch of the source chamber appears in Figure 1. The beam of 2-m.e.v. protons, well collimated and limited in cross-sectional area by a slit system placed between the Van de Graaff generator and the mass spectrometer, enters the vacuum-tight (except for the ion exit slit) source chamber through a 0.0025-mm. thick nickel window, 3.2 mm. in diameter. The beam passes successively through a 1.0-mm. high and 2.0-mm. wide defining aperture and a hole in a secondary electron repeller electrode held at 67.5 volts negative relative to the chamber. It then enters the main chamber where it ionizes the gas in a plane 1.0 cm. mean distance from the ion exit slit (an aperture 0.075 mm. by 2.0 mm.) of the source. The protons leave the chamber through a second thin nickel window, first going through another secondary electron repeller, which with its mate prevents electrons ejected by the protons from surfaces from entering the critical region of ionization adjacent to the slit. The beam is stopped and monitored by a deep air-cooled Faraday cup.

Intensities of approximately 0.03 μamp. were recorded in the cup. The temperature of the source chamber was measured as 23°C. The primary positive ions produced by the protons and the ionic products of reactions were driven by a field of 12.3 volts/cm. to the exit slit, through which they passed into the Nier-type accelerating and focusing system, where they were focused onto the 0.025-cm. by 1.43-cm. object aperture of the spectrometer. Extensive shielding by several layers of soft iron and Conetic essentially eliminated deflection of the proton beam by the fringe field of the magnet. The large chamber surrounding the source chamber was evacuated by a 270 liters/sec. mercury pump and trap while the tube and detector were each evacuated by 33-liters/sec. pumps and traps. The differential pumping was such that in a typical experiment the pressures in the chamber, tube, and detector were 3×10^{-5}, 2×10^{-6}, and 9×10^{-7} torr, respectively, when the pressure in the high pressure source was 0.7 torr.

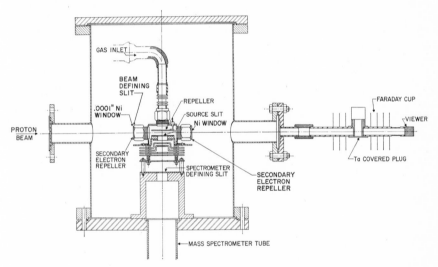

Figure 1. Source chamber and ion-accelerating system for m.e.v. proton bombardment of gases at relatively high pressures

A scintillation ion detector, described in detail elsewhere (*41*), detected virtually every ion which entered the detector chamber. Pulse counting techniques were used.

The pressure of gas in the source chamber was determined from the pressure in the gas reservoir (measured with a McLeod gage) by using Dushman's (*11*) relations for viscous and molecular flow in the higher and lower ranges of pressure, respectively.

Phillips research grade methane (99.99%) and ethylene (99.94%) and Matheson purified grade acetylene (99.6%) were each further purified twice by passing the gas through a trap of glass beads in a dry ice-trichloroethylene bath (dry ice alone for the C_2H_2), condensing the gas in activated charcoal in liquid N_2, evaporating a middle section into a likeactivated charcoal trap, and passing a second middle portion through another dry ice-trichloroethylene bath to a storage vessel. The gas inlet line and source chamber were thoroughly flushed with each gas prior to the experiments.

The extensive data from these experiments were processed by the CDC-3600 computer at this laboratory. The curves and histograms were machine plotted from the output data of the computer.

Results

Methane. The spectra of positively charged species in methane were recorded only up to mass 60. Relative intensities of several of the most prominent ions show the characteristic dependencies on source pressure given in Figure 2. Our data agree qualitatively with previously published work on methane (*15, 38*): CH_5^+, $C_2H_5^+$, $C_3H_5^+$, and $C_3H_7^+$ are the dominant polymeric species at higher pressures, and several higher weight products—principally $C_4H_7^+$, $C_4H_9^+$ and $C_4H_{11}^+$—are observed in low yield. In addition, the shapes of the curves showing the variation of yield with pressure are generally similar to the electron impact studies, but quantitative differences should be noted. In contrast to Wexler and Jesse's (*38*) observation that the yield of $C_2H_5^+$ increases slowly but continuously up to 0.4 torr while that of CH_5^+ goes through a maximum at approximately 0.15 torr and then decreases somewhat, and Field, Franklin, and Munson's (*13*) later finding of inverse behaviors for these two secondary ions, Figure 2 shows that after reaching maxima, both decrease only slightly up to 0.7 torr. The behavior of these secondary ions contrasts greatly with other secondary species and suggests that both are unreactive with methane; this agrees with the results of Field and Munson (*15*), who studied methane at pressures as high as 2 torr in a source chamber in which the mean distance between plane of ionization and exit slit was 0.20 cm.

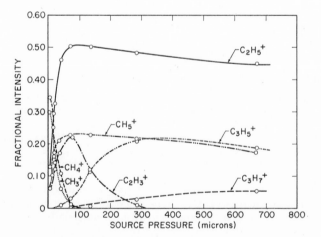

Figure 2. Relative intensities of several important ions as functions of the pressure of CH_4 in the source chamber of the mass spectrometer

In addition to CH_5^+ and $C_2H_5^+$, $C_2H_4^+$ also appears to be inert in methane since its relative abundance remains relatively constant between 0.05 and 0.7 torr. On the other hand, the secondary species, $C_2H_3^+$, reacts readily with methane. (Owing to an oversight the intensities of the reactive ions, $C_2H_2^+$ and C_2H^+, were not measured.) The relative abundances of the higher order species $C_3H_7^+$, $C_4H_7^+$, $C_4H_9^+$, and $C_4H_{11}^+$ increase with methane concentration. The yield of $C_3H_5^+$ increased to a maximum and then dropped only at the highest pressures, suggesting a slight reactivity of this ion with methane. One notes that both $C_2H_3^+$ and $C_3H_5^+$ are much more prominent and CH_5^+ somewhat less in the spectra obtained from the proton impact work than in previous patterns from electron bombardment and a much shorter mean ion path.

The cross-sections for the reactions of primary and secondary ionic species with the gas in the source chamber of the spectrometer were determined by the "beam model" (*38*). Reactions of primary ions with gas molecules as the ions move under the action of the electric field from the plane of formation toward the ion exit slit will attenuate the "beam" in exponential fashion, so that the intensity I_p at the exit slit will be:

$$I_p = I_p^{o} \exp\ [-\sigma_p{}^t(G)d] \tag{1}$$

where I_p^{o} is the intensity of the species in the plane of ionization at a distance d (cm.) from the exit slit, (G) is the concentration of gas (molecules cm.$^{-3}$), and $\sigma_p{}^t$ is the total cross-section (sq. cm. molecule^{-1}) for reaction of the primary species with the gas. The change of intensity of a secondary product species at any position x between the point of origin of the primary reactant and the exit is a balance between its formation and reaction,

$$\frac{dI_s}{dx} = I_p\sigma_p(G)\ -\ I_s\sigma_s{}^t(G) \tag{2}$$

Integration between proper limits gives:

$$I_s = \frac{I_p^{o}\sigma_p}{\sigma_s{}^t\ -\ \sigma_p{}^t}\ \{\exp\ (-\sigma_p{}^t(G)d)\ -\ \exp\ (-\sigma_s{}^t(G)d)\} \tag{3}$$

In Equation 3 σ_p is the partial cross-section of the primary species leading to the secondary ion of interest, and $\sigma_s{}^t$ is the total reaction cross-section (sq. cm. molecule^{-1}) of this secondary species. (Equations 2 and 3 correct omissions in the respective relations given in Ref. *38*.) It is readily seen from Equation 1 that a semi-logarithmic plot of the intensity of a primary species against gas concentration should be a straight line from whose slope the reaction cross-section may be calculated. The yield of a secondary ion should increase with gas pressure, pass through a maximum, and then if the ion is reactive, decrease. The cross-section $\sigma_s{}^t$ may be estimated from a semi-log plot of intensity *vs.* (G) provided $\sigma_s{}^t < \sigma_p{}^t$ since then the first exponential term of Equation 3 is negligible relative to the second term at higher gas concentrations, and I_s shows an exponential decrease with pressure. Actually, however, the intensity I_p^0 of the primary species in the plane of ionization increases with gas concentration, and consequently I_p and I_s must be normalized to correct for this effect. Normalization has customarily consisted of substituting fractional intensities for absolute intensities in Equations 1 and 3. Cross-sections for reaction of several primary and secondary ions with methane are given in Table I along with the results of earlier experiments (10, 13, 38) in which a beam of electrons served as the ionizing medium. In the latter studies the distance between the electron beam and the exit slit was either 0.20 or 0.32 cm. (in contrast to 1.0 cm. in this work), and the repeller field strength differed from the conditions of the proton experiments.

Table I.   Total Reaction Cross-Sections of Ions with CH_4

σ^t ($\times$ 10^{-16} sq. cm. molecule^{-1})

	Field Strength, volts/cm.			
Species	12.3 (this work)	12.5 (Ref. 38)	10 (Ref. 10)	6.25 (Ref. 13, 15)
C^+	5.3		39	42
CH^+	14	45	48	56
CH_2^+	15	36	40	41
CH_3^+	21	27	27	29
CH_4^+	23	39	38	38
CH_5^+	0.1	1.6		<0.07
$C_2H_2^+$		26		30
$C_2H_3^+$	5.0	10		6
$C_2H_4^+$	<0.1	1.9		<0.2
$C_2H_5^+$	<0.06	<0.1		<0.07

Ethylene. In contrast to the general inertness of the principal secondary ions in methane toward this molecule and the simple pattern of ions found in this gas at high source pressures, the secondary and higher order species formed when ethylene is irradiated appear to be quite reactive with the olefin. A complex pattern of positively charged species (more than 150 fragments) is observed at higher source pressures. As the histograms in Figure 3 show, the pattern of ions shifts toward higher weight polymeric species and becomes progressively more complex as the source pressure of C_2H_4 is increased incrementally from 0.002 to 1.26 torr. At the lowest pressure the primary ions $C_2H_4^+$ (mass number 28), $C_2H_3^+$, and $C_2H_2^+$ dominate the spectrum, but secondary ions ($C_2H_5^+$, $C_3H_3^+$, $C_3H_5^+$, $C_3H_7^+$, $C_3H_8^+$, $C_4H_5^+$, $C_4H_7^+$) are present, and a small amount of the higher order ion $C_5H_9^+$ is found. When the pressure is 0.022 torr, the primary fragments are depressed, and $C_3H_5^+$ is by far the most prominent species. The extents of reaction of the primary ions continue so that at 0.75 torr they are almost completely quenched. At the same time $C_5H_9^+$ becomes dominant, and the spectrum extends with no reduction in abundance up to (and probably beyond) mass 219 (probably $C_{16}H_{27}^+$). There is some indication of an approach to steady-state conditions above 0.75 torr as shown by the fact that the pattern changes only slightly when the pressure is raised to 1.26 torr. An interesting aspect of the patterns is the progression of fragments increasing in weight by 14 mass units. The ionic polymerization takes place through the principal chains of ions represented by the formulas $C_nH^+_{2n-1}$, $C_nH^+_{2n-3}$, $C_nH^+_{2n-5}$, and $C_nH^+_{2n-7}$.   The behavior of ethylene in the region 0.002–1.26 torr under proton bombardment is thus quite similar to that observed with a beam of ionizing electrons (*12, 39*) and a source of uncollimated alpha particles (*20*).   However, the chains of $C_nH_{2n}^+$ and $C_nH^+_{2n+1}$ ions found by Kebarle and Hogg (*20*) at 40 torr pressure were not observed in our experiments.   They reached steady-state conditions above 5 torr under their geometrical arrangement, and many more stabilizing collisions available to the polymeric species may be the reason they detected these chains.

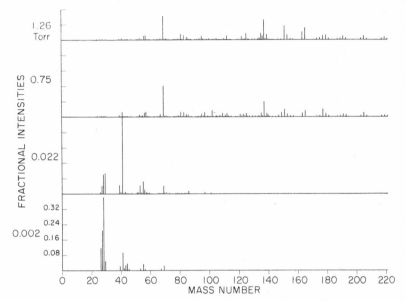

Figure 3.   Histograms of the spectra of positively charged ions in C_2H_4 at four different gas pressures

To illustrate further the similarity of our results on ethylene to earlier work, the pressure dependencies of the relative abundances of the species considered to take part in the principal ionic chain in ethylene— namely, (*39*) $C_2H_4^+$, $C_3H_5^+$, $C_4H_8^+$, $C_5H_9^+$, and $C_7H_{13}^+$—are drawn in Figure 4.   The consecutive nature of the ionic reactions shown by Figure 4 is quite similar to that of Figure 5 in Wexler and Marshall's paper (*39*) when one accounts for the difference in abscissa scales in the two figures. However, the peak of the relative intensity curve for $C_5H_9^+$ is lower here than in the electron impact work, and the curves for the various species rise and fall more gently.   The following observations also agree with previous findings: (a) $C_2H_4^+$ possesses, in addition to a first-order dependence on ethylene concentration, a second-order component formed by charge exchange;   (b) $C_3H_5^+$ is a second-order ion;   (c) $C_4H_8^+$ and $C_5H_9^+$ are at least third order;   (d) $C_7H_{13}^+$ is at least fourth order.   Moreover,

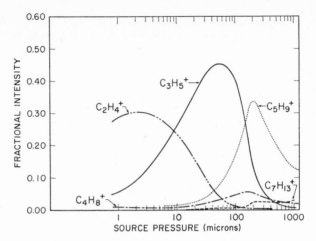

Figure 4.   Variations with pressure of the fractional abundances of the species in the principal chain of ion-molecule reactions in ethylene

a broad metastable peak positioned at mass 24.3 is observed, indicating the dissociation of excited $C_2H_4^+$ into $C_2H_2^+$ and H_2.

Total reaction cross-sections of the primary and secondary ions in C_2H_4 were determined from the slopes of the linear sections of the curves of the log of fractional intensity plotted against ethylene pressure. Curves for $C_2H_4^+$, $C_2H_2^+$, and $C_2H_5^+$, as example of such plots, appear in Figure 5.   Deviations from linearity seen for all the curves at the higher source pressures were also observed when an electron beam was used to ionize the gas (*39*), behaviors that may be caused by enhancement of the intensities by collisional decomposition of higher polymeric ions.   From these and similar curves the cross-sections listed in Table II were derived. The values are compared in the table with corresponding cross-sections obtained from electron impact data.

Acetylene.   Rapid ionic polymerization of acetylene takes place in the mass spectrometer on proton bombardment, as shown by the progressively more complex mass pattern as the pressure of acetylene is raised (Figure 6).   The primary ion $C_2H_2^+$ and the secondary products $C_4H_2^+$ and $C_4H_3^+$ are the main species at 0.002 torr, but the mass spectra at 0.022 torr has already shifted so that the primaries are negligible, and $C_4H_2^+$, $C_4H_3^+$, $C_6H_4^+$, $C_6H_5^+$, $C_8H_5^+$, and $C_8H_6^+$ are now prominent. Increasing the pressure to 0.74 torr gives the extensive spectra of ionic fragments (from a total of approximately 200) shown in the histogram of Figure 6.   Species as large as $C_{17}H_{14}^+$ (mass 218) were found.   As in ethylene, a steady-state condition is approached above 0.74 torr.   Of the numerous ionic fragments found at the higher source pressures, the yields of those containing an even number of carbon atoms are generally somewhat higher than those having an odd number.   However, because of extensive branching, the chains of consecutive ion-molecule reactions result in a much more formless spectra of transient ions than they do in ethylene (Figure 3). The patterns observed at the lower source pressures resemble those reported previously (*3, 10, 31, 33*), except that in these studies $C_8H_5{}^+$ is in higher yield than $C_8H_7{}^+$. Although the polymerization appears to proceed mainly by addition of C_2H_2 molecules at lower

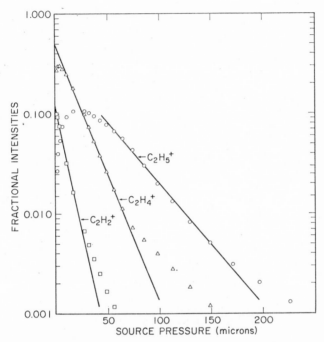

Figure 5. *Semi-logarithm plots of the fractional intensities of $C_2H_4{}^+$, $C_2H_2{}^+$, and $C_2H_5{}^+$ ions as functions of the pressure of C_2H_4*

Table II. Total Cross-Sections for Reactions of Ions with Ethylene

σ^t ($\times$ 10^{-16} sq. cm. molecule^{-1})

| Species | Field Strength, volts/cm. | | | |
	12.3 (this work)	12 (Ref. 39)	12 (Ref. 12)	12 (Ref. 14)
C_2H^+		135		32
$C_2H_2{}^+$	60	93	18	34
$C_2H_3{}^+$	22	47	17	32
$C_2H_4{}^+$	18	62	13	45
$C_2H_5{}^+$	8.5	28		
$C_3H_3{}^+$	4.2	6		
$C_3H_4{}^+$	6.4	15		
$C_3H_5{}^+$	5.8	23		
$C_3H_7{}^+$	3.9	17		
$C_4H_3{}^+$	7.0	19		
$C_4H_4{}^+$	3.5			
$C_4H_5{}^+$	2.6	6		
$C_4H_6{}^+$	3.4	5		
$C_4H_7{}^+$	4.1	22		

pressures (after the first step which produces $C_4H_2{}^+$ or $C_4H_3{}^+$ by loss of H_2 and H, respectively), this mechanism seems less important as the pressure is increased, owing to extensive competition from reactions involving loss of carbon and hydrogen-containing neutral fragments.

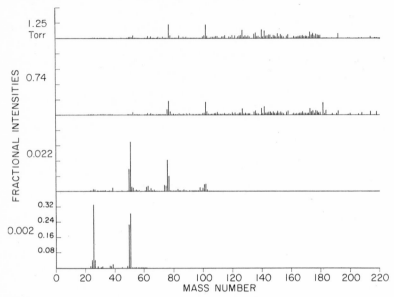

Figure 6. Histograms of the mass spectra of ionic species in C_2H_2 at four different source pressures

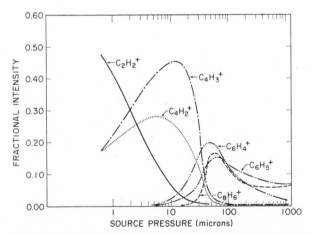

Figure 7. Characteristic dependencies of fractional intensities of several prominent ions on the pressure of acetylene in the source chamber of the spectrometer. To avoid confusion, only the smooth curves through the data points are presented

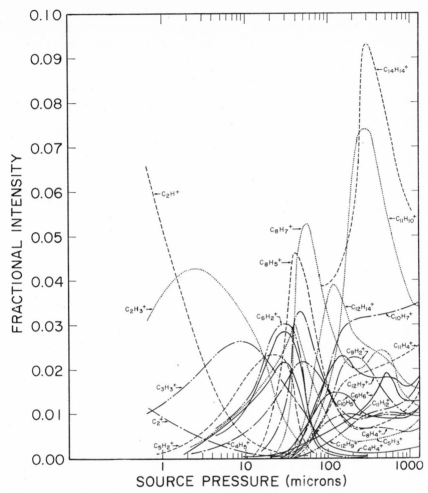

*Figure 8.   Variations of fractional intensities of many ionic species of
low abundance with pressure of C_2H_2*

Figures 7 and 8 present the characteristic pressure dependence curves
for several representative species, the plots in Figure 7 being for ions of
higher abundance.   The consecutive and branching nature of the ion-
molecule reactions is vividly illustrated here.   The intensities of the
primary ions $C_2H_2^+$, C_2H^+, and C_2^+ decrease rapidly as the pressure rises,
accompanied by increased yields of secondary species ($C_2H_3^+$, $C_4H_2^+$,
$C_4H_3^+$).   Further enhancement of the concentration of acetylene causes
the appearance of heavier polymers whose yields peak at progressively
higher pressures: first $C_6H_2^+$, $C_6H_3^+$, $C_6H_4^+$, $C_6H_5^+$, then $C_8H_4^+$, $C_8H_5^+$,
$C_8H_6^+$, $C_8H_7^+$, and finally others such as C_9H_2, $C_{10}H_5^+$, $C_{11}H_{10}^+$, $C_{14}H_{14}^+$,
and $C_{17}H_{10}^+$; the peaking behavior indicates that the polymeric ionic
transients are reactive with acetylene.   Other ions—e.g., $C_{10}H_7^+$, $C_{11}H_4^+$,

$C_{11}H_{12}{}^+$, $C_{12}H_7{}^+$, $C_{12}H_9{}^+$—appear to be much less reactive since their curves either reach a plateau or continuously rise over the entire pressure region investigated. From the relative positions of their yield curves on the pressure axis, one may conclude that $C_3H_3{}^+$ is of the same kinetic order as $C_4H_3{}^+$ and is therefore a secondary ion, but $C_4H_4{}^+$ is a tertiary species. $C_6H_4{}^+$ and $C_6H_5{}^+$ are at least of fourth kinetic order while $C_8H_5{}^+$, $C_8H_6{}^+$, and $C_8H_7{}^+$ are at least fifth order. The heavier fragments are apparently of higher (some much higher) order. However, the maxima for the C_8 and higher polymers are too close together to deduce reliable kinetic orders by this procedure. Except for $C_3H_3{}^+$, which Munson (*31*) claims is a tertiary ion, these observations agree with earlier results (*10, 31*).

The total reaction cross-sections of the individual primary and secondary species were derived and are compared in Table III with reactivities determined from previous electron impact studies (*10, 31*).

Table III.   Reactivities of Primary and Secondary Ions with Acetylene

$\sigma^t (\times 10^{-16}$ sq. cm. molecule^{-1})

	Field Strength, volts/cm.		
Species	12.3 (this work)	10 (Ref. 10)	12.5 (Ref. 31)
$C_2{}^+$	128	72	75
C_2H^+	153	70	72
$C_2H_2{}^+$	91	62	48
$C_2H_3{}^+$	38	20	
C_3H^+	51		
$C_3H_2{}^+$	47		
$C_3H_3{}^+$	14		
$C_4H_2{}^+$	46	33	
$C_4H_3{}^+$	50	18	

Discussion

Our new approach in "high pressure" mass spectrometry of combining a spectrometer and a Van de Graaff proton generator was prompted by two desires. We wished to use this technique to check on the results obtained by other methods to find out whether experimental artifacts account for previous observations. Our second wish was to extend such studies to higher and higher pressures in order to approach the conditions of conventional gas phase radiation chemistry. There are several advantages in using a collimated beam of energetic heavy particles as the ionizing medium for such studies: little attenuation and scattering of the proton beam by the gas in the source chamber, trivial deflection of the beam by the repeller field, eliminating the electron beam collimating magnet, and the availability of a relatively intense ionizing beam. In contrast, a low energy electron beam is greatly attenuated by interactions with gas molecules along the path between the entrance aperture and the critical region adjacent to the ion exit slit, the loss increasing with pressure. In addition, the collimating magnetic field and the electric repeller field combine to cause mass discrimination at the ion exit slit. Since many of the conclusions concerning mechanisms of consecutive ion-molecule reactions are drawn from the pressure dependencies of the ionic species, it was possible that phenomena observed in previous electron-impact studies were artifacts that reflected these inherent experimental difficulties.   An internal active source, on the other hand, suffers from lack of collimation so that primary ions are formed over a large volume.   Since the path lengths of primary and higher order ions in the source chamber are not known, quantitative measurements are precluded.   Here again, one may question the relevance of the observations to actual phenomena occurring in the source chamber.   However, the general concordance of our data, obtained with a technique we thought avoided these complications, with those of the earlier studies leads us to conclude that all the experimental arrangements give valid results.

Nevertheless, the reaction cross-sections of the primary and secondary ions measured by various authors using different arrangements show considerable scatter (cf. Tables I, II, and III).   The diversity of values may be caused by the fact that the methods used thus far give a phenomenological indication of cross-section rather than a true one since they measure a weighted mean reactivity which strongly depends on the velocities and internal energies of the reactants (*4, 17, 32*).   Consequently, experimental parameters such as field strength, mean distance of the travel of the ions, source temperature, and space charge influence the cross-section values.   Because of these effects, as well as systematic errors in measuring source pressures and scattering in the spectrometer proper, it may not be surprising that cross-sections obtained by various workers usually agree only within one order of magnitude.

The reactivities of the two principal secondary ions in methane were found to be so low that they were unmeasureable for $C_2H_5^+$ and just determinable for CH_5^+.   Because of the scatter of the data and the possibility that CH_5^+ was lost through proton transfer reactions with traces of impurities, the cross-section listed for this species is an upper limit. Probably, both ions do not react with CH_4, a conclusion which agrees with Field and Munson (*15*) who observed no reactivity of these secondary ions at pressures up to 2.0 torr and a mean distance of 0.2 cm. between the plane of ionization and ion slit.   These findings should be considered more reliable than the results of the earlier work with electron beams (in which the pressure was at most 0.4 torr and the distance at most 0.3 cm.) which suggested that one or the other secondary ion was somewhat reactive toward methane (*13, 38*).   The inertness of CH_5^+ and $C_2H_5^+$ is consistent with radiolysis studies of Ausloos *et al.* (*2*) who present evidence that these species live through at least 10^4 collisions with methane molecules before reacting via proton or hydride ion transfer with C_3H_8 or C_4H_{10} at low concentration.

Both this and previous studies demonstrate the existence of rather long chains of consecutive ion-molecule reactions in methane, ethylene, and acetylene, and thus they provide direct evidence for ionic mechanisms of condensation or polymerization in these gases.   Polymers have been found in relatively high yields among the radiolysis products of these gases (5, 25, 37). Sieck and Johnsen (37) have measured G(polymer) from methane as 2.1; from the lack of any scavenger effect of NO on the yield of polymer, they suggest that the mechanism of formation involves consecutive ion-molecule reactions, probably initiated by the hydrogen-deficient ions C^+, CH^+, and CH_2^+. However, if we take the total G-value calculated by the authors for the production of these ions, 0.48, and assume that these species produce polymer exclusively, then only 4.4 methane molecules on the average help form each polymer molecule. This value is much too low to account for the 12–20 carbon atoms measured by Sieck and Johnsen as taking part in each polymeric chain on methane radiolysis or the 18 carbon atoms reported by Davis and Libby (8). Although better agreement is obtained by assuming that CH^+ and C^+ are the only primary precursors of the polymer (15), the comparison suggests that polymer formation must compete with the production of other products that result from neutralization of various transient ions in the chains of consecutive ion-molecule reactions.

Irradiation of ethylene at atmospheric pressure with alpha particles or fast electrons leads to the formation of liquid condensation products with an ion pair yield of approximately 5 (22, 24, 26, 29). According to Lampe (22) 11 gaseous organic products, ranging from methane to n-hexane, and hydrogen are also produced, but they account for only about one-third of the ethylene consumed; therefore polymerization of C_2H_4 to nonvolatile compounds is the dominant reaction. Lind (24) has suggested that the polymerization proceeds through the formation of ion clusters, such as $C_2H_4^+ \cdot nC_2H_4$, which form the liquid products on electron capture. In contrast to this postulate, our data here and earlier results give experimental evidence that the polymerization proceeds through chains of rapid consecutive and competitive ion-molecule reactions, the principal chains being represented by the formulas $C_nH^+_{2n-1}$, $C_nH^+_{2n-3}$, $C_nH^+_{2n-5}$, $C_nH^+_{2n-7}$, $C_nH_{2n}^+$, and $C_nH^+_{2n+1}$. The fact that the main ionic species appear to differ in mass from adjacent ions by 14 mass units suggests that each step in the ionic chain propagation is accompanied by the formation of a methylene radical. Alternatively, the observation may reflect consecutive additions of C_2H_4 to precursors that differ by a CH_2 group. Since only liquid condensation products have been observed in the radiolysis of gaseous C_2H_4 at normal pressures, the carbon content of each molecule of the condensate is limited to at most 15–18 atoms. The magnitude of the ion pair yields gives roughly 10 carbon atoms per polymer molecule. The experimental finding of such high mass ionic species as $C_{16}H_{27}^+$ agrees with the results from the radiolysis studies. However, because the ionic polymerization probably proceeds to higher weight entities before electron capture terminates the chains, the neutralization must induce carbon-carbon bond rupture.

From the earliest days of radiation chemistry it has been known that acetylene polymerizes to a cuprene-like ("alprene") solid (5, 6, 25, 28). The characteristics of the polymerization—e.g., lack of effect of temperature, dose rate, and pressure on polymer yield and negligible effect of radical scavengers—led Lind (24) to postulate an ion cluster mechanism.

Since approximately 20 acetylene molecules disappear for each ion pair formed in the gas phase, it was suggested that the $C_2H_2^+$ ion attracts 19 acetylene molecules to form $(C_2H_2)_{20}^+$, which on ion-electron combination yields the polymer $(C_2H_2)_{20}$. On the other hand, Garrison (*16*) proposed that the polymer is built up by the chain of consecutive ion-molecule reactions beginning with $C_2H_2^+$ and involving simple addition of C_2H_2. In contrast to these conjectures, our data suggest that the radiation-induced polymerization proceeds through a complicated array of consecutive, competitive ion-molecule reactions. At higher pressures of C_2H_2 in the spectrometer the ionic mass spectra is extensive and formless (Figures 6–8), and no prominent chains stand out to indicate a preferred mechanism. Neutralization of the multitude of positive ions (which undoubtably extend beyond mass 218, the highest measured) would be expected to yield a great variety of radicals and molecules that react further to produce the "polymer." It is not surprising, then, that the structure of alprene has not been elucidated.

The data also bear on the validity of the two models that have been proposed to describe the mechanism of ionic chain propagation in the gas phase. In review, Lampe, Franklin, and Field (*23*) have proposed that the polymerization proceeds through the reactions of long-lived, undissociated, intermediate reaction complexes,

$$P^+ + M \rightarrow [PM^+] \tag{6}$$

$$[PM^+] \rightarrow S^+ + N_i \tag{7}$$

$$[PM^+] + M \rightarrow [PM_2^+] \tag{8}$$

$$[PM_2^+] \rightarrow T^+ + N_j \tag{9}$$

$$[PM_2^+] + M \rightarrow [PM_3^+] \tag{10}$$

$$[PM_3^+] \rightarrow Q^+ + N_k, \text{ etc.} \tag{11}$$

Here, a primary ion P^+ formed by the radiation field reacts with a gas molecule M to give an intermediate complex $[PM^+]$ which can either dissociate to a secondary species S^+ and a neutral fragment N_i or react with another molecule to produce another complex $[PM_2^+]$. The latter then dissociates into a tertiary ion T^+ or propagates the chain by forming a third intermediate $[PM_3^+]$. A quaternary ion Q^+ may result from dissociation of $[PM_3^+]$, or the chain may continue through reaction of $[PM_3^+]$. Wexler and Jesse (*38*), on the other hand, have suggested a model which states that *reactive* intermediate complexes are not involved in the propagation, but rather the polymerization proceeds by chains of simple consecutive and competitive ion-molecule reactions,

$$P^+ + M \rightarrow S^+ + N_i \tag{12}$$

$$S^+ + M \rightarrow T^+ + N_j \tag{13}$$

$$T^+ + M \rightarrow Q^+ + N_k, \text{ etc.} \tag{14}$$

The evidence accumulated here and in other studies indicates that ions may indeed form relatively long lived intermediate complexes on reaction with molecules, but they are vibrationally excited and must be stabilized by at least one nonreactive collision before they in turn can react to produce other complexes in the chain. The $C_4H_8{}^+$ species in ethylene is an ion of the type PM^+. It is observed (Figure 4) (*12, 39*) to be a tertiary ion and not the secondary ion required by Equation 6 of the reactive intermediate complex model. Further, $C_5H_9{}^+$ appears to be a fourth-order ion, and since its precursor is the secondary ion $C_3H_5{}^+$, the excited reaction complex $[C_5H_9{}^+]^*$ must be stabilized by one collision with an ethylene molecule in order to be observed. Note that according to the reactive complex model $C_5H_9{}^+$ would be the product from dissociation of the complex $[C_6H_{12}{}^+]$ and consequently would have to be a tertiary species. Additional evidence for stabilizing collisions comes from studies on acetylene. The $C_4H_4{}^+$ ion, the complex from the reaction of $C_2H_2{}^+$ with an acetylene molecule, is a tertiary rather than a secondary species. $C_6H_4{}^+$ and $C_6H_5{}^+$, formed from the secondary ions $C_4H_2{}^+$ and $C_4H_3{}^+$, respectively, are of the fourth and not third kinetic order (*10, 31*). In addition, the C_8 polymers are observed here to be of least a fifth kinetic order, and except for $C_8H_7{}^+$, the same finding has been reported by Volpi (*10*). However, Munson (*31*) states that $C_8H_6{}^+$ and $C_8H_7{}^+$ may be sixth-order ions. Despite the disagreement, the observed orders are higher than the fourth order required by the long lived reactive complex model. Other evidence for the required stabilizing collisions of complexes comes from the kinetic orders of polymeric species in water (*30*). Consequently, the observations can be accounted for by a combination of the two models that gives the following sequence of ion-molecule reactions:

$$P^+ + M \rightarrow [PM^+]^* \qquad (15)$$

$$[PM^+]^* \begin{cases} + M \rightarrow PM^+ + M^* & (16a) \\ \longrightarrow S^+ + N_i & (16b) \end{cases}$$

$$PM^+ + M \rightarrow [PM_2{}^+]^* \qquad (17)$$

$$S^+ + M \rightarrow [SM^+]^* \qquad (18)$$

$$[PM_2{}^+]^* \begin{cases} + M \rightarrow PM_2{}^+ + M^* & (19a) \\ \longrightarrow Q^+ + N_j & (19b) \end{cases}$$

$$[SM^+]^* \begin{cases} + M \rightarrow SM^+ (\equiv Q^+) & (20a) \\ \longrightarrow T^+ + N_l, \text{ etc.} & (20b) \end{cases}$$

Although collision-stabilized reaction complexes take part in chain propagation, the complex spectra of ions observed for ethylene and acetylene suggest that this mechanism undoubtedly must compete with consecutive reactions of species produced by unimolecular dissociation of the complexes and by collisional dissociation of other ions.

Acknowledgment

The authors wish to thank Robert Ginskey for his assistance in assembling the apparatus for this experiment.

Literature Cited

(1) Aquilanti, V., Galli, A., Giardini-Guidoni, A., Volpi, G. G., *J. Chem. Phys.* **43,** 1969 (1965); **44,** 2307 (1966).
(2) Ausloos, P., Lias, S. G., Gorden, Jr., R., *J. Chem. Phys.* **39,** 3341 (1963); **38,** 2207 (1963).
(3) Bloch, A., *Advan. Mass Spectrometry* **2,** 48 (1963).
(4) Boelrijk, N., Hamill, W. H., *J. Am. Chem. Soc.* **84,** 730 (1962).
(5) Chapiro, A., "Radiation Chemistry of Polymeric Systems," Chap. 3, Interscience, New York, 1961.
(6) Collidge, W. D., *Science* **62,** 441 (1925).
(7) Curran, R. K., *J. Chem. Phys.* **38,** 2974 (1963).
(8) Davis, D. R., Libby, W. F., *Science* **144,** 991 (1964).
(9) Derwish, G. A. W., Galli, A., Giardini-Guidoni, A., Volpi, G. G., *J. Chem. Phys.* **40,** 5 (1964).
(10) Derwish, G. A. W., Galli, A., Giardini-Guidoni, A., Volpi, G. G., *J. Am. Chem. Soc.* **87,** 1159 (1965).
(11) Dushman, S., "Scientific Foundations of Vacuum Technique," 2nd Ed. J. M. Lafferty, ed., pp. 82, 88, 108, John Wiley and Sons, Inc., New York, 1962.
(12) Field, F. H., *J. Am. Chem. Soc.* **83,** 1523 (1961).
(13) Field, F. H., Franklin, J. L., Munson, M. S. B., *J. Am. Chem. Soc.* **85,** 3575 (1963).
(14) Field, F. H., Franklin, J. L., Lampe, F. W., *J. Am. Chem. Soc.* **79,** 2419 (1957).
(15) Field, F. H., Munson, M. S. B. *J. Am. Chem. Soc.* **87,** 3289 (1965).
(16) Garrison, W. M., *J. Chem. Phys.* **15,** 78 (1947).
(17) Gioumousis, G., Stevenson, D. P., *J. Chem. Phys.* **29,** 294 (1958).
(18) Hummel, R. W., *Nature* **192,** 1178 (1961).
(19) Kebarle, P., Godbole, E. W., *J. Chem. Phys.* **36,** 302 (1962).
(20) Kebarle, P., Hogg, A. M., *J. Chem. Phys.* **42,** 668 (1965).
(21) Knewstubb, P. F., Tickner, A. W., *J. Chem. Phys.* **36,** 674, 684 (1962).
(22) Lampe, F. W., *Radiation Res.* **10,** 691 (1959).
(23) Lampe, F. W., Franklin, J. L., Field, F. H., "Progress in Reaction Kinetics," Vol. 1, G. Porter, ed., p. 69, Pergamon Press, London, 1961.
(24) Lind, S. C., Bardwell, D. C., Perry, J. H., *J. Am. Chem. Soc.* **48,** 1556 (1926).
(25) Lind, S. C., "The Radiation Chemistry of Gases," Chap. 9, Reinhold Publishing Corp., New York, 1961.
(26) McLennan, J. C., Patrick, W. L., *Can. J. Res.* **5,** 470 (1931).
(27) Melton, C. E., *J. Chem. Phys.* **33,** 647 (1960).
(28) Mund, W., Koch, W., *Bull. Soc. Chim. Belges* **34,** 241 (1925).
(29) Mund, W., Huyskens, P., *Bull. Acad. Roy. Belg.* **36,** 610 (1950).
(30) Munson, M. S. B., *J. Am. Chem. Soc.* **87,** 5313 (1965).
(31) Munson, M. S. B., *J. Phys. Chem.* **69,** 572 (1965).
(32) Pottie, R. F., Lorquet, A. J., Hamill, W. H., *J. Am. Chem. Soc.* **84,** 529 (1962).
(33) Rudolph, P. S., Melton, C. E., *J. Phys. Chem.* **63,** 916 (1959).
(34) Rudolph, P. S., Melton, C. E., *J. Chem. Phys.* **32,** 1128 (1960).
(35) Saporoschenko, M., *J. Chem. Phys.* **42,** 2760 (1965).
(36) Saporoschenko, M., *Phys. Rev.* **111,** 1550 (1958).
(37) Sieck, L. W., Johnsen, R. H., *J. Phys. Chem.* **67,** 2281 (1963).
(38) Wexler, S., Jesse, N., *J. Am. Chem. Soc.* **84,** 3425 (1962).
(39) Wexler, S., Marshall, R., *J. Am. Chem. Soc.* **86,** 781 (1964).
(40) Wexler, S., *J. Chem. Phys.* **41,** 1714, 2781 (1964).
(41) Wexler, S., *Argonne National Laboratory Rept.* ANL-**6288,** Jan.-Feb. (1961).

RECEIVED April 27, 1966. Based on work performed under the auspices of the U. S. Atomic Energy Commission.

13

Mass Spectrometric Study of Ions in Gases under Conventional Radiation Chemical Conditions

Rare Gas Sensitized Ionization of Ethylene, Pure Ethylene, and Ethylene and Nitric Oxide

P. KEBARLE, R. M. HAYNES, and S. SEARLES

University of Alberta, Edmonton, Alberta, Canada

Gases at 1–200 torr pressure were irradiated with alpha particles in the absence of electric fields. The xenon-sensitized ionization of C_2H_4 produces mainly $C_2H_4^+$. $C_2H_4^+$ plus ethylene leads to a chain with ionic intermediates $C_{2n}H_{4n}^+$. The rate constants k_{na} for addition of these ions to ethylene decrease rapidly, and polymerization stops around $C_{10}H_{20}^+$. At lower xenon pressures $C_nH_{2n}^+$ is not stabilized and loses an alkyl radical. The stabilization to decomposition ratio is studied as a function of xenon pressure. The reactions of $C_2H_3^+$ and $C_2H_2^+$ with C_2H_4 were studied by Ar, Ne, and He sensitization. In pure ethylene the polymerization does not continue significantly beyond mass 250. The $G(-\Delta C_2H_4) = 18$ by ionic reactions. Presence of NO causes formation of $C_nH_{2n}NO^+$.

Work on the alpha particle mass spectrometer was started in this laboratory some five years ago (18). Our principle objective was to create conditions for studying ions at pressures much higher than those used in conventional electron impact ion-molecule reaction mass spectrometers. We also wished to study the reaction of ions under conditions closely approximating those of conventional radiation chemistry—i.e., gases at near atmospheric pressures exposed to ionizing radiation in the absence of external electric fields. We felt that such an apparatus would provide information on successive ion-molecule reactions with high (kinetic) order dependence on the concentration of the reacting gas, slow ion-molecule reactions, collisional deactivation of excited ionic species, rate constants of ionic reactions with thermal ions, ion clusters, etc. Direct experimental information on any of these questions was exceedingly scarce. The high promise of the apparatus for studying ions obtained under conventional radiation chemical conditions unfortunately does not come without some unavoidable drawbacks. Thus, one must rely on mass flow and effusion for extracting the ions. This leads to poorly defined ionic reaction times. The history of the sample is complex since charge neutralization by diffusion to the walls, ion-electron, and ion-ion recombination could be competing reactions. In addition, a serious difficulty arises with impurities. The charge lifetimes under conventional conditions (and in the present apparatus) are of the order of one millisecond. Organic impurity molecules of low ionization potential can take over the charge from a given ion. The rate constants for such charge transfer reactions are typically 10^{-9} cc. molecule^{-1} sec^{-1}. At 30 torr pressure an impurity of 1 part per million (p.p.m.) consists of 10^{12} molecules cc.$^{-1}$. Using the above rate constant we calculate the half-life for charge takeover by the impurity as ~ 1 millisecond. Since this is equal to the lifetime of the ion we see that impurities at the p.p.m. level can still seriously affect the observations.

Studies with the high pressure ion source can be divided into two classes: ion-molecule reactions and ion-dipole molecule interactions. Previous work (20, 21) dealing with the ion-molecule reactions will be considered in this text where it relates to the new results. The study of ion-dipole (solvent) molecule interactions (14, 15, 22) is not considered part of this paper.

Apparatus and Method

A recent version of the apparatus is shown in Figure 1. The gas, supplied from a conventional gas handling system, which can be backed to 170°C., is irradiated in the ionization chamber. The radiation is supplied from an enclosed 200 mc. polonium alpha source. The polonium is deposited on a circular area of about $1/_8$-inch diameter on the side facing the ion source. To prevent spreading of the polonium, a double container is used. The radiation reaches the ion source through two 10^{-4}-inch stainless steel foils. To prevent early rupture of the foils, two stainless porous plugs are used, allowing pump out of the alpha source. The irradiated gas bleeds through a leak into the evacuated electrode chamber. There the ions carried by the gas are captured by the electric fields while the gas is pumped away. The ions are focused, accelerated, and then subjected to mass analysis and electron multiplier detection in a 90° sector field analyzer tube.

In "static" runs gas is supplied to the ion source only at a rate sufficient to compensate the outflow through the leak (0.5 cc./sec. for air, equal to conductance of leak). The gas mixtures were prepared in two 2-liter storage flasks of the gas handling system. Flow runs can be made by passing gas through the ion source. Different flow rates were obtained by interposing capillary tubes in series with the flow system. Flow rates with an average linear velocity of up to 10 meters sec.$^{-1}$ could be obtained. Since the distance from the foil window to the leak is about 3 cm., the contact time for irradiation at this velocity is some 3 msec.

In the normal runs one irradiates the total volume over the leak. Provisions are also made for placing a collimating slit between the leak and the alpha source. The collimating slit was cut in a turret of 6-mm. diameter which screwed onto a leak-carrying cone provided with threads. The slit was elevated over the plane of the leak by unwinding the turret a certain number of revolutions.

The ion source is normally at room temperature. However, the temperature can be varied up to a maximum of 200°C. by means of heaters mounted in the heater wells. These are used either for bake-out or runs at elevated temperature.

Reaction and Sampling Conditions (23)

General. The use of alpha particles instead of electrons as in conventional ion-molecule reaction mass spectrometers introduces a difference in primary ionization conditions which is not as great as might be supposed. Thus, the primary ion mass spectra produced by alpha particles are very similar to these produced by say 70-e.v. electrons (30). Secondary electrons produced by the alpha particles are responsible for more than 50% of the total ionization. The energies of these electrons peak in the range 20–100 e.v. so that again the primary ions will be similar to those produced by 70-e.v. electrons.

However, some of the conditions in the alpha ion source do differ significantly from those in conventional ion-molecule sources. The most important difference is caused by the absence of an electric field and the mode of sampling. Positive and negative particles are carried out by mass flow. Therefore it is necessary to understand the reaction and sampling conditions at least qualitatively. For this reason we are devoting this section to a description of the conditions and a discussion of some experiments which were done specifically to obtain a better understanding of the sample prehistory.

Intensity of Irradiation. As discussed below the ionic sample Sriginates from a small volume with a radius of approximately 1 mm., and one can visualize this volume as a sphere placed on top of the leak. oince the distance from the leak to the ion source (R = 3 cm.) is relatively large, we can use a point-source approximation to obtain j, the

---

Figure 1.   Ion source and electrode system   →

(1) Stainless steel block forming ion source.   (2) Alpha source, consisting of polonium deposited on a metal disc.   Metal disc enclosed in container with stainless foil window and stainless porous plug allowing pressure equalization across foil.   (3) Outer alpha source container with foil window and porous plug.   Double container prevents spreading of polonium into pressure equalization system.   (4) Porous stainless plug allowing pump-out of alpha source and pressure equalization across foils. (5) Gas supply to ion source and flow system (in the direction of the arrows).   (6) Tube leading to vacuum system of alpha source container.   (7) Insulating material allowing voltages different from ground to be applied to ion source.   (8) Cone-carrying metal foil at its truncated apex.   Foil has one or several leaks through which the gas and ions enter the pumping and electrode chamber.   (9) Heater and thermocouple wells for temperature control of ion source.   (10) Auxiliary electron gun for gas purity determinations.   (11–19) Electrodes focusing ion beam into magnetic mass analyzer

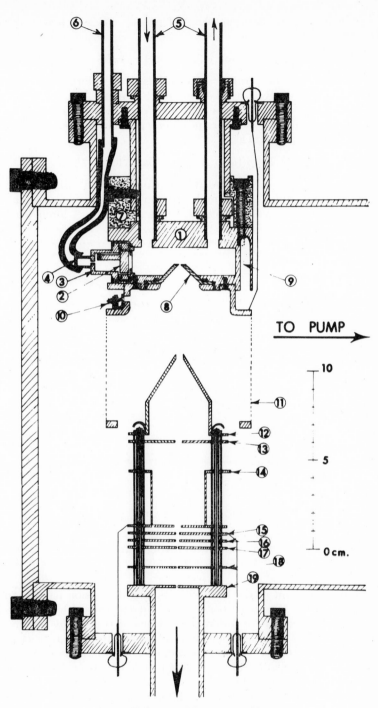

TO PUMP

TO MASS ANALYSIS

number of alpha particles per sec. and per sq. cm. which pass directly above the leak.

$$j = A(\text{mc.}) \times 3.7 \times 10^7/4\pi R^2$$

A is the manufacturer's rated activity based on calorimetric measurement of the heat evolved by the source. Since one 3-m.e.v. alpha particle produces 3×10^4 ion pairs in air of 1 mg. sq. cm. $^{-1}$ density we calculate I, the number of ion pairs produced per second above the leak in 1 cc. air at p torr pressure as:

$$I = 1.4 \times 10^7 \, p(\text{torr}) \, A \, (\text{mc.}) \, (\text{particles cc.}^{-1} \text{ sec.}^{-1})$$

Total Ionization with Movable Collimating Slit. To locate the region from which the sample originates, some experiments were done with a movable collimating slit. The slit was 1 $\times$ 5 mm. and was

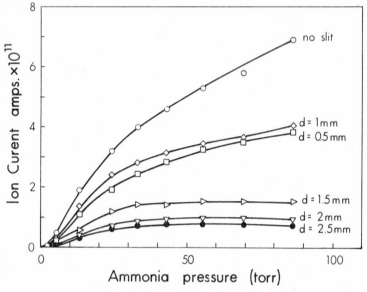

Figure 2. Total positive ion current collected on blanked-off first electrode; variation caused by interposing collimating slit; d is the height of the center of the slit over the level of the sampling leak

placed 5 mm. in front of the leak with its long dimension parallel to the plane of the leak. The total positive ion current caused by the effusing gas was then measured for different positions of the slit by making the blanked-off conical first electrode (Figure 1) negative with respect to the ion source. The total ion current obtained with ammonia gas is shown in Figure 2. The meaning of the results is seen more clearly in Figure 3a where we have plotted the percentage current observed (current in absence of the slit equal to 100) for different distances of the slit above the level of the leak. The three curves, taken at three representative

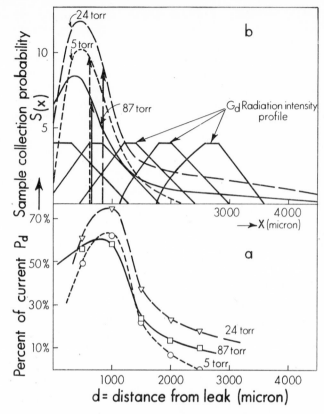

Figure 3. (a) *Total ion current in percent of current without collimating slit.* (b) *Plot of sample origin as a function of slit distance. Plot based on data from part a but corrects for intensity profile of slit*

pressures (5, 24, and 87 torr) show maxima for a distance of about 800 microns. The curves indicate that under normal (no slit) conditions most of the ions emerging through the leak originate from a region extending only about 2 mm. above the leak. In Figure 5b an attempt has been made to correct for the rather poor definition of the collimated beam. The trapeze-shaped $G_d(x)$ curves represent radiation intensity profiles derived from geometric considerations (*23*) for the different slit positions. The method by which the sample collection probability curves $S(x)$ were constructed is described elsewhere (*23*). The average ion distance is about 750 microns. Obviously, the sampling method mixes ions with a considerable range of reaction times. The lowest spread in the origin of the ions is observed at 5 torr. Low pressures would thus appear favorable for approximate kinetic studies.

A Simple Model for the Reaction and Sampling Conditions. A model proposed to represent the sampling conditions is shown in

Figure 4. The following data were used: leak radius r_o (40 micron), leak conductance $F = 1$ cc. sec.$^{-1}$, gas pressure (air) p (20 torr), diffusion coefficient (26) for ions $D_i = 2$ sq. cm. sec.$^{-1}$, for electrons $D_e = 2000$ sq. cm. sec.$^{-1}$ (at 20 torr air). The flow velocities were assumed independent of θ and ϕ (spherical polar coordinates). The spherically symmetrical flow pattern, which obviously overestimates the flow velocity for large values of θ was chosen because of its simplicity. The velocity of the radially directed flow at a distance r is $v = F/2\pi r^2$. The time required for outflow, $t = \dfrac{2\pi}{3F}(r^3 - r_0{}^3)$ is shown numerically on the left side of the abscissa.

One can calculate the charge density as a function of the vertical distance from the wall (z) in the absence of flow by solving the differential equation:

$$I = \alpha n^2 - \frac{D d^2 n}{dz^2} \tag{I}$$

I is the number of ions created per unit volume and time. The value used was $I = 1.4 \times 10^{10}$ ions cc.$^{-1}$ sec.$^{-1}$ which corresponds to irradiation with a 50-mc. source (see section on intensity of irradiation above); n is the number of ions per cc. Ion recombination coefficient

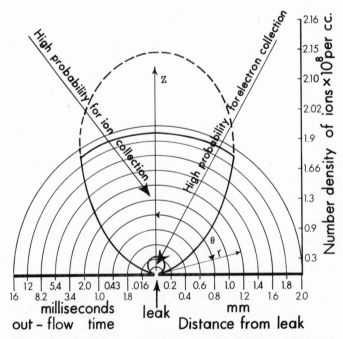

Figure 4. Sampling conditions; at 20 torr most of the ionic sample originates from a volume of approximately 1-mm. radius; electrons are collected much less efficiently

$\alpha = 10^{-6}$ cc. sec.$^{-1}$ The numerical values of n for different z are shown for orientation purposes on the right hand ordinate of Figure 4. The ion density n increases initially nearly in proportion to z, but as z increases, a limiting value is reached which is determined by gas phase recombination. In the presence of flow this solution holds in a region of the wall which is far removed from the leak.

The situation in the flow perturbed region is quite different. Mathematical difficulties arising from the complexity of the boundary conditions have led us to treat the flow region in a simplified manner. The large egg-shaped area in Figure 4 was obtained by imposing the requirement that for ions inside the area the time of diffusion to the wall should be longer than the time for outflow through the leak. The outflow time of the ion was assumed the same as that for the gas. The time for diffusion to the wall τ, was obtained from the approximate equation $\tau = z^2/D$. The condition for the egg-shaped boundary line is thus $z^2 =$

$\dfrac{2\pi D_i}{3F} (r^3 - r_o{}^3)$. The small egg-shaped boundary for the electrons was

obtained from the same equation by replacing D_i with D_e. We suggest that the majority of ions within the boundary enter the vacuum region. In a sense the ions are scooped out by the mass flow. Because the electrons diffuse much faster, only a much smaller number is caught in the same way. In the absence of mass flow, one would be sampling the ionic concentration at a distance of about 20–40 microns from the wall. This concentration would of course be low. We have flattened the top of the ion volume boundary with a lid (thick line at $r = 2$ mm.) because of the following consideration. Ions coming from the region, $r > 2$ mm. will have outflow times larger than 16 msec. These ions, even if they remained in the high collection probability region, would most likely disappear by gas phase recombination. The line was drawn for $t = 16$ msec. (i.e., $r = 2$ mm.) since this corresponds to the half-life for gas phase recombination as obtained from the equation:

$$t \approx 1/\alpha n.$$

According to the model, the gas entering the leak consists in a large part of discharged material, streaming in along the walls and a small part of relatively high charge density gas coming from the high probability area. The high probability area is thus a quasi-reaction chamber with an average reaction time of a few milliseconds. At 20 torr charge destruction is partly controlled by diffusion to the wall and partly by gas phase recombination. Change of ion source pressure should have the

following effect. Since: $D \propto \dfrac{1}{p}$, $F = $ constant with p and $I \propto p$, de-

crease of pressure will result in a shrinking of the high probability area and a movement of the lid towards higher z. Thus, for a pressure of 10 torr the high probability volume extends to a maximum z of only 1 mm., and the lid is completely above the high probability area.   Charge removal occurs now only by diffusion to the wall and outflow.   Pressures above 20 torr cause the high probability area to grow.   The lid cuts off a larger and larger fraction of the ellipsoid so that gas phase recombination becomes the controlling mechanism.

The above predictions will now be compared with the experimental results.   The high probability volume agrees well with the movable slit observations above.   The predicted low collection efficiency for electrons is also observed.   Figure 5 (bottom) shows the ratio of negative to positive ion current collected on the blanked-off conical electrode for different gases. For the rare gases this ratio is small especially at low pressures while

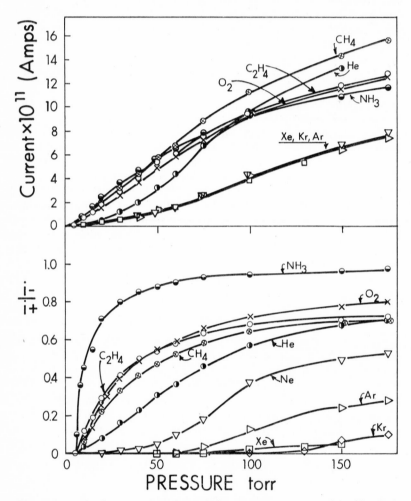

Figure 5.   Total ion current from different gases measured on blanked-off first electrode.   Rare gases show much lower negative currents. Negative current deficiency believed caused by electrons

gases like NH_3, C_2H_4, etc. have ratios which are much higher and approach unity at about 10 torr. Invariably, when the current ratio was high, the intensity of the negative ions found with the mass spectrometer was also high. The negative to positive ion ratio after mass analysis could not be determined accurately owing to multiplier calibration difficulties, but the results suggested strongly that the negative current collected on the cone electrode consisted mostly of negative ions. Thus few electrons emerge from the leak as predicted by the model.

Undoubtedly the sampling efficiencies of the different positive ions are also not identical so that the measured relative ion intensities cannot be expected to equal exactly the relative concentrations in the ion source. However, since the diffusion coefficients are inversely proportional to the square root of the molecular weight, in the mass range 30–200, we should not expect discriminations by factors larger than 2 for ions of similar nature—i.e. $C_2H_4{}^+$ and $C_4H_8{}^+$, etc. Therefore, all numerical results obtained from ion intensity measurements are of order of magnitude significance only.

Ions in the Rare Gas Sensitized Radiolysis of Ethylene (23)

Primary Species Causing Ionization of Ethylene. THE TERMOLECULAR FORMATION OF THE RARE GAS MOLECULAR ION $R^+ + 2R \rightarrow R_2{}^+ + R$. Since the ions observed in pure ethylene are numerous, one needs a method to identify the primary ions which initiate the reaction sequences. In conventional ion-molecule work, identification can be achieved by varying the energy of the ionizing electrons. Since this is not possible here, the technique of rare gas sensitization was applied instead. The rare gases were used at some 20 torr pressure while the ethylene concentration was kept in the range 0.001–1 torr. Under these conditions ionization of ethylene occurs almost exclusively on collision with excited atoms R^* or by charge transfer from R^+ and $R_2{}^+$. We found that the primary ionic fragmentation of ethylene—i.e., the composition of the C_2 ion group—varied with the pressure of ethylene. The C_2 ion composition also changed when at constant ethylene concentration the rare gas pressure was varied. This effect could be traced to a change of the rare gas ion ratio $R_2{}^+/R^+$. The change of the ratio can be explained if one assumes that charge transfer to ethylene depletes $R_2{}^+$, part of which is formed by the relatively slow termolecular reaction involving the atomic ion.

We can consider the following reaction sequence:

$$R \rightsquigarrow R^+ + e \tag{11}$$

$$R \rightsquigarrow R^* \tag{12}$$

$$R^+ + 2R \rightarrow R_2{}^+ + R \tag{13}$$

$$R^* + R \rightarrow R_2{}^+ + e \tag{14}$$

$$R^+ + C_2H_4 \rightarrow C_2H_4{}^+{}_{(excited)} + R \tag{15}$$

$$R_2{}^+ + C_2H_4 \rightarrow C_2H_4{}^+{}_{(excited)} + 2R \tag{16}$$

Applying a steady-state approximation $d[R_2{}^+]/dt = 0$, $d[R^+]/dt = 0$, and $d[R^*]/dt = 0$, we obtain Equation II.

$$\frac{[R_2{}^+]}{[R^+]} = \frac{a[R]^2}{[C_2H_4]} + b \qquad (II)$$

where

$$a = \left[1 + \frac{k_{12}}{k_{11}}\right]\frac{k_{13}}{k_{16}} \text{ and } b = \frac{k_{12}k_{15}}{k_{11}k_{16}}$$

We have neglected charge neutralization reactions with regard to $R_2{}^+$ and R^+ since the concentration of these ions is controlled by the rapid Reactions 15 and 16 with ethylene. According to Equation II a plot of $[R_2{}^+]/[R^+]$ vs. $[R]^2$ at constant $[C_2H_4]$ should give a straight line with slope $a/[C_2H_4]$ and intersection with the ordinate equal to b. Such a plot is given in Figure 6 for argon and three constant concentrations of ethylene. To obtain the plot in Figure 6, we have replaced the relative concentrations $[R_2{}^+]/[R^+]$ with the mass spectrometrically measured ion intensities. This procedure assumes that the ion intensities are proportional to the steady-state concentrations in the reaction volume. Considering the complexity of sampling conditions discussed above, the validity of this procedure is questionable. However, we have found consistently that sensible results can be obtained by its use.

The ethylene pressures used were 0.5, 1, and 2 millitorr. Thus, the slopes of the three lines should be in the ratios $2:1:0.5$. The lines in Figure 6 were drawn to give a best fit of the experimental points and comply with the above condition. The considerable scatter in the experimental points is possibly caused by inexact concentration ratios in the reaction mixture. In spite of some curvature, most noticeable for the 0.5-millitorr results, the experimental results are generally compatible with Equation II since they follow the required slope ratios, have a common intersection with the ordinate, and show approximate linearity with the square of the pressure.

The numerical results for argon are $a = 0.66 \times 10^{-22}$ and $b = 0.4$. Since $b = k_{12}k_{15}/k_{11}k_{16}$, we must make some further assumptions to obtain values of interest. Considering the nature of Reactions 15 and 16, we conclude that $k_{15}/k_{16} \approx 1$ which leads to $k_{12}/k_{11} \approx 0.4$. Substituting this value into the equation which defines a, we obtain $k_{13}/k_{16} \approx 4.75 \times 10^{-23}$. In a separate study (31) with a mass spectrometer for conventional ion-molecule reaction work we could determine the cross-section for Reaction 15 as $Q_f = 208 \times 10^{-16}$ sq. cm. at $E_r l = 0.55$ volt, where E_r is repeller field strength and l the ion path length in the ion source.

It could be shown in the same work that Q_f is proportional to $(E_r)^{-1/2}$. We feel therefore justified in using the Giomousis and Stevenson (10) equation: $k_{15} = Q_f \left(\frac{eE_r l}{2m}\right)^{1/2}$ to calculate the charge transfer rate constant k_{15} at thermal energies. Substituting the numerical values,

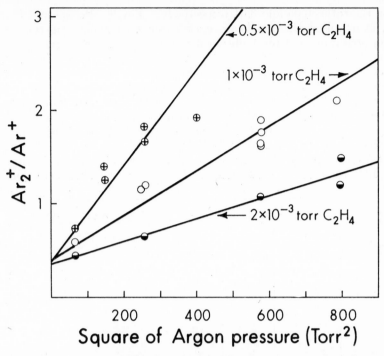

Figure 6. *Plot providing data for termolecular rate constant of reaction* $Ar^+ + 2Ar \rightarrow Ar_2^+ + Ar$

one obtains $k_{15} = 1.2 \times 10^{-9}$ cc. molecule $^{-1}$ sec $^{-1}$. Since we are assuming that $k_{15} \approx k_{16}$ we can use $k_{16} = 1.2 \times 10^{-9}$ and the ratio $k_{13}/k_{16} \approx 4.75 \times 10^{-23}$ to obtain $k_{13} \approx 5.7 \times 10^{-32}$ cc.^{2} atoms $^{-2}$ sec. $^{-1}$

It is also of interest to mention here that Stevenson's (*10*) theoretical equation, $k = 2\pi(e^2\alpha/\mu)^{1/2}$ predicts a value for $k_{15} = 3.5 \times 10^{-9}$. This is close to the experimental value 1.2×10^{-9} discussed in the text and suggests that Stevenson's theoretical equation has some validity for Reactions 15 and 16. Stevenson's equation predicts that k_{15} and k_{16} differ only by the square root of the reduced mass—i.e., $k_{15}/k_{16} = \left(\dfrac{\mu_{15}}{\mu_{16}}\right)^{1/2} =$

1.24 which supports the assumption $k_{15} \approx k_{16}$ made above.

We will now discuss the derived values for $k_{12}/k_{11} = 0.4$ and k_{13} and compare them with the literature. The rate constants k_{12}/k_{11} correspond to the ratio of excitation of argon to states Ar* which produce Ar_2^+ [Hornbeck-Molnar process (*16*)] and the ionization of Ar to Ar$^+$. Such ratios have been measured by several workers. Hornbeck (*17, 25*), in a study of pulsed discharges in the rare gases, found for argon at 8 torr pressure $k_{12}/k_{11} \approx 2$. The ratios for He and Ne were 1 and 0.5. Dahler *et al.* (*7*) in a mass spectrometric study at pressures up to 0.3 torr and electron voltages of 15 e.v. and 70 e.v. obtained for argon and

neon the ratios 0.05 and 0.01 respectively.   Finally, Becker and Lampe
(4), in a pulsed electron beam mass spectrometric investigation using
lower pressures (0.01 torr), obtained ratios for argon which are somewhat
lower than those of Dahler *et al.*   In making a comparison between these
different results the following should be taken into account.   An excited atom will be able to undergo the Hornbeck-Molnar (H-M) process
if its excitation lies within some 1.5 e.v. below its ionization potential
and if its lifetime is at least the same order as that required for a reactive
collision.   We may expect a number of excited atoms to participate in
the H-M process.   Recent work by Kaul (18) and the already quoted
work by Becker and Lampe (4) report three such states with lifetimes in
the 10^{-5} to 5×10^{-7} sec. range.   Both measurements were done at

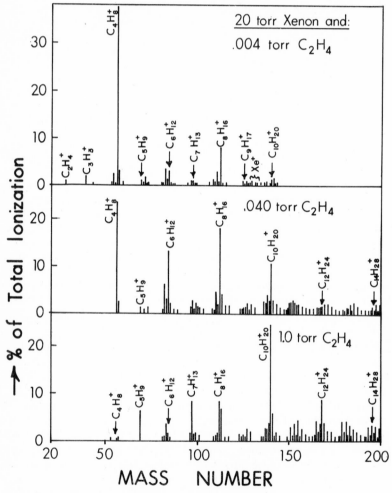

*Figure 7.   Ions from ethylene in xenon.   Ions mostly caused by $C_2H_4^+$.
Increase of ethylene pressure shows development of $C_nH_{2n}^+$ chain*

relatively low ion source pressures so that considerably shorter-lived states would not have been noticed.   The rate constants for the H-M Reaction 14 obtained by Becker and Lampe are in the range $k_{14} \approx 10^{-9}$ cc. atoms^{-1} sec.$^{-1}$ At the 20 torr pressure used in our experiments, states with much shorter lifetimes will be also able to react.   Thus, assuming Becker's rate constant, we calculate $k_{14}[Ar]$ at 20 torr as 6×10^8 sec.$^{-1}$ Atoms with lifetimes as short as 10^{-9} sec. could also be expected to react.   The much higher excitation to ionization ratio obtained in Hornbeck's and our work could therefore result from the much higher pressures used.   The early measurements of Maier-Leibnitz (27) of total excitation to ionization in argon are also of the order of unity and therefore agree with Hornbeck's and our value.   In comparing the difference between Hornbeck's and our value, one must consider the different modes of excitation.   For example, since we use alpha particles, electrons (δ rays) represent only roughly half the ionization and excitation agents.   We conclude that our excitation to ionization ratio is of a reasonably expected magnitude.

The rate constant we derived for the termolecular reaction, forming $Ar_2{}^+$, was $k_{13} \approx 5.7 \times 10^{-32}$ cc.^{2} atoms^{-2} sec.$^{-1}$.   A recently determined value for this reaction is 2×10^{-28} (7).   Thus, the two results differ by a factor of 10^4.   However, pulse discharge experiments (17, 29) give values for the termolecular rate constants which are of the same order of magnitude as our rate constant.   The rate constants for the termolecular recombination of (neutral) atoms are also all in the range 10^{-32} cc.^{2} atoms^{-2} sec.$^{-1}$.   There are, of course, important differences between the ion-atom and atom-atom recombination.   The cross-section for the primary collision forming the excited molecular complex will be larger for the ion.   The lifetime of the complex can be expected to be the same. The cross-section for collisional deactivation might again be larger for the ionic complex than the neutral complex.   On this basis one might guess that the termolecular rate constant for the ionic recombination could be larger by one to two orders of magnitude.   Thus classical calculations by Bates (3) for the ionic termolecular reaction give rate constants which are in the range 10^{-31}–10^{-32} (cc.^{2} atoms^{-2} sec.$^{-1}$).   However, the result of Dahler is some three orders of magnitude higher than this.

The $R_2{}^+/R^+$ ratios for the other rare gases and ethylene were examined, but less extensively.   The results were similar to those for argon (Figure 6).   We shall mention such data when needed in further discussion.

Ethylene in Xenon: Rate Constants for Ionic Polymerization. Some typical mass spectra obtained with ethylene in xenon are given in Figure 7.   The spectrum of 4 millitorr ethylene in 20 torr shows that $C_2H_4{}^+$ is the only visible ion of the C_2 group.   The spectrum is dominated by polymer ions of empirical formula $C_nH_{2n}{}^+$ (n = even) which obviously originate from an ionic polymerization initiated by $C_2H_4{}^+$. Other ions of significant intensities have the empirical formula C_kH_{2k-1} (k = uneven).   These ions are caused by loss of alkyl from excited addition products $C_nH_{2n}{}^+$ and will be discussed in the next section in connection with their collisional deactivation by the inert gas.   The $C_nH_{2n}{}^+$ and C_kH_{2k-1} ions account for some 85% of the total ionization for ethylene pressures in the millitorr range, showing that the $C_2H_4{}^+$ ion is the predominant species formed by excitation and charge transfer from xenon. This is of course expected since $Xe_2{}^+$ and $Xe^+(^2P_{3/2})$ can form only $C_2H_4{}^+$. The $Xe^+{}^2P_{1/2}I_p$ (13.4 e.v.) can produce also $C_2H_2{}^+$ and $C_2H_3{}^+$ as shown with the Cermack (5) and ion-molecule technique (31).   The ions $C_3H_3{}^+$ and $C_nH_{2n-2}{}^+$ (in Figure 7) originate from $C_2H_2{}^+$ while $C_4H_9{}^+$ arises from $C_2H_3{}^+$.   The reactions of $C_2H_2{}^+$ and $C_2H_3{}^+$ will be discussed later when the results with the other rare gases are considered since these ions are much more abundant there.

The relative simplicity of the xenon spectra makes this system suitable for studying the simple polymerization reaction leading to $C_nH_{2n}{}^+$. A number of spectra were therefore taken in which the xenon was kept constant at 20 torr, but the ethylene pressure was varied in the range 0.001–5 torr.   The spectra in Figure 7 are examples of such runs.   The most abundant ion in the millitorr range is $C_4H_8{}^+$.   The ions $C_6H_{12}{}^+$, $C_8H_{16}{}^+$, etc. are of much lower intensity, but still considerably larger than $C_2H_4{}^+$.   We shall see that this is caused by large differences in the rate constants of the reactions forming these ions. $C_2H_4{}^+$ reacts rapidly with ethylene, but $C_4H_8{}^+$, $C_6H_{12}{}^+$, etc. reacts much more slowly.   When the ethylene pressure is increased, a development of the polymerization chain $C_nH_{2n}{}^+$ towards higher n is observed.   However as the lower members ($C_2H_4{}^+$, $C_4H_8{}^+$, and $C_6H_{12}{}^+$) disappear, an equivalent development towards higher and higher mass does not occur.   Thus, the ions $C_{10}H_{20}{}^+$ and $C_{12}H_{24}{}^+$ remain of maximum intensity from 0.1–5 torr.   This must be caused by a continued slowing down of the polymerization reactions. This observation was confirmed by a study of the high mass range (m/e 200–1000).   All ion intensities were found to decrease gradually and become negligible around mass 300.   The percentage of total ionization above mass 200 was small ($\approx 10\%$) and did not increase substantially for an ethylene pressure rise from 0.2 to 5 torr.   The polymerization therefore stops in the mass range: 200–300.   In our earlier work (21) we had found considerably more ionization above mass 200.   We now attribute the previous results to the presence of impurities.

Estimates for the rate constants of the polymerization reaction can be obtained from the following treatment.

$$C_2H_4{}^+ + C_2H_4 \rightarrow (C_4H_8{}^*)^+ \qquad \text{addition (1a)}$$

$$(C_4H_8{}^*)^+ + Xe \rightarrow C_4H_8{}^+ \qquad \text{stabilization (2s)}$$

$$(C_4H_8{}^*)^+ \begin{cases} \nearrow C_3H_5{}^+ + CH_3 \\ \searrow C_4H_7{}^+ + H \end{cases} \qquad \text{decomposition (2d)}$$

$$C_4H_8{}^+ \rightarrow \text{neutrals} \qquad \text{charge removal (2c)}$$

$$C_4H_8{}^+ + C_2H_4 \rightarrow (C_6H_{12}{}^*)^+ \qquad \text{addition (2a)}$$

etc.

Applying a steady-state condition to the ions $(C_4H_8^*)^+$ and $C_4H_8^+$, we obtain Equation III:

$$\frac{[C_2H_4^+]}{[C_4H_8^+]} = a + \frac{b}{[C_2H_4]} \tag{III}$$

where:

$$a = \frac{(k_{2s}[Xe] + k_{2d})k_{2a}}{k_{1a}k_{2s}[Xe]} \text{ and } b = \frac{(k_{2s}[Xe] + k_{2d})k_{2c}}{k_{1a}k_{2s}[Xe]}$$

Equations of the same form hold for the other pairs $C_4H_8^+/C_6H_{12}^+$ etc. Figure 8 shows a plot of $(C_2H_4)_{n-1}^+/(C_2H_4)_n^+$ vs. the reciprocal ethylene concentration. The data cover an ethylene pressure range from 0.04–1 torr. To obtain the plot, we have replaced the ionic concentration ratio

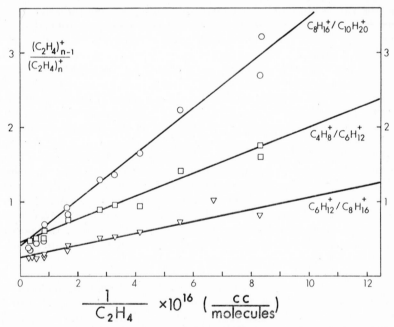

Figure 8. Plot used to determine average rate constant ratios of the $C_nH_{2n}^+$ chain. $(C_2H_4)_n^+$ indicates only empirical formula but not structure of ion

with the ratio of ion intensities measured with the mass spectrometer. The results give reasonably straight lines and thus obey Equation III. Since stabilization predominates over decomposition—i.e., $k_{2s}[Xe] > k_{2d}$, one can simplify the expressions for the intercept a and the slope b to $a \approx k_{2a}/k_{1a}$ and $b \approx k_{2c}/k_{1c}$. Reading off from Figure 4, we obtain: $k_{3a}/k_{2a} \approx 0.4$, $k_{4a}/k_{3a} \approx 0.26$, $k_{5a}/k_{4a} \approx 0.4$. The $C_2H_4^+$ ion was too small in the pressure range covered by Figure 8. A separate plot (22) for $C_2H_4^+/C_4H_8^+$ in the millitorr ethylene range gave $k_{2a}/k_{1a} \approx 0.002$. It is possible, using data from conventional ion-molecule reaction studies, to convert the above relative data into approximate absolute rate constants. Under conventional ion molecule reaction conditions, Reaction 1a is followed almost exclusively by decomposition (Reaction 2d) to $C_3H_5^+$ and $C_4H_7^+$. A sum of the cross-sections for the reactions leading to $C_3H_5^+$ and $C_4H_7^+$ should be a fair estimate of Reaction 1a. Using the data of Wexler (*34*) and Field (*9*) and applying Stevenson's (*10*) formula for conversion to a thermal rate constant, one obtains $k_{1a} \approx 10^{-9}$ cc. molecules^{-1} sec.$^{-1}$ Substituting this value into the above ratios, we obtain $k_{1a} = 10^{-9}$, $k_{2a} = 10^{-12}$, $k_{3a} = 8 \times 10^{-13}$, $k_{4a} = 2 \times 10^{-13}$, $k_{5a} = 8 \times 10^{-14}$ cc. molecules^{-1} sec.$^{-1}$. We see that the rate constants decrease by four orders of magnitude! From the slopes b we can obtain the values for the effective charge neutralization reactions: $k_{3c} = 3 \times 10^3$, $k_{4c} = 6.4 \times 10^2$, $k_{5c} = 6 \times 10^2$ sec.$^{-1}$ These rate constants thus predict millisecond charge lifetimes as was expected. We wish to emphasize that the values obtained above have only order of magnitude significance since it is obvious that the steady-state treatment we applied cannot be truly adequate for the complex reaction conditions and mode of sampling.

The large decrease of the rate constants for the addition reactions must be caused by structural effects. The largest decrease occurs in the reactivity of $C_4H_8^+$ which adds only $1/500$ as fast as $C_2H_4^+$. One could imagine the transition state of the $(C_4H_8^*)^+$ formed by Reaction 1a as having an initial structure $\cdot CH_2CH_2CH_2CH_2^+$. Two successive 1,2-hydride ion shifts or one 1,3-hydride ion shift will convert this structure to the more stable 1-butene ion. Conversion to the even more stable 2-butene ion structure is also conceivable since the $C_4H_8^+$ species is highly excited. Once a species like the 2-butene ion is deactivated, its reactivity towards ethylene addition might be low. Aside from a possible steric hindrance effect of the methyl groups one must consider that in the transition state for the formation of $C_6H_{12}^+$, the positive charge first needs to be visualized on a terminal CH_2 group. Such a structure is of high energy and would lead to a low rate constant. To check on the reactivity of the 2-butene ion, we studied the ion-molecule reactions of 2-butene with ethylene in a conventional ion-molecule reaction mass spectrometer (*32*). The $C_4H_8^+$ ion was obtained near its appearance potential. The reaction with highest cross-section was $C_4H_8^+ + C_2H_4 \rightarrow C_5H_9^+ + CH_3$. The cross-section for this process was compared with that for $C_2H_4^+$ addition to ethylene measured with the same apparatus. The cross-section for the 2-butene reaction was about $1/400$ as large. This decrease is of similar magnitude as that observed with the alpha particle system.

The decrease of reactivity of the higher $C_nH_{2n}^+$ ions must be caused by effects of the same nature as those suggested for $C_4H_8^+$. Since the charge will always seek a tertiary or quaternary position, one may expect that the higher $C_nH_{2n}^+$ ions will be branched and become progressively less reactive.

Collisional Deactivation of $(C_nH_{2n}^*)^+$ by Xenon. The excited $C_4H_8^+$, formed by addition of $C_2H_4^+$ to ethylene, if it is not deactivated, decomposes to $C_3H_5{}^+ + CH_3$ and $C_4H_7{}^+ + H$. These two decomposition modes are the major reactions observed with conventional ion-molecule mass spectrometers (*9, 34*). Under our conditions xenon is present at relatively high pressure, and efficient stabilization occurs. To study the relative rates of the decomposition and stabilization reactions, runs were made with constant ethylene concentration and variable xenon pressure. Three representative mass spectra with ethylene at 0.1 torr pressure are shown in Figure 9. The $C_3H_5{}^+$ ions are not present in these spectra. However, the higher homologs, $C_5H_9{}^+$ and $C_7H_{13}{}^+$, of the C_kH_{2k-1} group are found in high abundance. The absence of $C_3H_5{}^+$ could be caused by a

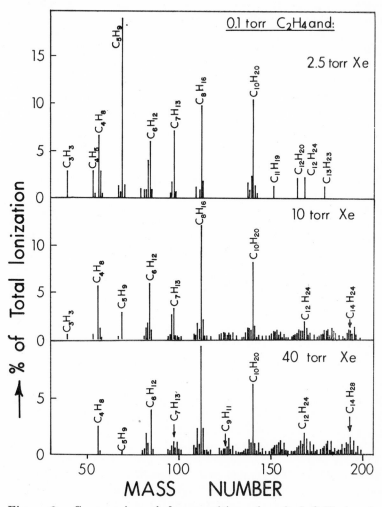

Figure 9. Suppression of decomposition of excited $C_nH_{2n}{}^+$ evidenced by the decrease of fragment ions $C_5H_9{}^+$ and $C_7H_{13}{}^+$ with xenon pressure

high reactivity of this ion with ethylene such that its steady-state concentration remains below the detection limit. For this to be the case its reactivity needs to be only as high as that of $C_2H_4^+$ since $C_2H_4^+$ which we know is formed, is below the detection limit at 0.1 torr ethylene. At millitorr ethylene pressures $C_2H_4^+$ becomes visible, but just barely. Unfortunately, under these conditions there is a large intensity decrease of the total C_kH_{2k-1} series so that the absence of $C_3H_5^+$ (Figure 7) cannot be taken as evidence that this ion is not formed. If $C_3H_5^+$, is not a precursor of $C_5H_9^+$, decomposition of the excited C_6H_{12} ion must have occurred. Since $C_{16}H_{12}^+$ has more degrees of freedom than $C_4H_8^+$, its preferential decomposition could be understood only on the basis of a structure which favors decomposition or by an "energy carry-over" from incompletely thermalized $C_4H_8^+$.

We shall see below that there is some evidence for "energy carry-over" in this system. We therefore cannot decide from our data whether the C_kH_{2k-1} chain starts at $C_3H_5^+$ or at $C_5H_9^+$. For this reason we are going to treat the C_kH_{2k-1} group as a whole.

The mass spectra (Figure 9) show that the C_kH_{2k-1} group decreases drastically as the xenon pressure is increased. Thus the peaks $C_5H_9^+$ and $C_7H_{13}^+$ which are among the highest at 2.5 torr xenon become unsignificant at 40 torr.

A plot of the stabilization to decomposition ratio (S/D) is shown in Figure 10. The S/D ratio was obtained by summing over the intensities of the groups $C_nH_{2n}^+$ (n even) and $C_kH_{2k-1}^+$ (k odd). Ions up to mass 160 were taken into consideration. The leveling off, at higher xenon pressures, is possibly caused by impurities which will generally contribute to the $C_kH_{2k-1}^+$ peaks but not to the $C_nH_{2n}^+$.

To obtain a simple interpretation for the significance of the slope of the S/D curve, we can consider the Reactions nd and ns.

$$(C_nH_{2n}^*)^+ \rightarrow C_{n-1}H_{2n-3}^+ + CH_3 \qquad (nd)$$

$$(C_nH_{2n}^*)^+ + Xe \rightarrow C_nH_{2n}^+ \qquad (ns)$$

Applying the steady-state condition and assuming that the rate constants for neutralization are the same, we obtain Equation IV

$$\frac{S}{D} = \frac{k_{ns}[Xe]}{k_{nd}} \qquad (IV)$$

which gives k_{ns}/k_{nd} as the slope of the curve. From Figure 10 we obtain for 0.1 torr ethylene $k_{ns}/k_{nd} = 2 \times 10^{-17}$ cc. molecule.$^{-1}$ Plots for 0.04 and 0.004 torr constant pressure of ethylene are also shown in Figure 10. The initial slopes at the two pressures are $k_{ns}/k_{nd} = 3.4 \times 10^{-17}$ (0.04 torr) and 11×10^{-17} (0.004 torr). Two alternative explanations can be offered for the change of k_{ns}/k_{nd} with ethylene pressure. The composition of the $C_nH_{2n}^+$ group depends on pressure. $C_4H_8^+$ is practically the only ion at 0.004 torr while at 0.1 torr this ion is of low abundance, the intensity being concentrated in the C_6, C_8, and C_{10} homologs. Higher abundance of the C_kH_{2k-1} group will be expected at higher ethyl-

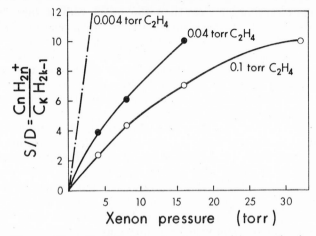

Figure 10. Stabilization to decomposition ratio for $C_nH_{2n}^+$. Slope at 0.004 torr C_2H_4 based on points outside the range of the graph.

ene pressures if decomposition to the C_kH_{2k-1} ions occurred from the $C_6H_{12}^+$ and higher homologs.

The second alternative that can be considered is incomplete thermalization. Initial excess energy in the $C_2H_4^+$ as well as excitation owing to energy released in the condensation reactions may not be completely removed between reactive encounters with C_2H_4. The accumulation of energy will cause increased decomposition. In 0.1-torr ethylene and 10-torr xenon 100 collisions with xenon will occur between a collision with ethylene. The above interpretation of the results suggests that 100 collisions are not sufficient for thermalization.

An interesting comparison can be made between deactivation of an ion and deactivation of a neutral species on basis of this work and studies done by Rabinovich (*11, 24*). This author has studied the inert gas deactivation of the C_4H_7 radical prepared by the adding H atoms to 2-butene. The excitation energy of the radical is 43 kcal./mole, and the excess energy over that required for decomposition to propylene and methyl is 10 kcal./mole (*11*). The k_s/k_d obtained for deactivation of the radical by krypton was (*24*) equal to 4×10^{-18} cc. molecule^{-1}. No value was obtained for xenon, but judging by the differences between Ar and Kr observed by Rabinovich one would estimate the xenon value to be only slightly higher. The $C_4H_8^+$ formed in our study has a total excitation of 43 kcal. (assuming the butene-1 molecular ion structure since decomposition to methyl should occur via this structure) (*8*) and an excess energy over that required for decomposition of 10–15 kcal. Thus, the energies of the butyl radical and the butene ion are very similar as are their structures and degrees of freedom. We can assume, as an approximation, that the unimolecular decomposition rate constants are the same. The ratio k_{ns}/k_{nd} found for 0.004-torr ethylene was 11×10^{-17}. This is a lower limit for the rate constant ratio of

$C_4H_8{}^+$ and is 25 times higher than the butyl radical ratio found by Rabinovich. This difference is sufficiently large to suggest, in spite of the uncertainty in the unimolecular decomposition rate constants, that the efficiency for deactivation of the ion is about one order of magnitude larger. This result could be expected if it is considered that according to the Stevenson equation (*10*) the cross-section for the ion-inert gas collision is about one order of magnitude larger than the radical-inert gas kinetic collision cross-section.

Ethylene in Kr and Ar—Reactions of $C_2H_2{}^+$ and $C_2H_3{}^+$ with C_2H_4. The results for the Kr, Ar, Ne, He sensitized ionization of ethylene are best discussed using the charge transfer fragmentation diagram shown in Figure 11. The data for the diagram were obtained from Cermack (*5*), Abbe and Adloff (*1*), Tal'roze (*33*), and this laboratory (*31*), and a more detailed discussion is given in Ref. (*31*). The charge transfer spectra obtained by Tal'roze and in this laboratory correspond to charge transfer from near thermal velocity primary ions.

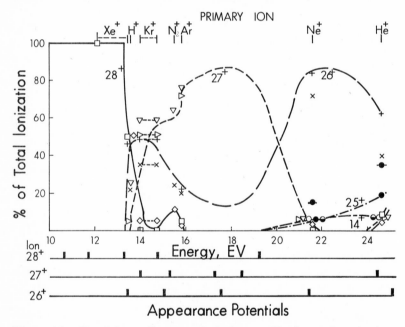

Figure 11. Breakdown diagram of ethylene. Abscissas given for ions 28⁺, 27⁺ and 26⁺ indicate outer and inner appearance potentials obtained by J. E. Collin (6)

This laboratory (32):   28⁺ □   27⁺ ▷   26⁺ +   25⁺ ●   14⁺ ○
Abbe and Adloff (1):   ◇   ▽   ×   ‑●‑   ◓

Three typical spectra of ethylene in argon are shown in Figure 12. The differences between the 2-millitorr ethylene spectra at 40 and 10-torr argon are mostly caused by a change of the $Ar_2{}^+/Ar^+$ ratio. As discussed above, $Ar_2{}^+$ increases with argon pressure owing to a rate increase of the termolecular Reaction 13. From the charge transfer diagram (Figure 11) we can read off the primary C_2 ions produced by Ar^+. The recombination energy of Ar_2^+ should be lower (by about 1.5–2 e.v. as will be shown below) so that the C_2 ions produced by Ar_2^+ should contain relatively more $C_2H_2^+$ and $C_2H_4^+$. The C_2 ions in Figure

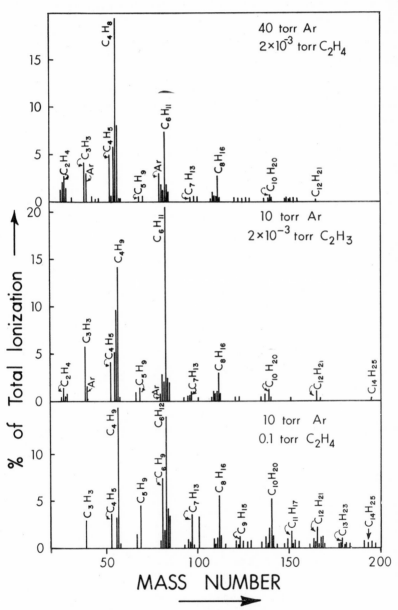

Figure 12. Ions in argon–ethylene mixtures

12 reflect this prediction.   The relative abundances of $C_2H_2^+$ and $C_2H_4^+$ are affected by the charge transfer Reaction 20.   Evidence for the occurrence of Reaction 20:

$$C_2H_2^+ + C_2H_4 \rightarrow C_2H_2 + C_2H_4^+ \tag{20}$$

was first obtained by Field (9) in conventional ion-molecule studies. We shall observe that the $C_2H_2^+$ abundance is consistently lower than expected—evidence that Reaction 20 occurs also under our conditions.

The charge transfer spectrum from Ar_2^+ can be estimated by plotting $C_2H_3^+/(C_2H_2^+ + C_2H_3^+ + C_2H_4^+)$ vs. $N = Ar_2^+/(Ar_2^+ + Ar^+)$.   Such a plot is shown in Figure 13.

The C_2 ion intensities are of course not primary charge transfer abundances but correspond approximately to relative steady-state

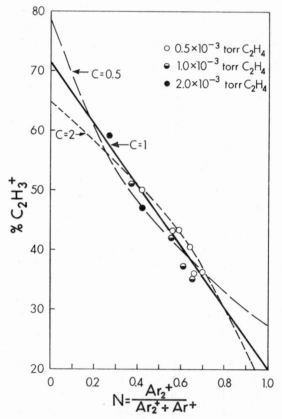

Figure 13.   Determination of % $C_2H_3^+$ abundance by charge transfer from Ar^+ ($N = 0$) and Ar_2^+ ($N = 1$).   Straight line extrapolation corresponds to k_{15} assumed equal to k_{16}.   Curved line extrapolations correspond to $k_{15} = 2k_{16}$ and $k_{15} = 0.5 k_{16}$

concentrations since this ion group reacts rapidly with ethylene.   The C_2 ions will represent the charge transfer abundances only if their rate constants for reactions with ethylene are the same.   Assuming this to be the case (justification for this assumption is given in Ref. *22*) and reading the linear extrapolation for $N = 0$ (the linear extrapolation corresponds to the assumption $k_{15} = k_{16}$ as shown in Ref. *22*), we obtain $C_2H_3^+$ owing to Ar^+ equal to 70%.   This compares well with the directly determined $C_2H_3^+$ abundance shown in the charge transfer diagram.   For $N = 1$ we obtain $C_2H_3^+ = 20\%$.   In the charge transfer diagram this abundance corresponds to a recombination energy $RE \approx 13.9$ e.v.   It is interesting that this recombination energy leads to an estimate for the bond dissociation energy of Ar^+ through the equation: $D(Ar^+-Ar) = I_p(Ar) - RE(Ar_2^+)$.   Substituting the ionization potential of Ar (15.8 e.v.), one obtains $D(Ar^+-Ar) = 1.9$ e.v. which is a reasonable value.   The charge transfer spectrum at $RE \approx 13.9$ e.v. changes steeply so that one can obtain only rough estimates for the relative abundances of the $C_2H_4^+$ and $C_2H_2^+$ ions produced by charge transfer from Ar_2^+.

The ion-molecule reaction chains initiated by the primary C_2 ion group can be discussed on the basis of Figure 12.   At 35-torr argon we observe the $C_nH_{2n}^+$ group caused by the simple polymerization of ethylene.   This reaction chain was discussed in the section dealing with ethylene in xenon.   A pair of ions which become most intense at 10-torr and 2-millitorr ethylene are $C_4H_3^+$ and $C_6H_{11}^+$.   We propose that they originate from reactions of the $C_2H_3^+$ ion according to the Reactions 21–24.

$$C_2H_3^+ + C_2H_4 \rightarrow C_2H_2 + C_2H_5^+ \tag{21}$$

$$C_2H_5^+ + C_2H_4 + Ar \rightarrow C_4H_9^+ + Ar \tag{22}$$

$$C_2H_3^+ + C_2H_4 + Ar \rightarrow C_4H_7^+ + Ar \tag{23}$$

$$C_4H_7^+ + C_2H_4 + Ar \rightarrow C_6H_{11}^+ + Ar \tag{24}$$

Reaction 21 is a proton transfer process which has been postulated in conventional ion-molecule work (*9*).   It is interesting to note that this reaction probably proceeds at least in part by a stripping-type mechanism which might not involve a deactivatable, condensation-type, activated complex.   Reaction 21 leads to a $C_nH_{2n+1}^+$ chain which does not grow much beyond $C_6H_{13}^+$ even at 1 torr.   The high intensity of the $C_4H_9^+$ ion at 0.1 torr shows that already this ion is unreactive with ethylene.

Reaction 23 initiates the simple argon deactivated condensation of $C_2H_3^+$ to ethylene which leads to a C_nH_{2n-1} chain.   The ion $C_4H_7^+$ is formed at low pressures in conventional mass spectrometers from the decomposition of the excited $C_4H_8^+$—i.e., Reaction 2d.   We think that this process can contribute little to the observed $C_4H_7^+$ and $C_6H_{11}^+$ under our conditions.   The formation of $C_4H_7^+$ from $C_4H_8^+$ was a minor reaction in the xenon runs where the competitive decomposition leading to the C_kH_{2k-1} chain was the important process.   We have high $C_nH_{2n-1}^+$

abundances in argon under conditions where the C_kH_{2k-1} chain is only minor. Furthermore, the C_nH_{2n-1} group in argon follows faithfully the abundance of the $C_2H_3{}^+$ ion.

The results at 0.1-torr ethylene show that the $C_6H_{11}{}^+$ ion reacts only slowly with C_2H_4. Thus, this ion is the last intense member of the C_nH_{2n-1} group while the $C_nH_{2n}{}^+$ series is fully developed up to $C_{10}H_{20}{}^+$.

The spectra in Figure 12 show also the species $C_3H_3{}^+$ and $C_4H_5{}^+$ in considerable abundances. These ions are probably products of the reactions of $C_2H_2{}^+$ with ethylene. Conventional ion-molecule studies (9, 12, 34) have shown that Reactions 25 and 26:

$$C_2H_2{}^+ + C_2H_4 \to (C_4H_6{}^*) + \begin{cases} C_3H_3{}^+ + CH_3 \quad \Delta H = -29 \text{ kcal./mole} \quad (25) \\ C_4H_5{}^+ + H \quad \Delta H = -20 \text{ kcal./mole} \quad (26) \end{cases}$$

occur at low ethylene pressure. The $C_3H_3{}^+$ and $C_4H_5{}^+$ ions could be formed by the same reactions in our system. Considering the efficient stabilization of the excited condensation products $C_nH_{2n}{}^+$ and $C_nH_{2n-1}{}^+$, the decomposition of the excited $C_4H_6{}^+$ ion should be at least one to two orders of magnitude shorter than that of $C_4H_8{}^+$ if the above assignments are correct. Reactions 25 and 26 are considerably more exothermic than 2a, and the higher excess energy will shorten the lifetime. However, structural differences in the activated complex could also be important. The $C_nH_{2n-2}{}^+$, group which could be assigned to a simple condensation of $C_2H_2{}^+$ with ethylene, was found in significant abundance only at millitorr C_2H_4 pressures and xenon as sensitizing gas (see Figure 7). Thus energy carry-over could be an additional contributing factor.

The assignment of the various reaction products to the primary C_2 ions can be checked by adding up the different groups and comparing their relative intensities with those observed for the C_2 ions. The procedure is as follows. We sum $C_nH_{2n}{}^+$ and $C_kH_{2k-1}{}^+$ and assign to $C_2H_4{}^+$, $C_nH_{2n-1}{}^+$, and $C_nH_{2n+1}{}^+$ and assign to $C_2H_3{}^+$, $C_nH_{2n-2}{}^+$, $C_nH_{2n-3}{}^+$, and $C_kH_{2k-3}{}^+$ and assign to $C_2H_2{}^+$. This procedure gives for 2×10^{-3}-torr-C_2H_4 in 35-torr Ar the abundances: $C_2H_4{}^+$, 44%; $C_2H_3{}^+$, 36%; $C_2H_2{}^+$, 20%. These values are almost identical to the C_2 ion abundances observed in the same spectrum. A similar balance but with somewhat less agreement is obtained for the 10-torr Ar spectrum.

The mass spectra of ethylene in krypton were intermediate between those in xenon and argon. These spectra are discussed in more detail elsewhere (23).

Ethylene in He and Ne—Reactions of Excited $C_2H_2{}^+$. A number of spectra with ethylene in He and Ne were obtained. From the Ne spectra a plot analogous to that of Figure 6 could be made. The % $C_2H_3{}^+$ owing to charge transfer from Ne$^+$ was equal to 12% which agrees with the direct measurement of 8% (see breakdown diagram, Figure 11). The % C_2H_3 produced by $Ne_2{}^+$ was equal to 40%. This value leads to a recombination energy of about 19.6 e.v. and to a bond dissociation energy $D(Ne^+—Ne) \approx 1.8$ e.v.

The mass spectra from ethylene in Ne were very similar to those of ethylene in He.   A mass spectrum of 1×10^{-3}-torr C_2H_4 in 20-torr He is shown in Figure 14.   The C_2 ion group contains noticeable amounts of C_2H^+.   The appearance of this ion is predicted from the breakdown graph.   The $C_2H_4^+$ ion and its associated ion-molecule products are present in considerable abundance.   According to the charge transfer diagram this ion cannot be produced in high yield either by He^+ or He_2^+ (the bond dissociation energy of He_2^+ has been estimated (*13*) as 3.1 e.v.).   Thus, the ethylene molecule-ion must be produced by charge transfer from $C_2H_2^+$—i.e., Reaction 20.   From the breakdown diagram

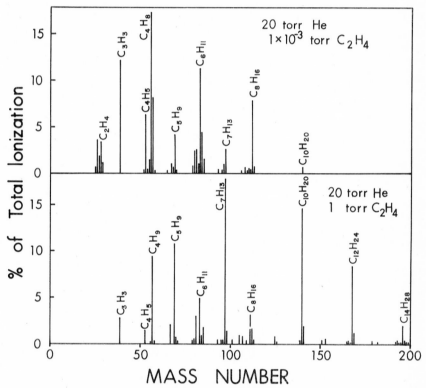

Figure 14.   Ions from Helium and ethylene

we expect $C_2H_2^+$ to be the ion of highest abundance, which is the case if the $C_2H_2^+$ and $C_2H_4^+$ intensities are combined.   The presence of $C_2H_3^+$ in the C_2 ion group is surprising since this ion should not be formed in any abundance by charge transfer from either He^+ or He_2^+.   This suggests that the vinyl ion is formed by a secondary reaction.   The ion-molecule products of $C_2H_3^+$ are the same as those observed in argon.

The mass spectrum of 1-torr ethylene in 20-torr He is also shown in in Figure 14.   Remembering that the (electron impact) ionization cross-section for ethylene is 20 times higher than that for He, we expect almost

50% direct ionization of C_2H_4. The primary ions are thus somewhat different from those at 1×10^{-3}-torr ethylene. The spectrum is, however, useful since it demonstrates that the reactions of the ions $C_4H_5^+$, $C_5H_9^+$, $C_6H_{11}^+$, $C_7H_{13}^+$ with ethylene are slow. The only chain that has developed to any extent is $C_nH_{2n}^+$. The 1-torr spectrum is remarkably similar to that of pure ethylene as will be seen below.

Ions in Pure Ethylene

Some typical spectra of the ions observed in pure ethylene are given in Figure 15. Experiments with C_2D_4 showed (23) that all major ions in the pure C_2H_4 spectra had their isotopic counterparts in the C_2D_4 spectra. Thus, the major ions in the ethylene spectra are genuine and not attributable to impurities. The flow experiments at 5-torr ethylene were obtained with a rate of 380 cc./sec. which corresponds to an average velocity over the leak of 300 cm./sec. and a contact time in the irradiated zone of about 6 msec. The flow flushes out impurities and stable reaction products from the ion source. It also changes the sampling conditions by removing ions with long reaction times. This combined effect produces cleaner spectra in which the major peaks have grown while peaks of small intensity have disappeared. This can be seen clearly from the spectra shown in Figure 15 showing 5-torr spectra with and without flow. We will use the uncluttered flow spectrum at 5 torr as basis for our discussion.

Building on the knowledge gained from the rare gas ethylene mixtures, we can identify the origin of all major ions. The series $C_nH_{2n}^+$ shows three prominent members: $C_{10}H_{20}^+$, $C_{12}H_{24}^+$, and $C_{14}H_{28}^+$. All these ions originate from condensation reactions initiated by $C_2H_4^+$. The intensities of the lower members $C_2H_4^+$, $C_4H_8^+$, $C_6H_{12}^+$ are small since these ions react rapidly with C_2H_4. The members $C_{10}H_{20}^+$, etc. are of high intensity since they react slowly with C_2H_4. The polymerization effectively stops at $C_{14}H_{28}^+$ and $C_{16}H_{32}^+$. The build-up of the $C_nH_{2n}^+$ (n even) series proceeds through a similar set of reactions as those discussed in the section dealing with C_2H_4 in xenon, only now ethylene acts also as quenching gas.

The ions $C_5H_9^+$ and $C_7H_{13}^+$ are the most intense members of the C_kH_{2k-1} series which originates from the $C_nH_{2n}^+$ group by alkyl radical loss. The high intensity of both ions testifies to their low reactivity with ethylene as was already observed with the rare gases. The $C_nH_{2n}^+$ and the C_kH_{2k-1} series are assigned to the $C_2H_4^+$ ion as precursor.

The chain C_nH_{2n+1} represented mainly by $C_4H_9^+$ and $C_6H_{13}^+$ is produced by Reactions 21 and 22 from the $C_2H_3^+$ ion. The vinyl radical ion is also responsible for the $C_nH_{2n-1}^+$ series represented largely by $C_6H_{11}^+$ and $C_8H_{15}^+$.

The ions: $C_3H_3^+$ (Figure 15 does not cover the mass range below 50, but judging by the 1-torr ethylene spectrum shown in Figure 14, $C_3H_3^+$ must have been present also here) $C_4H_5^+$, $C_5H_7^+$, and $C_6H_9^+$ are

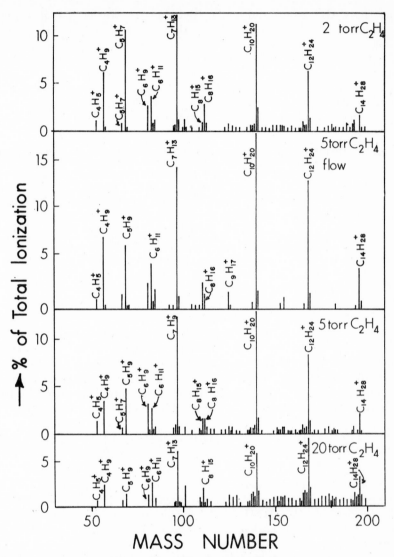

Figure 15.   Ions in pure ethylene

assigned to the precursor $C_2H_2^+$ since they are probably formed by Reactions 25 and 26 followed by some further addition of ethylene.

   The above assignments have been summarized in Table I.   Summing over the ion intensities for the different groups, one obtains the figures in the third row.   The total of assigned ions adds to some 86%.   Setting this equal to 100%, we obtain the groups in percent of the accounted ions.   The value resulting for the $C_2H_2^+$ group is low.   Assuming that the charge transfer Reaction 20 was operative, we must subtract from the $C_2H_4^+$ group and add to the $C_2H_2^+$. Wexler (*34*) in conventional low pressure studies has found that about $^2/_3$ of the $C_2H_2^+$ charge transfers to ethylene while the remainder reacts by the condensation processes of Reactions 25 and 26. The corrected values in the table were obtained by multiplying the $C_2H_2^+$ assignment by 3 and subtracting an equivalent amount from the $C_2H_4^+$ assignment. The result of this operation agrees well with primary alpha particle mass spectra (*30*) and electron impact spectra obtained at 50 volts.

Table I. Ion Product Balance from 5-torr Ethylene Spectra (Flow)

Primary Ion	$C_2H_4^+$	$C_2H_3^+$	$C_2H_2^+$
Assigned Products	$C_nH_{2n}^+$, $C_kH_{2k}^+{}_{-1}{}^a$	$\begin{array}{c}C_nH_{2n}^+{}_{+1}\\C_nH_{2n}^+{}_{-1}\end{array}$	$\begin{array}{c}C_3H_3^+,\ C_4H_{5+},\\C_5,H_7^+,\ C_6H_9^+\end{array}$
Product (%) of total ionization	60.8	17.4	7.7
% of accounted ions	71	20	9
% corrected for charge transfer from $C_2H_2^+$	53	20	27
% in alpha particle ionization[b]	53	20	23
% from 50-volt electrons	50	25	25

[a] n = even, k = odd
[b] From alpha-particle mass spectra at low pressure (*29*).

An estimate for the G value for ethylene removal by ionic reactions can be made from the ion intensities of the 5-torr spectrum. First, the total intensity of accounted ions is set equal to unity. Then we multiply the intensities of the given ions by the number of ethylene molecules used up in their formation. Some of the weighing factors used were:

$$C_nH_{2n}^+\left(\frac{n}{2}\right),\ C_kH_{2k-1}\left(\frac{k+1}{2}\right),\ C_nH_{2n+1}\left(\frac{n}{2}+1\right),\ C_nH_{2n-1}\left(\frac{n}{2}\right),\ \text{etc.}$$

Proceeding in this manner one finds that some 4.5 ethylene molecules are used up per ion formed. Using the established value of 3.88 ion pairs per 100 e.v. we find a G value for ethylene used up by ionic reactions at 5 torr pressure $G(-\Delta C_2H_4) \approx 17$. This shows that ionic mechanisms account for the major part of the ethylene consumed in gas phase radiolysis.

A simple order of magnitude estimate of the rate constants for reaction with ethylene can be made for the high intensity ions in the 5-torr spectrum. Since the average reaction time, limited by neutralization or removal from the ion source is a few milliseconds (*see* section dealing with sampling conditions and section on ethylene in xenon) we can take 1 msec. as the half-life of these ions in 5-torr ethylene. This leads to $k = 10^{-14}$ to 10^{-15} cc. molecule^{-1} sec.$^{-1}$ as a rate constant for further reaction with ethylene. The value for k_{5a} found by the kinetic treatment above was 8×10^{-14}.

The spectra at 20-torr ethylene (Figure 15) are considerably more complex. Part of this must be caused by the absence of flow. Unfortunately the flow experiments are not easily executed at high pressures since they require large quantities of purified material.   Some of the increase in complexity must also be caused by a continuation of the ion-molecule reactions.   Measurements in the 200–1000 mass range at 20 torr showed no significant increase of the high mass ions.   We expect that the proliferation of ionic products in the mass range 100–250 continues with pressure increase so that it remains questionable whether an adequate account of the ionic reactions in ethylene at some 100 torr pressure can be given and whether such a pursuit is really of scientific interest.

Ions in Ethylene Containing Nitric Oxide

Nitric oxide is a well known free-radical scavenger used extensively in systems where free radicals are generated by thermal and photochemical means.   NO has been used as radical scavenger also in radiolytic systems and to distinguish between free radical and ionic mechanisms. It has been pointed (2, 21) out that the low ionization potential of NO and other free radical scavengers may involve them also in the ionic mechanism by charge transfer reactions.   Taking advantage of the expected charge transfer effect Meisels (28) has used NO as charge scavenger in ethylene.   At 100-torr ethylene pressure adding small quantities of NO increased the butene yields.   Saturation was reached with some 10% NO.   Meisels interpreted the results by the charge transfer Reaction 30.

$$C_4H_8{}^+ + NO \rightarrow NO^+ + C_4H_8 \qquad\qquad (30)$$

Independently of Meisels we had became interested (21) in the effect of NO and chose ethylene as one system of study.   It is therefore interesting to compare some of the results even though our study is still not completed.

Before discussing our ethylene–NO spectra we wish to point out some of the findings of the previous sections here which bear on Meisels work.   We found that the rate constants for the simple chain C_nH_{2n+2} (Reaction 1a) decrease at the $C_4H_8{}^+$ level to 2×10^{-12} and then continue to decrease more slowly reaching values of 10^{-14} at $C_{10}H_{20}{}^+$.   It was further shown that in pure ethylene the chain $C_nH_{2n}{}^+$ is still present, which means that C_2H_4 itself can act also as an excess energy quencher. In a separate study with the Cermack (5) technique we measured relative charge transfer cross-sections from $C_2H_4{}^+$ and $C_4H_8{}^+$ to NO.   We found (32) that the cross-section from $C_2H_4{}^+$ is somewhat larger than that from $C_4H_8{}^+$ and that both cross-sections correspond to thermal rate constants in the range 10^{-9} cc. molecules^{-1} sec.$^{-1}$ (Work done after this paper was submitted indicates that the butene-2 ion does not transfer charge to NO.)   The above findings corroborate Meisels' work.   Thus the charge transfer occurs at the $C_4H_8{}^+$ level since 10% NO cannot compete efficiently with the fast $C_2H_4{}^+$ reaction with ethylene but can compete with the much slower $C_4H_8{}^+$ reaction.

Unfortunately a closer look into the system, afforded by the α-particle mass spectrometer, shows that the situation is considerably more complicated. Some representative spectra of ethylene–NO systems are shown in Figure 16. All empirical formula assignments were obtained with the use of $N^{15}O$. The top spectrum is that of 20-torr C_2H_4 and 0.1% NO. Spectra obtained at the same pressure and higher NO content did not change the picture materially. Thus at 10% NO, the peaks $C_6H_{14}NO$, $C_7H_{14}NO$, $C_8H_{16}NO$, etc. were still of nearly equal abundance. The only important change was the increase of the C_4H_8NO peak to nearly the intensity of the peaks just mentioned. The appearance of a new peak

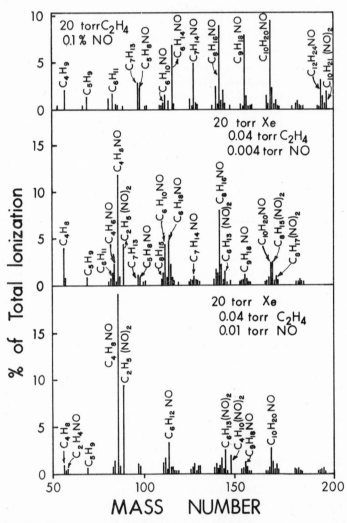

Figure 16. Effect of adding nitric oxide on ionic composition

$C_2H_5(NO)_2{}^+$ was also observed. The total ionization was essentially unaffected by adding NO, and no NO^+ could be detected.

To examine the situation under simpler conditions, runs with xenon as sensitizer were made using low pressures of ethylene and NO. Two spectra are shown in Figure 16. The simplest spectrum is obtained with 25% NO. $C_4H_8NO^+$ and $C_2H_5(NO)_2{}^+$ dominate the spectrum.

The observed ions indicate some interesting chemistry. Thus, in the species $C_nH_{2n}NO^+$ (n even or odd), the NO might be attached to the free electron of the molecular olefin ion forming a nitroso group. The structures $C_2H_5(NO)_2{}^+$ and $C_6H_{13}(NO)_2{}^+$ could be considered as protonated dinitroso compounds. In xenon $C_2H_4{}^+$ represents some 80% of the C_2 precursor ions. The $C_2H_5(NO)_2{}^+$ is thus formed via this ion. The most likely reaction seems the attack on $C_4H_8NO^+$ according to Reaction 31. This reaction is considered to proceed in two steps.

$$C_4H_8{}^+NO + 2NO \rightarrow C_2H_3NO + C_2H_5(NO)_2{}^+ \tag{31}$$

Thus, nitric oxide seems to react in a complex manner. Simple addition to existing ions and initiation of new reactions, which might involve even carbon bond scission, seem to occur. At present our study of this system is incomplete. We have not been able to reconcile the complexity of the spectra with the findings of Meisels which are otherwise supported by our rate constant determinations.

Literature Cited

(1) Abbe, J. C., Adloff, J. P., *Comp. Rend. Acad. Sci. Paris* **258**, 3003 (1964).
(2) Ausloos, P., Lias, S. G., Gorden, Jr., R., *J. Chem. Phys.* **39**, 3341 (1963).
(3) Bates, D. R., *Phys. Rev.* **77**, 118 (1950).
(4) Becker, P. M., Lampe, F. W., *J. Chem. Phys.* **42**, 3857 (1965).
(5) Cermak, V., Herman Z., *Nucleonics* **19**, 106 (1961).
(6) Collin, J. E., *Bull. Soc. Chim. Belges* **71**, 15 (1962).
(7) Dahler, J. S., Franklin, J. L., Munson, M. S., Field, F. H., *J. Chem. Phys.* **36**, 3332 (1962).
(8) Field, F. H., Franklin, J. L., "Electron Impact Phenomena," Academic Press, Inc., New York, 1957.
(9) Field, F. H., *J. Am. Chem. Soc.* **83**, 1523 (1961).
(10) Giomousis, G., Stevenson, D. P., *J. Chem. Phys.* **29**, 294 (1958).
(11) Harrington, R. E., Rabinovitch, B. S., Hoare, M. R., *J. Chem. Phys.* **33**, 744 (1960).
(12) Harrison, A. G., *Can. J. Chem.* **41**, 236 (1963).
(13) Herzberg, G., "Spectra of Diatomic Molecules" 2nd ed., p. 536, D. van Nostrand Co., Inc., New York, 1950.
(14) Hogg, A. M., Kebarle, P., *J. Chem. Phys.* **43**, 449 (1965).
(15) Hogg, A. M., Haynes, R. M., Kebarle, P., *J. Am. Chem. Soc.* **88**, 28 (1966).
(16) Hornbeck, J. A., Molnar, J. P., *Phys. Rev.* **84**, 621 (1951).
(17) Hornbeck, J. A., *Phys. Rev.* **84**, 1072 (1951).
(18) Kaul, W., *Proc. Intern. Conf. Ionization Phenomena Gases, 4th, Paris, 1963*, p. 169.
(19) Kebarle, P., Godbole, E. W., *J. Chem. Phys.* **39**, 1131 (1963).
(20) Kebarle, P., Hogg, A. M., *Advan. Mass Spectrometry* **3**, 401 (1965).
(21) Kebarle, P., Hogg, A. M., *J. Chem. Phys.* **42**, 668 (1965).
(22) Kebarle, P., Hogg, A. M., *Ibid.*, **42**, 798 (1965).
(23) Kebarle, P., Haynes, R. M., *Ibid.*, to be published.
(24) Kohlmaier, G. H., Rabinovitch, B. S., *Ibid.* **38**, 1692 (1963).
(25) Loeb, L. B., "Basic Processes in Gaseous Electronics," p. 703ff., University of California Press, Berkeley and Los Angeles, 1955.

(26) McDaniel, E. W., "Collision Phenomena in Gases," p. 490, John Wiley and Sons, Inc., New York, 1964.
(27) Maier-Leibnitz, H., *Z. Physik* **95,** 499 (1935).
(28) Meisels, G. G., *J. Chem. Phys.* **42,** 3237 (1965).
(29) Phelps, A. V., Brown, S. C., *Phys. Rev.* **86,** 102 (1952).
(30) Rudolph, P. S., Melton, C. E., private communication.
(31) Searles, S., Kebarle, P., *J. Chem. Phys.*, to be published.
(32) Searles, S., Kebarle, P., to be published.
(33) Tal'roze, V. L., *Pure Appl. Chem.* **5,** 455 (1962).
(34) Wexler, S., Marshall, R., *J. Am. Chem. Soc.* **86,** 781 (1964).
(35) Wiberg, K. B., Bartley, W. J., Lossing, F. P., *J. Am. Chem. Soc.* **84,** 3980 (1962).

RECEIVED May 10, 1966

Formation and Reactions of Ions in Ethylene Radiolysis

G. G. MEISELS

University of Houston, Houston, Tex. 77004

Phenomenological evidence for the participation of ionic precursors in radiolytic product formation and the applicability of mass spectral information on fragmentation patterns and ion-molecule reactions to radiolysis conditions are reviewed. Specific application of the methods in the ethylene system indicates the formation of the primary ions, $C_2H_4{}^+$, $C_2H_3{}^+$, and $C_2H_2{}^+$, with yields of ca. 1.5, 1.0, and 0.8 ions/100 e.v., respectively. The primary ions form intermediate collision complexes with ethylene. Intermediates $[C_4H_8{}^+]$ and $[C_4H_7{}^+]$ are stable (dissociation rate constants $\leq 10^7$ sec.$^{-1}$) and form C_6 intermediates which dissociate (rate constants $\leq 10^9$ sec.$^{-1}$). The transmission coefficient for the third-order ion-molecule reactions appears to be less than 0.02, and such inefficient steps are held responsible for the absence of ionic polymerization.

Ion-molecule reactions have been known for nearly 50 years, but have received little attention until about a decade ago (*51*) when their occurrence in a mass spectrometer was reported by several investigators (*19, 29, 55*). The present volume demonstrates the considerable current interest in this area.

One of the chief reasons for the recent extensive work in this field has been the recognition that ion-molecule reactions are highly relevant to radiation chemistry. The possibility that certain simple reactions, such as the formation of $H_3{}^+$, participate in the mechanism of product formation was appreciated much earlier (*14*), but wider applicability of this concept required that the generality of such reactions be demonstrated by an independent, unequivocal method. Mass spectrometry has been the predominant means of investigating ion-molecule reactions. The direct identification of reactant and product ions is appealing, at least, in part, because of the conceptual simplicity of this approach. However, the neutral products of ion-molecule reactions cannot be determined directly and must be inferred. Gross chemical measurements can serve as an auxiliary technique since they allow identification of uncharged species and permit the study of higher order reactions in homogeneous systems. Radiation chemistry has been an area which drew on mass spectrometric results to interpret its findings. Recently, it has been able to resolve seeming discrepancies in mass spectrometric investigations, to aid the investigator in determining correct mechanisms, and to suggest new reactions.

A major complication in applying radiation chemical techniques to ion-molecule reaction studies is the formation of nonionic initial species by high energy radiation. Another difficulty arises from the neutralization of ions, which may also result in the formation of free radicals and stable products. The chemical effects arising from the formation of ions and their reactions with molecules are therefore superimposed on those of the neutral species resulting from excitation and neutralization. To derive information of ion-molecule reactions, it is necessary to identify unequivocally products typical of such reactions. Progress beyond a speculative rationalization of results is possible only when concrete evidence that ionic species participate in the mechanism of product formation can be presented. This evidence is the first subject of this discussion.

Assigning a mechanism for the formation of products resulting from ionic intermediates is aided by our knowledge of the probable primary ions and the elementary ion-molecule reactions which they may undergo. The second subject to be examined is the applicability of fragmentation patterns and mass spectrometric ion-molecule reaction studies to radiolysis conditions. Lastly, the formation and the chemistry of the ionic species in ethylene radiolysis will be summarized.

Phenomenological Evidence for Ionic Precursors of Products

The arguments which have been advanced to support mechanisms of product formation involving ionic intermediates can be classified into two principal groups.

Inconsistency of Product Distribution with Known Reactions of Excited Species and Free Radicals. This argument has been used most widely but is often equivocal because it presumes a detailed knowledge of the formation and dissociation of excited species produced during radiolysis. The spectroscopy and the photochemistry of these states are often unknown, and conclusions are based solely on the behavior of the states with known behavior. Generally, triplet states are unimportant in radiation chemistry (41), and the relevant states are singlets whose absorption usually falls into the vacuum ultraviolet. A further complication arises from formation of superexcited states (41, 42) at energies above the ionization potential and their dissociation into neutral products. Recent photochemical studies at short wavelengths have indicated that superexcited states dissociate much like the singlet states (12).

A simplified experimental system results when free radical scavengers such as nitric oxide, iodine, or oxygen are added to the samples before radiolysis (*2, 48, 65*). This eliminates products resulting from free radical reactions and allows one to study molecular detachment processes and, in the presence of other additives, certain ion-molecule reactions. The possibilities of charge transfer (*35*) and energy transfer (*34*) may complicate the results and interpretation, and the study of ionic sequences resulting in free radicals is essentially precluded by the use of scavengers. Radical reactions have been studied extensively by other techniques, and a thorough analysis of such reactions in a radiolytic system can be helpful in deducing a mechanism (*32*).

Perhaps the most powerful variant of this approach is the use of labelled starting materials or additives and analyzing the products for isotopic distribution. This technique is valuable in assessing the importance of molecular detachment processes. Moreover, unique distributions result from proton, hydride, and H_2^- transfer particularly in the presence of radical scavengers and these have been studied extensively (*4, 6*).

The Application of Electrostatic Fields. The use of electric fields as a diagnostic tool in the radiolysis of gases was first introduced by Essex (*13*). Certain revisions of the original interpretation were required (*6, 37*) largely because the importance of ion-molecule reactions had been rediscovered.

This approach is quite complex in practice but is particularly intriguing because it appears direct and simple in principle. It is based on the knowledge that applying an electrostatic field during radiolysis has three main consequences: (a) it leads to the neutralization of ions at the electrode surface rather than homogeneously in the gas phase; (b) it shortens the lifetime of the charged species in the gas phase; (c) it leads to a shift in the energy distribution of all species toward a higher value. While this shift is relatively small for molecular and radical ions, it is considerable for electrons, which may obtain average energies of several electron volts.

Although the increase in the mean energy of the ions will not be enough to excite neutral molecules, it will decrease the cross-section of ion-molecule reactions. This decrease, coupled with the shortening of the ion lifetime, will lead to a reduction of the total number of collisions the charge may experience whether or not it undergoes chemical change on collision. The net effect which one might observe chemically would be a shorter chain length for ionic polymerization if that were the major mode of reaction. However, the charge will still make more than 10^3 collisions before neutralization at the electrodes, and one would expect that primary fragmentation processes, the first few ion-molecule reactions, and products arising from them would not be affected. In the presence of an electric field, ions will be neutralized at or near the electrodes, and thus the recombination energy may dissipate near the surface. The inhibition of homogeneous neutralization may thus lead to a reduction in product yields even at relatively low applied fields. In summary, it appears that the yield of products resulting from ionic precursors should be essentially independent of applied fields or decreased by them.

The increase in the electron energy may have several consequences. It may lead to dissociative or nondissociative electron attachment (54, 61). This would give rise to a step enhancement as in N_2O (8). The most important possibility is electronic excitation of the molecular species, which should manifest itself by an increased yield of all products arising from excited intermediates as the mean energy of the electron swarm rises with field strength.

From this discussion one would expect a clear distinction between ionic and nonionic types of precursors. Two complications exist. The first is caused by the possibility that the same product or intermediate may be produced by a mechanism involving ionic species and by one involving nonionic ones. For example, there can be little doubt that hydrogen may be produced from ethylene by dissociation of both an excited state and an excited ion,

$$C_2H_4^* \rightarrow C_2H_2 + H_2 \tag{1}$$

$$(C_2H_4^*)^+ \rightarrow C_2H_2^+ + H_2 \tag{2}$$

Both reactions are known from photochemistry and mass spectrometry. Enhancement of the hydrogen yield by electrostatic fields therefore cannot be used to argue against Reaction 2.

The second complication results from the nature of the excitation act. The degradation spectrum of electrons resulting from high energy radiation has a relatively high mean energy (42) well in excess of the ionization potential. This results in the excitation of the substrate molecule to optically allowed and superexcited states. On the other hand, applying electrostatic fields at field strengths below those causing secondary ionization results in an average value of the electron energy well below the lowest excited level of the substrate molecule. Excitation is therefore caused by the high energy tail of the distribution, with a maximum number of electrons having sufficient energy to excite only the lowest state, generally a triplet or other optically forbidden level. One must recognize therefore that using the applied field technique will not lead to the same distribution of excited species as does high energy radiation, and products resulting from ionic intermediates will be indistinguishable from those having highly excited and superexcited states as precursors. Fortunately, the dissociation of superexcited states seems to lead to the same products as that of the singlet states below the ionization limit (12).

Application to Ethylene Radiolysis. The predominant products of the vacuum ultraviolet photochemistry of ethylene are hydrogen, acetylene, ethane and butane, with minor amounts of butene-1 and higher hydrocarbons (40, 49). Although these are also the chief identified products in the radiolysis (26, 32, 48, 65), minor but significant amounts of methane, propane (27), and other hydrocarbons are observed as well. Moreover, ca. 40% of the ethylene consumed results in unknown and presumably higher molecular weight or polymeric products. Adding oxygen as a scavenger eliminates all volatile products except hydrogen, methane, acetylene, and certain higher olefins (32, 37, 48).

The radiolysis of equimolar amounts of ethylene and perdeutero-ethylene indicated a similarity with photochemistry by showing that hydrogen is eliminated in a molecular process (*48*). Acetylene was produced in the unmixed form only when nitric oxide was present, but considerable isotopic mixing was observed in the scavenger-free radiolysis, pointing out an important difference from photochemistry. This result will be discussed in more detail below. Moreover, radiolysis of CH_2CD_2 and CHDCHD demonstrated a significant difference in the distribution of the hydrogens from that observed in the vacuum ultraviolet photochemistry (*2*).

The reactions of free radicals in ethylene are well known (*5, 24*), and the applicability of this information to radiation chemistry has been demonstrated (*32*). Kinetic analysis of radical reactions revealed that the formation of methyl radicals and methane cannot be ascribed to excited precursors alone (*32, 37*).

Electrostatic fields applied slightly above the onset of the saturation region had little effect on product distribution (*37*). This presumably indicates that homogeneous ion-electron recombination is the same as neutralization at the electrodes, or that one is simply not observing the products of neutralization in either case.

A further increase in the electrostatic field has dramatic effects on the product distribution before secondary ionization sets in. Methane and ethane yields follow the predictions for products having ionic and nonionic precursors almost ideally (Figure 1).

The average energy of the electron swarm in ethylene near the onset of secondary ionization is only about 2.2 e.v. while the lowest energy levels of ethylene correspond to the spin-forbidden triplet state at 4.5 e.v. and a singlet state of uncertain assignment at 6.5 e.v. (*43*). The dissociation of the former is largely quenched at 100 torr (*11*) so that the contribution of the latter should be important in our system even though only a small fraction of the electron swarm will be sufficiently energetic to excite it (Figure 1).

A primary process leading to vinyl radicals

$$C_2H_4^* \rightarrow C_2H_3 + H \tag{3}$$

accounts for 16% of the dissociation events induced by the electrostatic field (*37*); it is not observed in the 2537-A. mercury photosensitized photolysis (4.9 e.v.) and is unimportant in the direct photolysis at 1470 A. (8.43 e.v.) and 1236 A. (10.03 e.v.) (*40, 49*). It seems reasonable to assume that vinyl radical formation results predominantly from the 6.5-e.v. singlet. Although the energy of that state is attainable by mercury resonance radiation at 1849 A. (6.70 e.v.), the extinction coefficient is small, and no search for C_2H_3 has been made in the direct photolysis (*40*). This state should be readily attainable by the mercury (6^1P_1) sensitization technique (*64*). A study of the ethylene system using that method indicates that vinyl radical formation is considerably more important there than in the applied field radiolysis (*45*). This observation strongly supports the present interpretation.

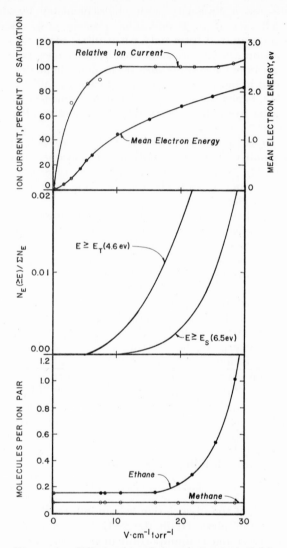

*Figure 1.   Effects of applying electrostatic fields
during radiolysis*

*Top: typical saturation curve and variation of mean
electron energy with applied field.   Middle: fraction
of the electron swarm exceeding the specific energy at
each field strength.   Calculated assuming constant
collision cross-section and Maxwell-Boltzman distribution.   Bottom: variation of products typical of
involvement of ionic precursors (methane) and excited
intermediates (ethane) with applied field strength*

Two of the many products of ethylene radiolysis—methane and propane—show no or only negligible variation with field strength. Methane is produced by a molecular elimination process, as evidenced by the inability of oxygen or nitric oxide to quench its formation even when these additives are present in 65 mole % concentration (*34*). Propane is completely eliminated by trace amounts of the above scavengers, suggesting methyl and ethyl radicals as precursors:

$$CH_3 + C_2H_5 \nearrow \begin{array}{l} C_3H_8 \qquad\qquad (4a) \\ \\ CH_4 + C_2H_4 \quad (4b) \end{array}$$

The observed product distribution indicates that Reaction 4 consumes virtually all methyl radicals. The formation of ethyl radicals is rapidly enhanced by electrostatic fields, clearly evident from the large increase in the yields of butane and ethane. These result predominantly from Reactions 5a and 5b.

$$2C_2H_5 \nearrow \begin{array}{l} C_4H_{10} \qquad\qquad (5a) \\ \\ C_2H_6 + C_2H_4 \quad (5b) \end{array}$$

The species participating in propane formation whose yield is not affected by the applied field must therefore by the methyl radical. We conclude that methane and methyl radicals are neutral products of ion-molecule sequences.

Applicability of Mass Spectrometric Information to Radiation Chemistry

Mass spectrometric studies yield principally three types of information useful to the radiation chemist: the major primary ions one should be concerned with, their reactions with neutral molecules, and thermodynamic information which allows one to eliminate certain reactions on the basis of endothermicity. In addition, attempts at theoretical interpretations of mass spectral fragmentation patterns permit estimates of unimolecular dissociation constants for excited parent ions.

Fragmentation Patterns. It has long been known that the fragmentation of simple molecules is relatively independent of the energy of the incident electrons at energies exceeding *ca*. 40–50 e.v. (*25, 53*). This might lead one to expect similar ion distributions in mass spectrometry and radiation chemistry, and remarkable agreement between predicted and observed products has been reported (*20, 21, 22*). Such correlations may be fortuitous (*2, 51*) since mass spectral patterns are obtained at charge lifetimes of the order of 10^{-5}–10^{-6} sec. while collisional deactivation may occur within 10^{-10} sec. at pressures of 1 atmosphere. This possibility was demonstrated drastically by calculating the fragmentation at 10^{-11} sec., predictable from the original statistical theory of mass spectra (*51*), and it was suggested that fragmentation of ethylene ion may be completely inhibited at 1 atmosphere. More recent versions of this theory (57) based on the variation of the effective number of oscillators with increasing energy, have shown that the probability of fragmentation rises sharply with excess energy above the reaction threshold, but that this effect levels off rapidly. Hence, the importance of collisional deactivation should be considerably less than that suggested originally. The variation of the fragmentation pattern with the lifetime between collisions has been calculated by this method (58), and only those fragment ions which arise from two or more successive dissociation steps are seriously affected by the shortened period. The expected minor decrease in fragmentation and increase in parent ion abundance with increase in pressure was verified later (3), and parent ions were found to be somewhat more common than in the mass spectrometer.

Energy carry-over may be another factor contributing to a lessening of the fragmentation dependence of pressure. The ion to be deactivated by collision possesses excess energy and may be able to undergo ion-molecule reactions endothermic for the ground state ion. The products of the excitation reactions may be indistinguishable from those of the fragment ion. There is considerable precedent for the participation of excitation energy in the thermodynamic balance of an ion-molecule reaction (9, 30).

Therefore, mass spectral fragmentation patterns can be used only as a guide. In combination with W, the energy required to form an ion pair by high energy radiation (63), fragmentation patterns can give a lower limit of the parent ion yield and indicate the nature of the fragment ions. If the latter arise from two successive fragmentation processes, their yield should be substantially smaller than expected from the pattern. If they are the result of only one fragmentation, their yield in the radiolysis will be larger if their mass spectral abundance is small because of successive dissociation, and the same or smaller when successive dissociation processes are not important.

Ion-Molecule Reactions. The list of ion-molecule reactions observed by mass spectrometry is highly impressive at this time; we can easily count several hundred. Most of these were observed at relatively low pressures and in the presence of a draw-out or pusher field in the ionization chamber. Using this information to account for the radiation chemical product distribution requires one to recognize its restrictions to this use.

The first complication to be considered is the presence of an electrostatic field during the mass spectrometric study of the reaction. Only few quantitative studies have allowed for the possible contribution of "hard collisions" to cross-section (25), and the possibility that competitive reactions of the same ion may depend on ion energy is generally neglected in assigning ion-molecule reaction sequences. These effects, however, do not preclude qualitative application of mass spectrometric results to radiation chemistry.

A much more difficult and complex problem is the effect of pressure on successive ion-molecule reactions. In radiolytic experiments, the charge survives over 10^5 collisions, each of which might change its chemical identity, and the ion will always be of thermal velocity. Moreover, the time between successive collisions is of the order of 10^{-10} sec. while it is more than 2 orders of magnitude longer in most mass spectrometric experiments. Thus, intermediate ions undergoing further reactions might be quite different in radiolysis and in mass spectrometry.

Two approaches have been used to elucidate the nature of higher order ion-molecule reactions. In the first, the sequence of reactions is deduced by following the change in product ion distribution as the source pressure is increased to several tenths of a torr (*16, 38, 62*). This allows one to estimate rate constants under mass spectrometric conditions and usually permits identification of the reaction sequences which give rise to tertiary and quaternary product ions. The second approach relies on sampling ions from a high pressure (several hundred torr) volume under irradiation with alpha particles (*23, 46*). This technique is more difficult because it requires sampling of charged species through an orifice. Moreover, the gross distribution of ions makes it difficult to assign precursor ions and the reaction sequence which leads to a particular species. Nonetheless, it represents an interesting approach to radiolysis studies.

Application to Ethylene Radiolysis. The predominant ions in the mass spectrum of ethylene (*1*) are ethylene, vinyl, and acetylene ions, which together account for over 85% of the total ionization. A total of 38% of all ions are $C_2H_4^+$, and since W(ethylene) $= 25.9$ e.v./ion pair, the parent ion should be produced with a yield of at least 1.5 ions/100 e.v. absorbed in ethylene. Similar calculations for the probable yields of the other major ions lead to estimates of 0.96 vinyl ions/100 e.v. and 0.94 acetylene ions/100 e.v. Successive dissociations are relatively unimportant in ethylene.

The ion-molecule reactions in ethylene were among the first to be studied in detail by mass spectrometric techniques (*19, 50, 55*). Initially, only second-order reactions were observed, and their nature and cross-sections are now well established. An important step was made when the investigations were extended to higher pressures (*16, 38, 62*). Two alternative mechanisms, were proposed to account for the formation of higher order ions (i.e., those where at least two neutral entities must have reacted with a primary ion). The first possibility is that the intermediate, second-order complex (i.e., $C_4H_8^+$, $C_4H_7^+$, or $C_4H_6^+$) is short lived and dissociates before colliding with ethylene. Higher order ions then result primarily by ethylene addition to product ions. Alternately, the intermediate, second-order complex may be relatively long lived and lead to higher order reaction products by collisions with neutral ethylene molecules. The sequence of reactions suggested by Field (*16*) is in a simplified form below.

$$C_2H_4^+ + C_2H_4 \rightarrow [C_4H_8^+] \tag{6}$$

$$[C_4H_8^+] \nearrow \; C_3H_5^+ + CH_3 \tag{7a}$$
$$\searrow \; C_4H_7^+ + H \tag{7b}$$

$$[C_4H_8^+] + C_2H_4 \rightarrow [C_6H_{12}^+] \tag{8}$$

$$[C_6H_{12}^+] \begin{cases} \nearrow C_5H_9^+ + CH_3 & (9a) \\ \rightarrow C_4H_8^+ + C_2H_4 & (9b) \\ \searrow C_3H_5^+ C_3H_7 & (9c) \end{cases}$$

$$C_2H_3^+ + C_2H_4 \rightarrow [C_4H_7^+] \tag{10}$$

$$[C_4H_7^+] \rightarrow C_2H_5^+ + C_2H_2 \tag{11}$$

$$[C_4H_7^+] + C_2H_4 \rightarrow [C_6H_{11}^+] \tag{12}$$

$$[C_6H_{11}^+] \begin{cases} \nearrow C_5H_7^+ + CH_4 & (13a) \\ \searrow C_6H_5^+ + 3H_2 & (13b) \end{cases}$$

$$C_2H_2^+ + C_2H_4 \rightarrow [C_4H_6^+] \tag{14}$$

$$[C_4H_6^+] \begin{cases} \nearrow C_2H_4^+ + C_2H_2 & (15a) \\ \rightarrow C_3H_3^+ + CH_3 & (15b) \\ \searrow C_4H_5^+ + H & (15c) \end{cases}$$

$$[C_4H_6^+] + C_2H_4 \rightarrow [C_6H_{10}^+] \tag{16}$$

$$[C_6H_{10}^+] \begin{cases} \nearrow C_6H_7^+ + H_2 + H & (17a) \\ \rightarrow C_5H_5^+ + CH_3 + H_2 & (17b) \\ \searrow C_4H_6^+ + C_2H_4 & (17c) \end{cases}$$

To distinguish between the two interpretations on the basis of mass spectrometric information alone is difficult and has not yet been accomplished. There are, however, striking differences. Reaction 13a provides a means for forming molecular methane while the mechanism based on a short lived second-order $[C_4H_7^+]$ ion does not. Reactions 3–14 suggest a chain of steps capable of producing radical and molecular species while the earlier interpretation could only account for an essentially constant, pressure independent yield and ionic polymerization. Lastly, Field's mechanism suggests a lifetime of greater than 10^{-8} sec. for the intermediate second-order complex. All of these features can be examined in the radiation chemistry of ethylene.

Yields and Reactions of Major Ions in Radiolysis

Ethylene Ion and Its Sequents. CHARGE EXCHANGE. The second-order intermediate butene ion, $C_4H_8^+$ may have a lifetime exceeding 10^{-8} sec. before unimolecular fragmentation. This should allow its neutralization by charge exchange with all substances whose ionization potential is smaller than the recombination energy of the butene ion. As a first approximation one may assume that this energy equals the ionization potential of the butenes (9.58 e.v. for butene-1 and 9.13 e.v. for butene-2) (60). Neutralization by charge exchange is exothermic by less than 2 e.v. even for the additive of lowest ionization potential and should lead to the formation of stable butene:

$$C_4H_8^+ + CA \rightarrow C_4H_8 + CA^+ \tag{18a}$$

where CA represents the charge acceptor.   Alternately, encounter of the two species may lead to transfer of a group

$$C_4H_8{}^+ + CA \rightarrow X^+ + Y \qquad\qquad (18b)$$

where Y represents any formula except C_4H_8.   The yield of butene observed in the presence of charge acceptors should therefore be equal to or less than the yield of the butene ion.

Enhancement of the total butene yield is observed when various additives whose ionization potential falls below about 9.4 e.v. are present during ethylene radiolysis (*35*).   This is consistent with the above interpretation (Figure 2).   In the vacuum ultraviolet photolysis of cyclobutane the yield of butenes varies with the ionization potential of the additives in the same way as observed here (*12*).   The maximum enhancement corresponds closely to the yield of $C_4H_8{}^+$, as expected from our mechanism.

Considerable support exists for Reaction 18a (*35*).   The application of an electrostatic field during radiolysis of ethylene-nitric oxide (*I.P.* 9.25 e.v.) mixtures showed no enhancement of the butene yields, consistent with an ionic mechanism.   When mixtures of C_2D_4 and C_2H_4 are irradiated in the presence of nitric oxide, product butene consists almost entirely of C_4H_8, $C_4D_4H_4$, and C_4D_8—evidence for a molecular association mechanism.

The separation of the product butenes into their isomers and subsequent isotopic analysis leads to the distribution summarized in Table I. The 2-butenes have an isotopic composition close to that reported earlier for the total butenes while a sizable fraction of butene-1 seems to have arisen by processes involving more than two ethylene molecules.   If we assume that the mechanism for the formation of butenes in the absence of a charge acceptor is not affected by the additive, we may calculate from the gross yields (Table III of Ref. *35*) that in the nitric oxide scavenged radiolysis 45% of the butene-1, 6.4% of *cis*-butene-2, and 4.6% of *trans*-butene-2 result from nonionic processes.   This is substantiated by our results, and one may conclude that nonionic processes make a constant contribution $G(C_4H_8, \text{ nonionic}) \approx 0.15$ molecules/100 e.v. to the yield of butenes in the presence of charge acceptors.   Since the maximum $G(C_4H_8) = 1.62$ molecules/100 e.v., it follows that $G(C_4H_8{}^+)$ $\simeq 1.47$ ions/100 e.v.

A comparison of the mass spectrometric fragmentation of the product butenes and the isotopic distribution of the propenyl ion resulting from the ion-molecule reaction provides further evidence.   Fragmentation of the butenes in a mass spectrometer can be restricted readily to propenyl ion by selecting the proper ionizing voltage.   Fragmentation of $C_4H_4D_4$ resulting from radiolysis is given in Table II along with the isotopic distribution resulting from the ion-molecule reaction in the ionization chamber of an Atlas CH-4 mass spectrometer.   It was operated at reduced ionizing voltage so that only reactions of $C_2H_4{}^+$ were observed.   The intensities of the perprotonated and the perdeuterated species are not given since they yield no further information than that in Table I.   The distribution

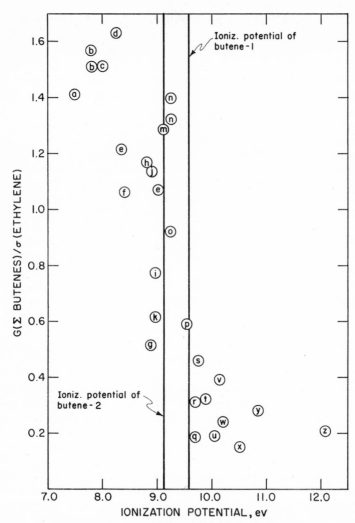

Figure 2. *Enhancement of total butene yields from 100-torr ethylene with ionization potential of additive present in 10% concentration, 3 torr oxygen added when necessary to inhibit free radical reactions.* *The letter symbols indicate ionization potentials from Ref. 58 in parenthesis; values in e.v.*

(a) *Triethylamine (7.50)*
(b) *Trimethylamine (7.82)*
(c) *Diethylamine (8.01)*
(d) *Dimethylamine (8.24)*
(e) *Dihydropyran (8.34)*
(f) *2-Methylfuran (8.39)*
(g) *Isopropylamine (8.72)*
(h) *Toluene (8.82)*
(i) *Ethylamine (8.86)*
(j) *Furan (8.89)*
(k) *Methylamine (8.97)*
(l) *Cyclopentene (9.01)*
(m) *2-Methylbutene-1 (9.12)*

(n) *Nitric oxide (9.25)*
(o) *Benzene (9.25)*
(p) *Diethylether (9.53)*
(q) *Dichloroethylene (9.66)*
(r) *Acetone (9.69)*
(s) *Propylene (9.73)*
(t) *Cyclohexane (9.88)*
(u) *Cyclopropane (10.06)*
(v) *Ammonia (10.15)*
(w) *Acetaldehyde (10.21)*
(x) *Ethylene (10.52)*
(y) *Methanol (10.85)*
(z) *Oxygen (12.08)*

Table I.   Isotopic Composition of Butenes Produced in Radiolysis of C_2H_4–C_2D_4–Nitric Oxide Mixtures

m/e	Ion	Butene-1	cis-Butene-2	trans-Butene-2
		Fractional Abundance[a]		
56	$C_4H_8{}^+$	16.2	23.2	21.0
57		5.7	0.8	0.2
58		8.5	1.5	0.5
59		9.6	4.4	2.2
60	$C_4H_4D_4{}^+$	29.8	41.9	45.3
61		5.6	0.7	0.0
62		4.0	1.5	1.0
63		5.4	2.5	0.5
64	$C_4D_8{}^+$	15.2	23.5	29.3
	56 + 60 + 64	61.2	88.6	95.6

[a] Monoisotopic spectra corrected for 2.8% C_2D_3H in C_2D_4.

Table II.   Isotopic Composition of $C_3(H,D)_5{}^+$ Formed by Dissociation of $C_4H_4D_4$

m/e	Ion	Radiolysis (Fragmentation[a])		Mass Spectrometer Ion-Molecule Reaction
		cis-Butene-2	trans-Butene-2	
42	C_3H_4D	11.5	10.2	10.6
43	$C_3H_3D_2$	39.3	39.1	39.8
44	$C_3H_2D_3$	39.4	40.6	39.9
45	C_3HD_4	9.8	10.1	9.6

[a] Monoisotopic, corrected for 2.8% C_2D_3H in C_2D_4.

of the mixed ions $C_3H_4D^+ : C_3H_3D_2{}^+ : C_3H_2D_3{}^+ : C_3HD_4{}^+$ is $1:4:4:1$ from the 2-butenes and the ion-molecule reaction. The random distribution would have been $1:6:6:1$, and it is not apparent how the deviation could be ascribed to a simple isotope effect. The present result suggests that the ion neutralized by charge exchange is the same as that produced in the ion-molecule reaction; this is perhaps best demonstrated by the sequence below.

$$C_2H_4{}^+ + C_2H_4 \searrow \quad \overset{C_4H_4D_4}{\underset{(C_4H_4D_4{}^+)}{\overset{\uparrow CA}{\Big\rangle}}} \searrow \quad \overset{e^- \text{ (in mass spectrometer)}}{C_3(H,D)_5{}^+ + C(H,D)_3}$$

An identical isotopic constitution of the propenyl ion resulting from both sources would be fortuitous if different mechanisms were operative.

The stability of the second-order intermediate butene ion is apparently at least that suggested by Field. Kinetic analysis of the competition between charge exchange with nitric oxide and further reaction of butene ion with ethylene (*35*) indicates that the charge transfer occurs about 70 times faster than Reaction 8. If the cross-section for charge transfer involving thermal species is determined by ion-induced dipole forces (*43*), this observation would suggest that the transmission coefficient for the ion-molecule Reaction 8 is about 0.01. As an alternative one might assume a transmission coefficient of unity for Reaction 8, which results in $k_{18,NO} \simeq 5 \times 10^{16}$ mole^{-1} cc. sec.$^{-1}$ This is about the magnitude of the rate constants for neutralization of two oppositely charged ions (28) and much larger than expected. We must therefore prefer the first alternative at this time. No measured cross-section for Reaction 18 is available, but if it is calculated from the polarizability and the dipole moment using the approach of Moran and Hamill (39) $k_{18,NO} \simeq 7.6 \times 10^{14}$ mole^{-1} cc. sec.$^{-1}$ and $k_8 = 1.1 \times 10^{13}$ mole^{-1} cc. sec.$^{-1}$ result.

METHYL RADICAL FORMATION. Reaction 7a cannot contribute to the methyl radical yield because of the lifetime of the intermediate butene ion complex. In the next section it will be shown that the secondary $C_4H_7{}^+$ complex is also relatively stable. One can argue by analogy that the complex $C_4H_6{}^+$ must also be long lived. Methyl radical formation should therefore result from third or higher interreactions. Dissociation of the tertiary complexes $C_6H_{12}{}^+$ and $C_6H_{10}{}^+$ may produce methyl radicals by Reactions 9a and 17b.

The dependence of the methyl radical yield on pressure (35) indicates that at least two processes must exist for its formation: a yield of 0.58 radical/100 e.v. appears to be essentially pressure independent up to ca. 600 torr, while the formation of 0.79 radical/100 e.v. can be inhibited at higher pressures. Kinetic analysis (35) shows that the pressure dependence agrees with a mechanism consisting of a unimolecular dissociation (rate constant k_f) yielding methyl radical in competition with a bimolecular process (rate constant k_q) which inhibits its formation with $k_q/k_f = 6.3 \times 10^5$ mole^{-1} cc. If we associate the two processes with the known ion-molecule reactions—7a and 15b—we should be able to derive the yields of the precursor primary ions provided that k_{9a}/k_9 and k_{17b}/k_{17} can be obtained from mass spectrometry. Although there is no agreement on these values, one can estimate them. Assuming that product ions produced in Reactions 9b and 17c will react identically to those produced by Reactions 6 and 14, respectively, one can use mass spectrometric values (16, 62) of $k_{9a}/k_9 = 0.9$ and $k_{17b}/k_{17} = 0.73$ making the further assumption that these ratios do not depend on pressure. Their application to the yields leads to $G(C_2H_4{}^+) = 0.64$ or 0.87 ions/100 e.v. and $G(C_2H_2{}^+) = 0.79$ or 1.08 ions/100 e.v. Although the acetylene yields seem reasonable, those for the ethylene ion must be rejected. Charge exchange experiments have indicated values of the order of 1.5 ions/100 e.v., and a minimum yield of 1.5 parent ions/100 e.v. can be calculated from mass spectral data and W; hence, the low values for $G(C_2H_4{}^+)$ are unsatisfactory on theoretical grounds as well.

The kinetic data fit a mechanism of successive reactions sequent to only one primary ion equally well, provided that the first step can yield 1.37 methyl radical/100 e.v. and is pressure dependent and that the succeeding pressure independent step yields methyl radicals with a lesser efficiency and leads to a pressure independent yield of 0.58 methyl radicals/100 e.v. If the first step is either Reaction 9a or Reaction 17b, one can once more use the rate constant ratios given earlier to estimate the yields of the possible primary precursor ions. Hence, either $G(C_2H_2{}^+) = 1.9$ ions/100 e.v., or $G(C_2H_4{}^+) = 1.52$ ions/100 e.v. The former alternative may be rejected since it corresponds to twice the acetylene ion yield predicted from mass spectrometry and W. Apparently one observes the competition between Reaction 9 and the deactivation.

$$C_6H_{12}{}^+ + C_2H_4 \rightarrow C_8H_{14}{}^+ \qquad (19)$$

followed by

$$C_8H_{14}{}^+ \nearrow CH_3 + (products)^+ \qquad (20a)$$
$$\searrow (products)^+ + products \qquad (20b)$$

with $k_{20a}/k_{20} \simeq 0.38$. Reaction 20 must occur about one or two orders of magnitude faster than 9 unless all subsequent dissociative steps whose precursor is $C_8H_{14}{}^+$ ion yield methyl radicals with the same branching ratio, an improbable possibility. Conversely, dissociation of the $[C_4H_8{}^+]$ precursor must be one or two orders of magnitude slower.

The ratio k_q/k_f can now be identified as k_{19}/k_{9a}. We can calculate an upper limit for k_{19} from ion-molecule reaction rate theory by assuming that this reaction occurs with a collision efficiency. This leads to $k_{9a} \leq 1 \times 10^9 \sec.^{-1}$ (7).

An interesting aspect is the suggestion that the stability of the intermediate ion decreases with increasing complexity. This is consistent with recent versions (57) of the statistical theory of mass spectra. Applying the group heat of formation concept (17) indicates that adding an ethylene unit to an olefinic ion is exothermic by approximately 0.4 e.v. (18) while the strength of the weakest bond must be assumed to be about constant. Thus, each chemical addition step adds energy to the ion, and the energy effect on the rate constant should outweight the opposite influence of the increase in the number of oscillators, which become fully effective only at very high excess energies.

Vinyl Ion and its Sequents. The charge exchange technique is not applicable here, and one is restricted to a kinetic examination of product yields. The connection with methane formation by Reaction 13a is obvious. The molecular nature of methane formation has been indicated above, but further evidence against a short life of the butene ion complexes may be derived from the isotopic distribution of the methanes produced in the radiolysis of nearly equimolar mixtures of C_2H_4 and C_2H_4. A short lived secondary intermediate would require that Reaction 7a be the main source of methyl radicals. If these result in methane by hydrogen atom abstraction as suggested (62), we should be able to calculate the isotopic constitution of the methanes. The distribution of the deuterated methyl radicals resulting from the ion-molecule reaction 7a was given earlier. Assuming equal probability of hydrogen or deuterium abstraction, one would expect the distribution $CH_4:CH_3D:CH_2D_2:CHD_3:CD_4$ to be about $1:1.7:1.3:1.7:1.3:1$; the actual distribution at 207 torr total pressure is approximately $1.1:0.9:1.1:0.8:0.9$ so that all the methanes are produced in approximately equal yield (47). The discrepancy is well outside of experimental error and cannot be readily ascribed to an isotope effect in the abstraction reaction.

Kinetic examination of the methane yield shows behavior quite similar to that of methyl radical: a pressure dependent yield of 0.406 molecule/100 e.v., a pressure independent yield of 0.126 molecule/100 e.v., and a rate constant ratio of $k_q/k_f = 1.5 \times 10^6$ mole^{-1} cc. for the competing steps.

One can be fairly certain that at least one of the processes is Reaction 13, and we may assume that competition between Reaction 13a and 21:

$$[C_6H_{11}{}^+] + C_2H_4 \rightarrow [C_8H_{15}{}^+] \tag{21}$$

is responsible for the pressure dependence leading to $k_{13a} \leq 4.2 \times 10^8$ sec.$^{-1}$ The choice between a parallel or a successive pressure independent reaction can be made as follows. The rate constants k_9 and k_{13} are about the same. The stability of the analogous complex dissociating by Reaction 17 should therefore be of the same order of magnitude. The rapid fragmentation should again be ascribable to a fourth- or higher order process. Thermodynamics suggests that the most probable precursor for such a dissociation is still the vinyl ion since the detachment of methane from an ion of the type $C_nH_{2n-1}{}^+$ leaves a radical ion whose heat of formation is considerably less than that of the corresponding alkene or alkyne ion (18). Ascribing the formation of methane to precursor primary vinyl ion alone permits one to estimate the yield of $C_2H_3{}^+$. The mass spectrometrically derived ratio $k_{13a}/k_{13} = 0.53$ may be used to infer $G(C_2H_3{}^+) \simeq 1.0$ ions/100 e.v.

Now $k_{13} \leq 0.8 \times 10^9$ sec.$^{-1}$, only slightly smaller than the upper limit $k_9 \leq 1.1 \times 10^9$ sec.$^{-1}$ Apparently the unimolecular dissociation rate constants of all secondary complexes are less than $ca.$ 5×10^7 sec.$^{-1}$, those of the tertiary complexes less than 10^9 sec.$^{-1}$, and those of the quaternary complexes probably of the order of 10^{10} sec.$^{-1}$ These conclusions substantiate the view (16) that the mass spectrometrically observed tertiary ions arise predominantly from dissociation of the intermediate addition complexes $C_6H_{12}{}^+$, $C_6H_{11}{}^+$, and $C_6H_{10}{}^+$. Higher order ions, however, should arise principally from reactions of the dissociation products of the above complexes (62).

The stability of the butenyl and butadiene ions precludes the contribution of Reactions 11a and 15a to the mechanism of acetylene formation in the radiolysis, and this product should arise from excitation processes only. The distribution of isotopically substituted acetylenes in the radiolysis and in the vacuum ultraviolet photolysis of equimolar mixtures of C_2H_4 and C_2D_4 should therefore be the same. This is not observed experimentally. While the photolysis yields essentially only C_2D_2 and C_2H_2, even at total conversions of over 40% of the original ethylenes (49), Sauer and Dorfman (48) report that the distribution in the gamma radiolysis is $C_2D_2:C_2HD:C_2H_2 = 0.32:0.45:0.23$. The formation of C_2HD is completely inhibited by nitric oxide without affecting the total yield of acetylenes. When C_2D_2 is initially added to C_2H_4, C_2HD becomes the predominant acetylene product although the total number of hydrogens in the product is not materially altered. These results indicate that acetylene is initially produced unmixed, but exchanges subsequently. The only radical mechanism which could account for these observations would involve vinyl radicals, which are not important in ethylene radiolysis (*32, 48*) and add rapidly to ethylene. Positive ions are not involved in acetylene formation, and it is therefore difficult to see how they could be responsible for the observations. We suggest, therefore, that the exchange results from electron attachment and subsequent negative ion-molecule collisions of $C_2H_2^-$. Such an exchange mechanism would be inhibited by nitric oxide because its electron affinity is large (about 0.9 e.v.) (*15*). The exchange should depend strongly on dose rate since the electron attachment coefficient for acetylene must be quite small.

Acetylene Ion. No evidence for the contribution of ion-molecule reactions originating with acetylene ion to product formation has been obtained to date. By analogy with the two preceding sections, we may assume that the third-order complex should dissociate at pressures below about 50 torr. Unfortunately, the nature of the dissociation products would make this process almost unrecognizable. The additional formation of hydrogen and hydrogen atoms would be hidden in the sizable excess of the production of these species in other primary acts while the methyl radical formation would probably be minor compared with that resulting from ethylene ion reactions. The fate of the acetylene ion remains an unanswered question in ethylene radiolysis.

Fortunately, an estimate of its primary yield can be obtained nonetheless by analyzing the distribution of the isotopic hydrogens in the radiolysis of dideuteroethylenes. It has been established that the hydrogen elimination accompanying acetylene ion formation from 1,1-dideuteroethylene as well as from the 1,2 dideuteroethylenes is random while the hydrogen produced in the radiolysis as well as in the photolysis is not (*2*). The $H_2 : HD : D_2$ product ratio in the photolysis of CH_2CD_2 is about 0.14 : 0.4 : 0.2, almost entirely independent of wavelength (*40*) while the corresponding distribution resulting from electron impact in a mass spectrometer (inferred from the distribution of the acetylene ions at low ionizing voltages) is 0.25 : 0.64 : 0.11. From the distribution in the radiolysis (0.31 : 0.51 : 0.18) (*2*) one may calculate that the contribution of the step leading to the simultaneous formation of acetylene ion and molecular hydrogen is about 50%. This is a very crude estimate at best since the isotopic analyses are difficult for these small quantities.

The total yield of hydrogen under the conditions of these measurements was about 1.6 molecules/100 e.v. If one-half resulted from the primary dissociation also leading to acetylene ion, a yield of 0.8 acetylene ions/100 e.v. may be estimated. This value is a minimum since acetylene ion production can also be accompanied by hydrogen atom formation and is highly uncertain but consistent with the mass spectral fragmentation pattern of acetylene and W which lead to an estimate of *ca.* 0.94 acetylene ions/100 e.v.

Cationic Polymerization and Neutralization. Adding one C_2H_4 unit to a mono-olefinic ion should be exothermic by about 0.4 e.v. (*18*). Although the entropy change resulting from the condensation would reduce the free energy increase, ionic polymerization should proceed spontaneously. The cross-section of encounters is large because of ion-induced dipole forces, and an ion experiences more than 10^4 collisions before neutralization. Hence, the chain length of ionic polymerization should be large if the addition step has no activation energy, a common assumption for ion-molecule reactions. Mass spectrometric investigations (*23*) have in fact shown polymeric ions consisting of up to seven ethylene moieties.

Radiolytic ethylene destruction occurs with a yield of *ca.* 20 molecules consumed/100 e.v. (*36, 48*). Products containing up to six carbons account for *ca.* 60% of that amount, and can be ascribed to free radical reactions, molecular detachments, and low order ion-molecule reactions (*32*). This leaves only eight molecules/100 e.v. which may have formed ethylene polymer, corresponding to a chain length of only 2.1 molecules/ion. Even if we assumed that ethylene destruction were entirely the result of ionic polymerization, only about five ethylene molecules would be involved per ion pair. The absence of ionic polymerization can also be demonstrated by the results of the gamma ray initiated polymerization of ethylene, whose kinetics can be completely explained on the basis of conventional free radical reactions and known rate constants for these processes (*32*). An increase above the expected rates occurs only at pressures in excess of *ca.* 20 atmospheres (*10*). The virtual absence of ionic polymerization can be regarded as one of the most surprising aspects of the radiation chemistry of ethylene.

Several explanations for this seeming inconsistency can be offered. By far the most attractive is based on unreactivity of certain intermediate ions, and this interpretation is supported by the observation that the reaction of butene ion with ethylene (Reaction 8) appears to occur with a collision efficiency of only about 0.015. The mass spectrometric observation of Reaction 17c (*16*) indicates that there may be similar low efficiency reactions in sequences initiated by other ions as well.

The rate constants for unimolecular dissociation of the intermediate ions suggested earlier indicate that all ions containing seven or more carbon atoms arise from reactions of the dissociation products of Steps 9, 13, and 17 when pressures are of the order of a few torr and of Step 20 and its analogues at pressures in excess of a few hundred torr. The product ions are generally quite complex, and the simple exothermicity rule given earlier will not apply. Thus, we may well expect that there will be inefficient ion-molecule reactions in the sequences originating with these ions as well.

The existence of a single step with a collision efficiency of 10^{-2} in the sequence of reactions would be insufficient to account for the absence of ionic polymerization since an over-all efficiency of about 10^{-5} is required by this mechanism within the first five reactions. Thus, at least two low efficiency steps are required in each series. Although this interpretation is only tentative, it suggests that the assumption of constant reaction rate constants in the kinetic analysis of mass spectrometric data may be an oversimplification.

The eventual fate of any ion is its neutralization, either by a free electron or by a negative ion formed by electron attachment.   In ethylene radiolysis at high dose rates, electron capture processes should be insignificant (*29*), and the recombination energy of the positive ion will become available on neutralization, a portion of which may be in the form of excitation (*59*).

At low dose rates, such as those observed in the gamma radiolysis of ethylene, electron capture may yield $C_2H_2^-$ when conversions are appreciable.   This species would then be involved in the neutralization step, slightly reducing the available energy.   The participation of $C_2H_2^-$ would be favored at lower dose rates and higher conversions and may possibly account for the isotope effect in the exchange between the acetylenes, and the irreproducibility of the acetylene yield under these conditions (*26, 31, 48, 65*).   Generally, higher dose rates have given higher acetylene yields.

The positive charge should reside on a complex entity, and there is no ready means for assessing the products of the neutralization process. Although we know that neutralization must yield 3.8 intermediates/100 e.v., there is no chemical evidence for their contribution to the product distribution.   This cannot be interpreted by neutralization yielding predominantly hydrogen atoms, ethyl radicals, or methyl radicals.   One can quantitatively account for these intermediates on the basis of the distribution of primary species and second- and third-order ion-molecule reactions (*36*).

The conclusions on the occurrence of ion-molecule reaction in the radiolysis of ethylene are not seriously affected by the uncertainties in the neutralization mechanism.   It must be assumed that neutralization results in the complex species which constitute the "ionic polymer,"— i.e., the fraction of the ethylene disappearance which cannot be accounted for by the lower molecular weight products containing up to six carbon atoms.

Acknowledgment

The author is indebted to Union Carbide Corp. for permission to quote unpublished results obtained during his association with its Sterling Forest Research Laboratory and to the Atomic Energy Commission for partial support of this research.   We are deeply grateful to M. C. Sauer (Argonne National Laboratory) for transmitting unpublished results of his work on ethylene and for his encouragement to use it in this presentation.

Literature Cited

(1) American Petroleum Institute Research Project 44, "Catalog of Mass Spectra Data," Texas A & M University, College Station, 1963.
(2) Ausloos, P., Lias, S. G., *J. Chem. Phys.* **36,** 5 (1962).

(3) Ausloos, P., Lias, S. G., *Trans. Faraday Soc.* **39**, 36 (1965).
(4) Ausloos, P., Lias, S. G., Sandoval, I. B., *Discuss. Faraday Soc.* **36**, 66 (1963).
(5) Benson, S. W., DeMore, W. B., *Ann. Rev. Phys. Chem.* **16**, 397 (1965).
(6) Borkowski, R. P., Ausloos, P., *J. Chem. Phys.* **40**, 1128 (1964).
(7) Bieman, K., "Mass Spectrometry—Organic Chemical Applications," Mc-Graw-Hill Book Co., New York, 1962.
(8) Burtt, B. P., Kircher, J. F., *Radiation Res.* **9**, 1 (1958).
(9) Cermak, V., Herman, Z., *J. Chim. Phys.* **57** 717 (1960).
(10) Colombo, P., Kuckacka, L. E., Fontana, J., Chapman, R. N., Steinberg, M., *Trans. Am. Nuclear Soc.* **7**, 313 (1964).
(11) Cvetanovics, R. J., Callear, A. B., *J. Chem. Phys.* **23**, 1182 (1955).
(12) Doepker, R. D., Ausloos, P., *J. Chem. Phys.* **43**, 3814 (1965).
(13) Essex, Harry, *J. Phys. Chem.* **58**, 42 (1954).
(14) Eyring, H., Hirschfelder, J. O., Taylor, H. S., *J. Chem. Phys.* **4**, 479 (1936).
(15) Farragher, A. L., Page, F. M., Wheeler, R. C., *Discuss. Faraday Soc.* **37**, 203 (1964).
(16) Field, F. H., *J. Am. Chem. Soc.* **83**, 1523 (1961).
(17) Franklin, J. L., *J. Chem. Phys.* **21**, 2029 (1953).
(18) Franklin, J. L., Field, F. H., "Electron Impact Phenomena," Academic Press, New York, 1956.
(19) Franklin, J. L., Field, F. H., Lampe, F. W., *J. Am. Chem. Soc.* **78**, 5697 (1956).
(20) Futrell, J. H., *J. Am. Chem. Soc.* **81**, 5291 (1959).
(21) Futrell, J. H., *J. Phys. Chem.* **64**, 1634 (1960).
(22) Gevantman, L. H., Williams, R. R., Jr., *J. Phys. Chem.* **56**, 369 (1952).
(23) Kebarle, P., Hogg, A. M., *J. Chem. Phys.* **42**, 668 (1965).
(24) Kerr, J. A., Trottman-Dickenson, A. F., *Progr. Reaction Kinetics* **1**, 105 (1961).
(25) Kubose, D. A., Hamill, W. H., *J. Am. Chem. Soc.* **85**, 125 (1963).
(26) Lampe, F. W., *Radiation Res.* **10**, 691 (1959).
(27) Lampe, F. W., *J. Am. Chem. Soc.* **82**, 1551 (1960).
(28) Mahan, B. H., Person, J. C., *J. Chem. Phys.* **40**, 392 (1964).
(29) Massey, H. S. W., Burhop, E. H. S., "Electronic and Ionic Impact Phenomena," Oxford University Press, London 1952.
(30) Meisels, G. G., *J. Chem. Phys.* **31**, 285 (1959).
(31) Meisels, G. G., *J. Chem. Phys.* **41**, 51 (1964).
(32) Meisels, G. G., *J. Am. Chem. Soc.* **87**, 950 (1965).
(33) Meisels, G. G., *Nature* **206**, 287 (1965).
(34) Meisels, G. G., *J. Chem. Phys.* **42**, 2328 (1965).
(35) Meisels, G. G., *J. Chem. Phys.* **42**, 3237 (1965).
(36) Meisels, G. G., Sworski, T. J., *J. Phys. Chem.* **69**, 815 (1965).
(37) Meisels, G. G., Sworski, T. J., *J. Phys. Chem.* **69**, 2867 (1965).
(38) Melton, C. E. and Rudolph, P. E., *J. Chem. Phys.* **32**, 1128 (1960).
(39) Moran, T. F. and Hamill, W. H., *J. Chem. Phys.* **39**, 1413 (1963).
(40) Okabe, H., McNesby, J. R., *J. Chem. Phys.* **36**, 601 (1962).
(41) Platzman, R. L., *Vortex* **23**, No. 8 (1962).
(42) Platzman, R. L., *Radiation Res.* **17**, 419 (1962).
(43) Rapp, D. E., 11th Annual Meeting, ASTM Committee E-14, San Francisco, Calif., May 1963.
(44) Robin, M. B., Hart, R. R., Kuebler, N. A., *J. Chem. Phys.* **44**, 1803 (1966).
(45) Ruland, N. L., Ph.D. Thesis, University of Houston, 1966.
(46) Samuel, A. H., Halliday, F. O., *Stanford Res. Inst. Quart. Prog. Rept.*, Project No. PHU-4443, under contract AF 33(657)-11156, July 15 and October 15, 1964.
(47) Sauer, M. C., Jr., unpublished results.
(48) Sauer, M. C., Dorfman, L. M., *J. Phys. Chem.* **66**, 322 (1962).
(49) Sauer, M. C., Dorfman, L. M., *J. Chem. Phys.* **35**, 497 (1961).
(50) Schissler, D. O., Stevenson, D. P., *J. Chem. Phys.* **24**, 926 (1956).
(51) Stevenson, D. P., *Radiation Res.* **10**, 610 (1959).
(52) Stevenson, D. P., "Mass Spectrometry," C. A. McDowell, ed., McGraw-Hill Book Co., New York, 1963.
(53) Stevenson, D. P., Schissler, D. O., "The Chemical and Biological Action of Radiations," Vol. V, M. Haissinsky, ed., Academic Press, London, 1961.
(54) Stockdale, J. A., Hurst, G. S., *J. Chem. Phys.* **41**, 255 (1964).
(55) Tal'roze, V. L., Lyubimova, A. K., *Dokl. Akad. Nauk. S.S.S.R.* **86**, 909 (1952).

(56) Tate, J. T., Smith, P. T., Vaughan, A. L., *Phys. Rev.* **48,** 525 (1935).
(57) Vestal, M., Wahrhaftig, A. L., Johnston, W. H., *J. Chem. Phys.* **37,** 1276 (1962).
(58) Vestal, M., Wahrhaftig, A. L., and Johnston, W. H., "Theoretical Studies in Basic Radiation Chemistry," ARL 62-426 (1962).
(59) Von Koch, H., Lindholm, E., *Arkiv Fysik* **19,** 123 (1961).
(60) Watanabe, K., Nakayama, T., Mottl, J., *J. Quant. Spectry. Radiative Transfer* **2,** 369 (1962).
(61) Wentworth, W. E., Chen, E. T., Lovelock, J. E., *J. Phys. Chem.* **70,** 445 (1966).
(62) Wexler, S., Marshall, R., *J. Am. Chem. Soc.* **86,** 781 (1964).
(63) Whyte, G. N., *Radiation Res.* **18,** 265 (1963).
(64) Wolff, C. M., Pertel, R., *J. Opt. Soc. Am.* **54,** 1168 (1964).
(65) Yang, K., Manno, P. J., *J. Phys. Chem.* **63,** 752 (1959).

RECEIVED May 3, 1966.

15

Investigating Ion-Molecule Reactions by Analyzing Neutral Products Formed in the Radiolysis and Photoionization of Hydrocarbons

P. AUSLOOS, S. G. LIAS, and A. A. SCALA

Radiation Chemistry Section, Institute of Basic Standards, National Bureau of Standards, Washington, D.C.

The analysis of neutral products from the radiolysis and photoionization of suitable deuterium labeled hydrocarbons or hydrocarbon mixtures provides information concerning (a) the relative rates of H^+, H^-, H_2^-, and H_2 transfer reactions, and (b) the structure of the reacting ion or reaction complex. The reaction cross-section of a given ion with various alkanes generally increases with increasing polarizability of the neutral molecule. The actual increase in rate is, however, faster than that of the collision cross-section given by: $2\pi e(\alpha/\mu)^{1/2}$. Good quantitative and qualitative agreement exists between the information on reactions of parent ions obtained from gas phase radiolysis studies and that derived from photoionization experiments carried out at wavelengths slightly above the ionization energy of the molecule.

Although the mass spectrometer is the most versatile and in many instances the only tool for studying ion-molecule reactions, in certain systems valuable information can be gained by examining the neutral products formed by these reactions. In the past, workers investigating the effects of ionizing radiation in closed systems interpreted their experimental observations solely on the basis of previous mass spectrometric findings. However, in recent years this attitude has been modified considerably. Indeed, novel information has been derived from a conventional analysis of neutral products in hydrocarbon systems which, in some cases, has inspired mass spectrometric investigations. The approach used in those studies is similar to that used to study free radical reactions where major advances were achieved without the need to detect free radicals directly. At any rate, examining the neutral product formed in an ion-molecule reaction will provide information which complements that derived from detecting the charged product formed in the same reaction.   Besides leading to the discovery of new types of ion-molecule reactions, analysis of neutral products formed in the radiolysis or photoionization of hydrocarbons where the ions have thermal velocities can yield accurate relative rate constants of particular ion-molecule reactions as well as unique information concerning the structure of the reacting ion and/or reaction complex.   In some instances the effect of pressure on the decomposition of the reaction complex can also be readily investigated in a closed system.   This will contribute to our understanding of ion-molecule reactions occurring in the condensed phase radiolysis and photoionization of hydrocarbons.

Here we present new data on various ion-molecule reactions occurring in the radiolysis and photoionization of hydrocarbons. We will also review some earlier findings which will illustrate the kind of information which can be derived from the approach mentioned above.

Experimental

Our experimental techniques have been described extensively in earlier papers (2, 13).   The gamma ray irradiations were carried out in a 50,000-curie source located at the bottom of a pool.   The photoionization experiments were carried out by krypton and argon resonance lamps of high purity.   The krypton resonance lamp was provided with a CaF_2 window which transmits only the 1236 A. (10 e.v.) line while the radiation from the argon resonance lamp passed through a thin ($\sim$0.3 mm.) LiF window.   In the latter case, the resonance lines at 1067 and 1048 A. are transmitted.   The intensity of 1048-A. line was about 75% of that of the 1067-A. line.   The number of ions produced in both the radiolysis and photoionization experiments was determined by measuring the saturation current across two electrodes.   In the radiolysis, the outer wall of a cylindrical stainless steel reaction vessel served as a cathode while a centrally located rod was used as anode.   The photoionization apparatus was provided with two parallel plate nickel electrodes which were located at equal distances from the window of the resonance lamp.

In all experiments, unless otherwise stated, approximately 5% oxygen was added to the reaction mixture to remove free radicals from the system and thereby simplify the derivation of the modes of formation of the hydrocarbon products.

Hydride Ion Transfer Reactions

Field and Lampe (23) established the occurrence of the hydride transfer reaction in the gas phase in 1958 by detecting secondary ions of mass one unit lower than the parent compound.   Subsequently, Futrell (24, 25) attempted to account for most lower hydrocarbon products formed in the radiolysis of hexane and pentane by assuming that hydride transfer reactions play a dominant role in radiolysis.   More recently, Ausloos and Lias (2) presented experimental evidence which indicated that some of the products in the radiolysis of propane are, in part, formed by hydride transfer reactions. For instance, on the basis of an isotopic analysis of the ethane produced in the radiolysis of CH_3-CD_2CH_3, $CD_3CH_2CD_3$, and C_3D_8-C_3H_8 mixtures, they concluded (2, 3) that ethane is mainly, although not exclusively, formed by the H^- transfer reaction:

$$C_2H_5^+ + C_3H_8 \rightarrow C_2H_6 + C_3H_7^+ \tag{1}$$

On the other hand, the formation of ethylene was ascribed mainly to the unimolecular decomposition of a neutral excited propane molecule. These interpretations were later confirmed (4) by examining the effect of an applied electrical field on the neutral products in the radiolysis of propane. The yields of those products which were originally ascribed to ion-molecule reactions remained unchanged when the field strength was increased in the saturation current region while the yields of hydrocarbon products, which were ascribed to the decomposition of neutral excited propane molecules, increased several fold because of increased excitation by electron impact. In various recent radiolysis (14, 17, 18, 34) and photoionization studies (26) of hydrocarbons, the origins of products from ion-molecule reactions or neutral excited molecule decompositions have been determined using the applied field technique. However, because of recent advances in vacuum ultraviolet photolysis and ion-molecule reaction kinetics, the technique used in the above studies has become somewhat superfluous.

As a result of the conclusions reached in these studies, a simple competition method was devised (12, 32) to determine relative rates of hydride transfer reactions rather accurately. For example, to obtain relative reaction rates of ethyl ions with various additives, a suitable source of fully deuterated ethyl ions such as C_3D_8 or iso-C_4D_{10} was irradiated in the presence of a perprotonated additive (RH), leading to the formation of C_2D_6 and C_2D_5H by Reactions 2 and 3.

$$C_2D_5^+ + C_nD_{2n+2} \rightarrow C_2D_6 + C_nD^+_{2n+1} \tag{2}$$

$$C_2D_5^+ + RH \rightarrow C_2D_5H + R^+ \tag{3}$$

Provided that C_2D_6 and C_2D_5H are not produced by any other mechanisms, the following relationship exists:

$$k_3/k_2 = (C_2D_5H/C_2D_6)(C_nD_{2n+2}/RH)$$

Earlier studies (12, 32, 41) were concerned mainly with the reactions of $C_2D_5^+$ and $C_3D_7^+$ ions. These measurements have now been extended (Table I) to include hydride ion transfer reactions involving the $C_4D_9^+$ ion. In addition, relative rates of hydride transfer from cycloalkanes to the various carbonium ions have been determined for the first time. Both iso-C_5D_{12} and n-C_5D_{12} have been selected as convenient sources of $C_4D_9^+$ ions. The $C_4D_9^+$ ions which are produced by the unimolecular fragmentation process:

$$C_5D_{12}^+ \rightarrow C_4D_9^+ + CD_3 \tag{4}$$

react with C_5D_{12} or with the additive RH:

$$C_4D_9{}^+ + C_5D_{12} \rightarrow C_4D_{10} + C_5D_{11}{}^+ \tag{5}$$

$$C_4D_9{}^+ + RH \rightarrow C_4D_9H + R^+ \tag{6}$$

giving C_4D_{10} and C_4D_9H as neutral products. Similarly, both C_4D_{10} and iso-C_4D_{10} have been used as suitable sources for $C_3D_7{}^+$ ions. Whenever necessary, appropriate corrections were made for the formation of butane or propane by $H_2{}^-$ transfer reactions or by molecular elimination processes. The rates of the hydride ion transfer reactions given in Table I have arbitrarily been expressed relative to the rate of reaction with cyclobutane.

Table I. Relative Rates of Hydride Transfer Reactions[b] at 300°K.

	$C_4D_9{}^+$	$C_3D_7{}^+$	$C_2D_5{}^+$	[a]$(Q/Q_c)_{C_2D_5}{}^+$
Cyclopropane		<0.02	<0.05	
Isobutane		0.58	0.87	
Butane		0.78		1.05
Cyclobutane	1.00	1.00	1.00	1.00
Neopentane		0.049	1.05	1.06
Isopentane	1.26	1.04	1.09	1.07
Pentane	1.42		1.07	1.06
Cyclopentane	1.56	1.44	1.14	1.02
Hexane	2.37	2.13		
Methylcyclopentane	2.36	1.91	1.29	
Cyclohexane	3.51	2.41	1.36	1.09
Heptane	4.04	3.88	1.65	1.18
Methylcyclohexane	3.50	2.69		
Cyclopentene		0.71	0.34	
Cyclohexene		0.81	0.49	

[a] Ratio of collision cross-section of $C_2D_5{}^+$ with specified alkane to collision cross-section of $C_2D_5{}^+$ with cyclobutane.
[b] Pressure of reaction mixtures = 40 torr.

Several conclusions can be drawn from the results. Within experimental error (estimated at 5%) the same values for the relative rates were obtained when either iso-C_5D_{12} or n-C_5D_{12} was used as a source of $C_4D_9{}^+$ ions. Similarly, the relative rates observed for propyl ion reactions were the same regardless of the origin of the ion. This is not surprising since the structure of the reacting propyl or butyl ion is apparently the same regardless of whether its source is the branched or straight chain alkane molecule. This is demonstrated by the facts that in all experiments the C_4D_9H and C_3D_7H species formed in Reactions 6 and 7, respectively,

$$C_3D_7{}^+ + RH \rightarrow C_3D_7H + R^+ \tag{7}$$

have the structure $CD_3CD_2CDHCD_3$ or CD_3CDHCD_3. We may surmise that the $C_3D_7{}^+$ and $C_4D_9{}^+$ ions acquire the secondary structure prior to or during reaction. Although reshuffling of the deuterium atoms in the parent alkane ion or its butyl fragment ion results in the formation of the thermodynamically more stable sec-$C_4D_9{}^+$ structure, there is no evidence of rearrangement, involving the carbon skeleton of the molecule —i.e., there is apparently no isomerization yielding the energetically still more stable $tert\text{-}C_4D_9{}^+$ structure. It has also been demonstrated that the unreactive $tert$-butyl ions formed in the radiolysis of neopentane (33) do not revert to the sec-butyl ion structure.

Hydride transfer is essentially the only mode of reaction between the alkyl ions and the neutral alkane molecules except in the case of cyclopropane. This is seen from the fact that the ion pair yields of products having the reactant ions as precursors (that is, $C_4D_{10} + C_4D_9H$ for the butyl ion, $C_3D_8 + C_3D_7H$ for the propyl ion, and $C_2D_6 + C_2D_5H$ for the ethyl ion) are constant for all mixtures, except those containing cyclopropane or unsaturated additives.

Although the hydride transfer reactions:

$$sec\text{-}C_3D_7{}^+ + (CH_2)_3 \rightarrow C_3D_7H + C_3H_5{}^+ \tag{8}$$

$$C_2D_5{}^+ + (CH_2)_3 \rightarrow C_2D_5H + C_3H_5{}^+ \tag{9}$$

are exothermic by approximately 5 and 25 kcal., respectively, they do not occur to any appreciable extent. In contrast, H^- transfer reactions from the higher cycloalkanes to the various alkyl ions are quite efficient and constitute the only mode of reaction. However, in experiments where cyclopropane is added to the ion source, the yields of products originating from D^- transfer reactions with the parent molecule, are strongly reduced. Thus, an alternative reaction between the alkyl ion and cyclopropane occurs. By analogy (27, 40) with the established reaction of other fragment ions with cyclopropane, the most probable process can be written as follows:

$$C_nD_{2n+1}{}^+ + (CH_2)_3 \rightarrow [C_nD_{2n+1}(CH_2)_3]^+ \rightarrow$$
$$C_{n+1}H_2D_{2n+1}{}^+ + C_2H_4 \tag{10}$$

From the observed drop in yield, one can calculate the rate of Reaction 10 relative to hydride transfer with cyclobutane (on the rate scale used in Table I) as 1.55 for the ethyl ion and 0.83 for the propyl ion.

A low ion pair yield of products resulting from hydride transfer reactions is also noted when the additive molecules are unsaturated. Table I indicates, however, that hydride transfer reactions between alkyl ions and olefins do occur to some extent. The reduced yield can be accounted for by the occurrence of two additional reactions between alkyl ions and unsaturated hydrocarbon molecules—namely, proton transfer and condensation reactions, both of which will be discussed later. The total reaction rate of an ion with an olefin is much higher than reaction with a saturated molecule of comparable size. For example, the propyl ion reacts with cyclopentene and cyclohexene at rates which are, respectively, 3.05 and 3.07 times greater than the rate of hydride transfer with cyclobutane. This observation can probably be accounted for by a higher collision cross-section and/or a transmission coefficient for reaction which is close to unity.

According to theory (*22*), the rate constant for reaction between an ion and a molecule can be expressed in terms of the polarizability of the neutral species and of the reduced mass of the reacting pair

$$k = \chi 2\pi e(\alpha/\mu)^{1/2}$$

where α is the polarizability, μ is the reduced mass, and χ is the probability of a reactive collision. The expression $2\pi e(\alpha/\mu)^{1/2}$ is simply the collision cross-section for the pair. The collision cross-section for the ethyl ion with several of the additive molecules has been calculated, and values relative to the cross-section for collision with cyclobutane are given in the last column of Table I. Similar calculations for the propyl and butyl ions, although not given in Table I, would show that increases in collision cross-section with increasing molecular weight of additive molecule would be smaller for the propyl ion and butyl ion than for the ethyl ion. The experimental results for the relative reaction rates given in Table I show that the opposite trend actually prevails in the reaction rates—namely, that the increments in rate with increasing molecular weight of the neutral reactant are greatest when the hydride ion is transferred to $C_4D_9{}^+$ and smallest when $C_2D_5{}^+$ is the reacting ion. In addition, the increase in rate with increasing size of the neutral molecule is always greater than would be predicted from the change in collision cross-section. Hence, the probability of a reactive collision involving $C_3D_7{}^+$ or $C_4D_9{}^+$ is usually less than unity. For ethyl ion reactions with larger alkanes, however, there are indications that the probability for a reactive collision is close to unity. The fact that the ethyl ion reacts within experimental error at the same rate with the three pentane isomers and with cyclopentane (Table I) indicates that purely steric requirements for reaction are absent, provided that reaction is exothermic at every site in the molecule. By contrast, $C_3D_7{}^+$ and $C_4D_9{}^+$ react with different isomer molecules at widely varying rates. This is probably related to the fact that the larger alkyl ions may sometimes react selectively at certain sites of the neutral alkane molecule. Radiolysis experiments carried out with $CD_3CH_2CH_2CD_3$ as an additive indicate that the $C_3D_7{}^+$ ion reacts exclusively as follows:

$$C_3D_7{}^+ + CD_3CH_2CH_2CD_3 \rightarrow CD_3CDHCD_3 + CD_3CHCH_2CD_3{}^+$$

$$(11)$$

The fact that the propyl ion does not remove a primary hydrogen from butane is also confirmed (*6*) by the photoionization of $CD_3CH_2CH_2CD_3$ at 11.5–11.7 e.v. Similarly, only the tertiary hydrogen of isobutane is involved in the hydride transfer process to $C_3D_7{}^+$ (*13*). In both instances, the obvious explanation must reside in the endothermicity of the alternative mode of reaction. Although the values of ΔH_f of the various alkyl ions are not well known (*21*), data in the literature indicate that reaction at the primary carbon atom is indeed endothermic for the *sec*-$C_3D_7{}^+$ ion. On the other hand, even if reaction is exothermic at more than one site in the additive molecule, there may still be some selectivity. Note that in the radiolysis of $(CH_3)_2CDCH_2CH_3$ the $C_4H_8D{}^+$ ion, which has the structure $CH_3CDCH_2CH_3{}^+$, undergoes the D^- transfer reaction:

$$C_4H_8D^+ + (CH_3)_2CDCH_2CH_3 \rightarrow CH_3CD_2CH_2CH_3 + C_5H_{11}{}^+$$

$$(12)$$

with approximately the same probability as the H^- transfer reaction:

$$C_4H_8D^+ + (CH_3)_2CDCH_2CH_3 \rightarrow CH_3CDHCH_2CH_3 + C_5H_{10}D^+$$

$$(13)$$

notwithstanding that the latter reaction is statistically favored by a factor of 2.

The above discussion has been concerned with H^- transfer reactions to alkyl ions. In addition, there is mass spectrometric (16) and radiolytic (18) evidence that H^- can also be transferred to smaller olefinic ions $(C_nH_m{}^+)$

$$C_nH_m{}^+ + RH \rightarrow C_nH_{m+1} + R^+ \qquad (14)$$

as well as to carbonium ions having the formula $C_nH^+{}_{2n-1}$

$$C_nH^+{}_{2n-1} + RH \rightarrow C_nH_{2n} + R^+ \qquad (15)$$

In contrast with the alkyl ions which undergo hydride transfer as essentially the only mode of reaction with alkanes, the $C_nH_m{}^+$ and $C_nH^+{}_{2n-1}$ ions undergo Reactions 14 and 15 in competition with other modes of reaction, some of which will be discussed later. Experimentally it is somewhat more difficult to determine the relative rates of reactions such as Reaction 14, because in contrast with the reactions involving carbonium ions, the neutral product is a free radical rather than a stable hydrocarbon molecule. The rate of Reaction 14 can, however, be determined fairly accurately by using a free-radical scavenger such as H_2S (18). Experiments of this sort have determined that the probability of the transfer of a hydride ion from various alkanes to $C_3D_6{}^+$ depends strongly on the structure of the alkane. Hydride transfer is usually favored when the H^- donor is a branched alkane containing one or more tertiary H atoms.

$H_2{}^-$ Transfer Reactions

$H_2{}^-$ transfer reactions of the type

$$C_nH_m{}^+ + AH_2 \rightarrow C_nH_{m+2} + A^+ \qquad (16)$$

where AH_2 is a saturated hydrocarbon and $C_nH_m{}^+$ is an unsaturated hydrocarbon ion or a cyclopropane ion, were first observed in the radiolysis of propane (3) and in various mass spectrometric studies (16, 36) on simple alkanes. More recently, a systematic investigation (18) has been carried out on the relative rates of the $H_2{}^-$ transfer reactions from various alkanes to $C_3D_6{}^+$. The $C_3D_6{}^+$ ions were produced by irradiating cyclo-C_5D_{10} in a closed system with gamma rays. The $C_3D_6^+$ ion produced in the major fragmentation process:

$$\text{cyclo-}C_5D_{10}^+ \rightarrow C_2D_4 + C_3D_6^+ \qquad (17)$$

was shown to react with cyclo-C_5D_{10} and with the added alkanes as follows:

$$C_3D_6^+ + \text{cyclo-}C_5D_{10} \rightarrow C_3D_8 + C_5D_8^+ \qquad (18)$$

$$C_3D_6^+ + AH_2 \rightarrow CD_3CDHCD_2H + A^+ \qquad (19)$$

Since C_3D_8 or $C_3D_6H_2$ were not produced by any other reaction in the system, rates of Reaction 19 relative to that of reference Reaction 18 could simply be derived from the product ratio: $C_3D_6H_2/C_3D_8$. Very good agreement was reached between the rates determined in this radiolysis system and those obtained by a photoionization technique (*26*). The latter method consisted of photolyzing propylene-d_6 at 1236 A. (10 e.v.) in the presence of alkanes whose ionization potential lies at energies higher than 10 e.v. In such a system, $C_3D_6^+$ is the only ion initially produced. Thus the only primary reactions which need be considered are the reactions of $C_3D_6^+$ with propylene and with the alkane additive. Furthermore, from the measured saturation ion current one can derive the number of $C_3D_6^+$ ions initially produced in the photoionization experiment. Some of the relative rate data derived from such a study are given in Table II and can be compared with those determined in the radiolysis of cyclo-C_5D_{10}-AH_2 mixtures.

Table II. Relative Rates of the Reaction
$C_3D_6^+ + AH_2 \rightarrow C_3D_6H_2 + A^+$

	Photoionization of C_3D_6 at 1236 A.	Radiolysis of cyclo-C_5D_{10}
cyclo-C_4H_8	0.089	0.074
cyclo-C_5H_{10}	1.0	1.0
cyclo-C_6H_{12}	1.24	1.03
C_4H_{10}	0.51	0.65
iso-C_4H_{10}	0.21	0.23
neo-C_5H_{12}	0.00	0.00
iso-C_5H_{12}	0.46	0.45
C_5H_{12}	0.96	1.12

It is clear from the data in Table II that the photoionization technique is useful for studying ion-molecule reactions especially when the wavelength is chosen such that the parent ion undergoes no fragmentation or at most a few low energy fragmentations. The unique advantage of such a system resides in the fact that in contrast with radiolysis, a wide selection of additives whose ionization energy is above the energy of the incident photon can be introduced. An extensive discussion of the effect of additive structure on the rate of the H_2^- transfer reaction is given elsewhere (*18*). Furthermore, neutral product analysis yielded interesting information concerning the structure of the reaction complex which cannot be derived from other experimental techniques. For example, the C_3D_7H formed in the HD^- transfer reaction

$$C_3D_6^+ + (CH_3)_3CD \rightarrow C_3D_7H + C_4H_8^+ \qquad (20)$$

has the structure CD_3CDHCD_3, indicating that the reaction complex must have a well defined configuration in which the H atom on the terminal carbon atom of isobutane is transferred almost exclusively to the center carbon atom of $C_3D_6^+$. This stereospecificity is also confirmed by the fact that C_3D_7H formed in Reaction 21 consists mainly of CD_3-CD_2CD_2H.

$$C_3D_6^+ + CD_3CH_2CH_2CD_3 \rightarrow C_3D_7H + CD_2CHCH_2CD_3^+ \qquad (21)$$

H_2 Transfer Reactions

Recently, an important new type of reaction was discovered (7, 19) which may be designated as a H_2 transfer reaction:

$$C_nH_m + AH_2^+ \rightarrow C_nH_{m+2} + A^+ \qquad (22)$$

where C_nH_m is cyclopropane or an unsaturated hydrocarbon with fewer carbon atoms than the parent alkane ion, AH_2. This reaction is essentially the same as the H_2^- transfer reaction discussed above except that the charges of the reactants are reversed. Reaction 22 competes with the H atom transfer reaction

$$C_nH_m + AH_2^+ \rightarrow C_nH_{m+1} + AH^+ \qquad (23)$$

which is analogous to the H^- transfer process, Reaction 14.

The H_2 transfer reaction, which has been observed in photoionization studies (6) as well as in radiolytic investigations (7, 19) is useful in determining the degree of fragmentation of the parent ion at high pressures. Indeed, it is the only known reaction of a parent alkane ion which yields a stable and readily recognizable product. Since for larger hydrocarbons not more than 1% olefin (C_nH_m) has to be added to the system in order to intercept all parent alkane ions, most primary ion-molecule reactions involving fragment ions of the alkane will not be greatly affected.

Table III presents the relative rates of H_2 transfer reactions from cyclo-C_5H_{10} and C_5H_{12} to propylene, ethylene, acetylene, and cyclopropane. These values were obtained by irradiating pentane-C_nD_m-O_2 mixtures with gamma rays, or with the argon resonance lines at 1048–1067 A. The results obtained by the two irradiation techniques are in fair agreement.

When both reactants have comparable ionization potentials, there is a close relationship between the H_2 and H_2^- transfer reactions. For instance, a low efficiency of the H_2 transfer reaction from the alkane to a neutral olefin molecule (at least in the case of cyclohexane) is paralleled by a low efficiency of the corresponding H_2^- transfer process. Such a relationship can be accounted for by resonance phenomena. Unfortunately, not enough information is available on those systems where the

Table III. Relative Rates of H₂ Transfer Reactions

	Pentane		Cyclopentane	
	Gamma Rays	Photoionization	Gamma Rays	Gamma Rays (liquid phase)
Propylene	1.00	1.00	1.00	1.00
Ethylene	0.200	0.149	0.17	1.69
Acetylene	0.149	0.137		0.86
Cyclopropane	0.134		0.088	1.11

ionization potential of the alkane and the unsaturated molecule differ by more than 1 e.v.

Again, analysis of neutral products provides interesting information concerning the structure of the reaction complex and the reacting ion. The most striking result was obtained in the radiolysis and photoionization of cyclo-C_6H_{12}–cyclo-C_3D_6 mixtures. H_2 transfer from $C_6H_{12}^+$ to cyclo-C_3D_6 yielded exclusively $CD_2HCD_2CD_2H$, indicating that an H_2 molecule is transferred to two adjacent carbon atoms of cyclopropane with the simultaneous cleavage of the C-C bond. On the other hand, $CD_2HCDHCD_3$ is the only deuterium labelled propane produced when propylene-d_6, instead of cyclopropane-d_6, is added to the perprotonated alkane. Both observations indicate that we are dealing with a loose reaction complex in which little or no reshuffling of hydrogen atoms occurs.

Table III shows that in the gas phase at a pressure of 40 torr the relative rates of the H_2 transfer reactions from the cyclopentane ion to the various additives differ drastically from those derived from liquid phase radiolysis experiments. This indicates that the changes in density may profoundly affect the relative rates of the two competitive reactions, Reactions 22 and 28. Experimental results, which will be described in a later publication, indicate that in the liquid phase an increased importance of the H_2 transfer reaction to some of the additives occurs at the expense of the H atom transfer reaction, Reaction 23.

Proton Transfer Reactions

Several types of proton transfer reactions can be studied conveniently by a neutral product analysis. Until now, the most extensive investigations have been concerned with (1) proton transfer from H_3^+ and CH_5^+ to various hydrocarbon molecules, and (2) the transfer of a proton from carbonium ions to larger olefins or other organic compounds.

Proton transfer from species such as H_3^+ and CHO^+ to alkanes, followed by the decomposition of the protonated alkane was first demonstrated as occurring by Lindholm and co-workers (15, 39). Subsequently, the occurrence of proton transfer reactions from CH_5^+ and H_3^+ to higher alkanes was shown to occur (10, 11) by analyzing products formed in the radiolysis of CH_4 or H_2 containing trace amounts of deuterated higher alkanes. Furthermore, a most interesting investigation of a proton transfer chain reaction involving CH_5^+ and CH_4 has been carried out in a closed system by Lawrence and Firestone (30, 31).

In both the mass spectrometric and radiolytic investigation, they suggested that in all cases the protonated higher alkane undergoes decomposition shortly after being formed.   On the basis of the recent mass spectrometric study by Aquilanti and Volpi (1) one cannot entirely exclude the possibility that the $C_2H_7^+$ ion is stabilized at sufficiently high pressure.   If, in the radiolytic study (11), the $C_2H_7^+$ ion is largely stabilized, then one must conclude that this species as mentioned before (10) reacts with the interceptor molecule essentially as an ethyl ion.   At any rate, for protonated higher alkanes, one may expect decomposition to occur even at pressures close to atmospheric.   For instance, protonated pentane formed in a H_2-C_5H_{12} system was shown to decompose as follows:

$$C_5H_{13}^+ \rightarrow C_4H_9^+ + CH_4 \tag{24}$$

$$C_5H_{13}^+ \rightarrow C_3H_7^+ + C_2H_6 \tag{25}$$

$$C_5H_{13}^+ \rightarrow C_2H_5^+ + C_3H_8 \tag{26}$$

The relative probabilities of Reactions 24, 25, and 26 were, respectively, 1.00, 0.25, and 0.12 at a hydrogen pressure of about 1 atmosphere (9). These numbers could be derived either by analyzing the stable alkanes formed in the unimolecular decompositions (Reactions 24–26) or from the products of the hydride transfer reactions between C_5H_{12} and the alkyl ions.   Elimination of H_2 from protonated pentane may also occur, but it is difficult (although not impossible) to establish this reaction through neutral product analysis.

Proton transfer from H_3^+ and CH_5^+ to cyclopropane yields a $C_3H_7^+$ ion, which at atmospheric pressures is largely stabilized by collision (9). This ion reacts as a sec-propyl ion with an added interceptor molecule (9).   Hence, the protonated cyclopropane ion undergoes ring opening to acquire the sec-propyl ion structure.   Similarly, it has been shown that protonated cyclobutane rearranges to the sec-$C_4H_9^+$ structure.

Studies of the transfer of a proton from carbonium ions to larger olefins or other organic compounds have been concerned largely with reactions involving the $C_2D_5^+$ and sec-$C_3D_7^+$ ions.

$$C_2D_5^+ + M \rightarrow C_2D_4 + MH^+ \tag{27}$$

$$sec\text{-}C_3D_7^+ + M \rightarrow C_3D_6 + MH^+ \tag{28}$$

M is an unsaturated hydrocarbon or an organic compound such as CH_3OH, CH_3I, CH_3NO_2, $(CH_3)_2CO$, CH_3NH_2, etc.   When M is an olefin, Reaction 27 or 28 will compete with a hydride transfer process (see earlier discussion) and a condensation process.   For instance, in the radiolysis of C_3D_8-CH_3CHCH_2 mixtures (9), the relative rates of Reactions 29, 30, 31, and 32

$$C_2D_5^+ + C_3D_8 \rightarrow C_2D_6 + C_3D_7^+ \tag{29}$$

$$C_2D_5^+ + C_3H_6 \rightarrow C_2D_4 + C_3H_6D^+ \tag{30}$$

$$C_2D_5{}^+ + C_3H_6 \rightarrow C_2D_5H + C_3H_5{}^+ \tag{31}$$

$$C_2D_5{}^+ + C_3H_6 \rightarrow C_5D_5H_6{}^+ \tag{32}$$

at a pressure of 30 torr are 1.00, 1.07, 0.16, and 0.93, respectively. However, because Reactions 30 and 31 have $C_3D_5H_6{}^+$ as a common precursor, an increase in pressure may favor the condensation Reaction 32. Obviously, further experimentation is necessary to elucidate the effect of pressure on ion-molecule reactions involving olefins.

Condensation Reactions

Condensation reactions essentially include all reactions in which a strongly bound reaction complex, which may or may not be stabilized by collision, is produced.

$$A^+ + B \rightarrow AB^{+*} \tag{33}$$

$$AB^{+*} + M \rightarrow AB^+ + M \tag{34}$$

$$AB^{+*} \rightarrow \text{Fragments} \tag{35}$$

The charged species formed in the fragmentation process (Reaction 35) usually has a higher molecular weight than its precursor ion, A^+. Further reaction of the ion formed in Reaction 35 will lead to the formation of a product ion with a still higher molecular weight. Because a large number of ion-molecule reactions fall into this category, only a few examples which illustrate the advantages and limitations of the analytical method will be discussed.

The well established reaction:

$$CH_3{}^+ + CH_4 \rightarrow C_2H_7{}^+ \rightarrow C_2H_5{}^+ + H_2 \tag{36}$$

is a condensation reaction. As mentioned above, Aquilanti and Volpi (*1*) indicate that ample evidence exists that $C_2H_7{}^+$ can be collisionally stabilized at sufficiently high pressures. In a closed system, the occurrence of a reaction such as Reaction 36 can readily be demonstrated by an interceptor technique, which consists of adding to the system a larger hydrocarbon with which the product ethyl ion will react to form ethane. Such a technique, however, does not necessarily distinguish (*10*) between the $C_2D_7{}^+$ and the $C_2D_5{}^+$ species. Similarly, the presence of the tertiary ion, $C_3D_7{}^+$, in the radiolysis of CD_4 has been demonstrated (*10*) by an interceptor reaction such as 7. Furthermore, on the basis of the deuterium labeling of the propane produced in this reaction, it was concluded that the $C_3D_7{}^+$ ion has the secondary structure. Note that the consecutive reaction chain can be interrupted by introducing a suitable additive in trace amounts. Otherwise, in a closed system, neutralization will be the competing process. In various mass spectrometric studies (*38, 43*) it has been demonstrated that at sufficiently elevated pressures, ions of very high molecular weight can be formed. Such ionic species could not, as yet, be clearly pinpointed by analyzing neutral products although polymer products have been analyzed by Sieck and Johnsen (*42*). In agreement with a recent mass spectrometric investigation (*38*), they ascribed their formation to condensation reactions involving C^+ and CH^+.

Neutral or positively charged unsaturated hydrocarbons often undergo condensation-type reactions. Some of these have been mentioned previously in this communication. Of particular interest is Meisels' study (*35*) on the radiolysis of ethylene. He has shown that it is actually feasible to derive rate constants for the decomposition of some of the condensation products by a simple analysis of neutral products. Although the data of Kebarle and Hogg (*29*) demonstrate that the ion-molecule reaction mechanism occurring in such a high pressure system can be exceedingly complex, by judiciously introducing selected additives, the reaction can be interrupted or considerably simplified with the result that useful quantitative information can be derived more readily (*28, 34*). More extensive discussion on the subject is presented by Meisels (*36*) and Kebarle (*28*) in this volume.

Acknowledgment

This research was supported by the U. S. Atomic Energy Commission.

Literature Cited

(1) Aquilanti, V., Volpi, G. G., *J. Chem. Phys.* **44**, 2307 (1966).
(2) Ausloos, P., Lias, S. G., *J. Chem. Phys.* **36**, 3163 (1962).
(3) Ausloos, P., Lias, S. G., Sandoval, I. B., *Discuss. Faraday Soc.* **36**, 66 (1963).
(4) Ausloos, P., Gorden, R., Jr., *J. Chem. Phys.* **41**, 1278 (1964).
(5) Ausloos, P., Lias, S. G., *J. Chem. Phys.* **41**, 3962 (1964).
(6) Ausloos, P., Lias, S. G., *J. Chem. Phys.* **45** (in press).
(7) Ausloos, P., Lias, S. G., *J. Chem. Phys.* **43**, 127 (1965).
(8) Ausloos, P., Scala, A. A., Lias, S. G., *J. Am. Chem. Soc.* **88**, 1583 (1966).
(9) Ausloos, P., Lias, S. G., *Discuss. Faraday Soc.* **38**, 36 (1965).
(10) Ausloos, P., Lias, S. G., Gorden, R., Jr., *J. Chem. Phys.* **39**, 818 (1963); **40**, 1854 (1964).
(11) Ausloos P., Lias, S. G., *J. Chem. Phys.* **40**, 3599 (1964).
(12) Borkowski, R. P., Ausloos, P., *J. Chem. Phys.* **40**, 1128 (1964).
(13) Borkowski, R. P., Ausloos, P., *J. Chem. Phys.* **38**, 36, (1963).
(14) Carmichael, H. H., Gorden, R. Jr., Ausloos, P. J., *J. Chem. Phys.* **42**, 343 (1965).
(15) Chupka, W. A., Lindholm, E., *Arkiv Fysik* **25**, 349 (1965).
(16) Derwish, G. A. W., Galli, A., Giardini-Guidoni, Volpi, G., *J. Chem. Phys.* **41**, 2998 (1964).
(17) Doepker, R. D., Ausloos, P., *J. Chem. Phys.* **44**, 1641 (1966).
(18) Doepker, R. D., Ausloos, P., *J. Chem. Phys.* **44**, 1951 (1966).
(19) Doepker, R. D., Ausloos, P., *J. Chem. Phys.* **42**, 3746 (1965).
(20) Draper, L. M., Green, J. H., *J. Chem. Phys.* **68**, 1429 (1964).
(21) Elder, F. A., Giese, C., Steiner, B., Inghram, M., *J. Chem. Phys.* **36**, 3292 (1962).
(22) Eyring, H., Hirschfelder, J. O., Taylor, H. S., *J. Chem. Phys.* **4**, 479 (1936).
(23) Field, F. H., Lampe, F. W., *J. Am. Chem. Soc.* **80**, 5587 (1958).
(24) Futrell, J. H., *J. Am. Chem. Soc.* **81**, 5921 (1959).
(25) Futrell, J. H., *J. Phys. Chem.* **64**, 1634 (1960).
(26) Gorden, R., Jr., Doepker, R., Ausloos, P., *J. Chem. Phys.* (in press).
(27) Harrison, A. G., Tait, J. M. S., *Can. J. Chem.* **40**, 1986 (1962).
(28) Kebarle, P., ADVAN. CHEM. SER. **58**, 210 (1966).
(29) Kebarle, P., Hogg, A. M., *J. Chem. Phys.* **42**, 668 (1965).

(30) Lawrence, R. H., Jr., Firestone, R. F., *J. Am. Chem. Soc.* **87**, 2288 (1965).
(31) Lawrence, R. H., Jr., Firestone, R. F., ADVAN. CHEM. SER. **58**, 278 (1966).
(32) Lias, S. G., Ausloos, P., *J. Chem. Phys.* **37**, 877 (1962).
(33) Lias, S. G., Ausloos, P., *J. Chem. Phys.* **43**, 2748 (1965).
(34) Meisels, G. G., Sworsky, I. J., *J. Phys. Chem.* **69**, 2867 (1965).
(35) Meisels, G. G., *J. Chem. Phys.* **42**, 2328 (1965).
(36) Meisels, G. G., ADVAN. CHEM. SER. **58**, 243 (1966).
(37) Munson, M. S. B., Franklin, J. L., Field, F. H., *J. Phys. Chem.* **68**, 3098 (1964).
(38) Munson, M. S. B., Field, F. H., *J. Am. Chem. Soc.* **87**, 3294 (1965).
(39) Pattersson, E., Lindholm, E., *Arkiv Fysik* **24**, 49 (1963).
(40) Pottie, R. F., Lorquet, A. J., Hamill, W. H., *J. Am. Chem. Soc.* **84**, 579 (1962).
(41) Sandoval, I. B., Ausloos, P. J., *J. Chem. Phys.* **38**, 2454 (1963).
(42) Sieck, L. W., Johnsen, R. H., *J. Phys. Chem.* **67**, 2281 (1963).
(43) Wexler, S., Jesse, N., *J. Am. Chem. Soc.* **84**, 3425 (1962).

RECEIVED May 6, 1966.

16

Proton Transfer and Neutralization Reactions in Irradiated Gases at Atmospheric Pressure and Between −78° and 25° C.

ROBERT H. LAWRENCE, JR.[1] and RICHARD F. FIRESTONE

The Ohio State University, Columbus, Ohio

The occurrence of proton transfer reactions between D_3^+ ions and CH_4, C_2H_6, and ND_3, between methanium ions and NH_3, C_2H_6, C_3D_8, and partially deuterated methanes, and between ammonium ions and ND_3 has been demonstrated in irradiated mixtures of D_2 and various reactants near 1 atm. pressure. The methanium ion-methane sequence proceeds without thermal activation between −78° and 25°C. The rate constants for the methanium ion-methane and ammonium ion-ammonia proton transfer reactions are 3.3×10^{-11} cc./molecule-sec. and 1.8×10^{-10} cc./molecule-sec., respectively, assuming equal neutralization rate constants for methanium and ammonium ions (7.6×10^{-4} cc./molecule-sec.). The methanium ion-methane and ammonium ion-ammonia sequences exhibit chain character. Ethanium ions do not undergo proton transfer with ethane. Propanium ions appear to dissociate even at total pressures near 1 atm.

High pressure mass spectrometry has recently provided much detailed kinetic data (5, 12, 13, 14, 15, 17, 22, 24, 26, 29) concerning ionic reactions heretofore unobtainable by other means. This information has led to increased understanding of primary reaction processes and the fate of ionic intermediates formed in these processes but under conditions distinctly different from those which prevail in irradiated gases near room temperature and near atmospheric pressure. Conclusive identification and measurements of the rate constants of ionic reactions under the latter conditions remain as both significant and formidable problems.

This investigation was undertaken to establish the ionic mechanism responsible for exchange reactions occurring at pressures ranging from 0.85 to 0.98 atm. in irradiated deuterium, hydrocarbon and deuterium, ammonia gaseous mixtures at 25°C. and lower temperatures. New tech-

---

[1] Present address: U.S.A.F. Weapons Laboratory, WIRB-1, Kirtland AFB, N. M.

niques have made it possible to evaluate rate constants for proton and deuteron transfer steps in methane and ammonia, to indicate conditions under which even relatively slow ion-molecule reactions may compete effectively with neutralization at total pressures near 1 atm., and to demonstrate that proton and deuteron transfer and certain neutralization steps proceed without thermal activation. In addition, the character of the proton (deuteron) transfer sequences in ethane and propane is shown to be markedly different from that in methane.

Experimental

Experimental apparatus and procedures used are essentially those described previously (8). Modifications are described below.

Reagents. Nonisotopically labelled hydrocarbon gases used were Phillips research grade and were further purified by trap-to-trap distillation.

Chromatographic analyses of purified CH_4 and C_2H_6 indicated that no organic impurities were present at levels exceeding 10^{-3} mole %. Mass spectrometric analyses failed to detect impurities of any kind. CH_3D CH_2D_2, CHD_3, CD_4, and C_2H_5D were purchased from Merck, Sharp, and Dohme of Canada, Ltd. Samples of C_2D_6 and C_3D_8 were generously contributed by Dr. J. R. McNesby (N.B.S.) and Jean Futrell (U.S.-A.F. Aerospace Research Labs), respectively. NH_3 was obtained as the anhydrous liquid from Verkamp Co. and was purified by trap-to-trap distillation. No impurities were detectable on the mass spectrometer in NH_3 purified this way. A sample of ND_3 was graciously donated by M. S. B. Munson (Humble Oil). D_2, purchased from The Matheson Co., was mixed with carrier-free tritium (O.R.N.L.), and the mixtures were purified by passage through a heated palladium thimble.

Irradiation Procedure. Reaction mixtures were prepared at room temperature by transferring desired quantities of reactants from their storage bulbs to the reaction vessel, a 500-cc. spherical borosilicate glass flask attached to the vacuum line by a section of glass capillary tubing and a 4-mm. bore threaded glass valve with a Teflon plug (Fischer and Porter 795-609). Prior to each experiment this vessel was baked under vacuum at 500°C. for 12 or more hours.

Temperatures above 25°C. were maintained as described previously (8). Temperatures below 25°C. (other than 0°, −78°, and −196°C.) were maintained by immersing the reaction vessel in a suitable liquid (pentane or 2,3-dimethylpentane) which was cooled by passing liquid nitrogen through a coil of copper tubing immersed in the liquid hydrocarbon. The liquid nitrogen flow rate was regulated by a thermocouple actuated relay (Barber-Coleman Amplitrol) and suitable solenoid valves to maintain constant temperatures within ±3°C.

Sampling Procedure. The sample extraction technique previously described was used in this work (8). However, a heated palladium thimble was also used to separate hydrogen and hydrocarbon fractions of the samples. No exchange occurred during the separation process in agreement with observations of other workers (30). In experiments using NH_3 as a minor additive, the ammonia fraction was separated by means of appropriate cold traps.

Product Analyses. 100-e.v. yields were obtained with the expression $G_i = dx_i/dt[x_jPA/10RTI]$, where x_i is the mole fraction of product i relative to reactant j (CH_4, C_2H_6, NH_3, etc.), x_j is the mole fraction of reactant in the reaction mixture, A is Avogadro's number, and I is the dose rate (e.v./cc. sec.). Reaction rates were determined from the slopes of x_i vs. time plots. All rates and 100-e.v. yields reported are initial values—i.e., rates or yields at zero time and zero dose, respectively. Mass spectrometric analyses were performed with a Consolidated 21-620 instrument equipped with an isotope ratio accessory. Chromatographic analyses were performed with an F and M 609 flame ionization gas chromatograph. Calibration standards were rigorously used except mass spectrometer analyses for di-, tri-, and tetra-deutero ethanes and propanes. Sensitivity factors for the latter were estimated from published fragmentation pattern data (3, 18).

Dosimetry. Ion current measurements required for absolute dosimetry were performed with a Cary 31 ionization chamber and vibrating reed electrometer. Dry nitrogen was used as filling gas for the chamber, and a W value of 34.9 e.v./ion pair was assumed for H-3 beta rays in N_2 (27). Deuterium pressures in each of the reaction mixtures were great enough to ensure that less than 1% of the H-3 beta rays reached the walls of the reaction vessel (7).

Results and Discussion

Ionic Reactions in TD/D_2:Methane Mixtures. Previous investigation of the radiolysis of D_2 containing small quantities of CH_4 demonstrated that at low conversions all products anticipated from the H atom abstraction sequence except CH_3D are absent from 125° to −196°C. and that the temperature coefficient of the rate of CH_3D formation between 25° and 125°C. is much too small for a purely atomic and free-radical reaction sequence (8). These observations are confirmed by new data presented in Table I. The new data also demonstrate the initial value of $G(CH_3D)$ is independent of temperature at 25°C. and below.

Table I.   100-e.v. Yields in the TD/D_2:CH_4 System[a]

T, °C.	CH_3D	CH_2D_2	CHD_3	CD_4	$CH_3D/CH_2D_2/CHD_3/CD_4$
−196	3.1	0.0	0.0	0.0	
−100	3.6	0.0	0.0	0.0	
−78	3.6	0.0	0.0	0.0	
−50	3.4	0.0	0.0	0.0	
−25	3.1	0.0	0.0	0.0	
0	4.4	0.0	0.0	0.0	
25	4.3	0.0	0.0	0.0	
50	4.8	0.2	0.0	0.0	1.0/0.04/0.0/0.0
75	5.5	0.5	0.3	0.0	1.0/0.09/0.05/0.0
100	6.4	1.1	0.4	0.0	1.0/0.17/0.04/0.0
125[b]	6.1	2.0	0.45	0.0	1.0/0.33/0.074/0.0
150[b]	10.0	1.3	0.47	0.2	1.0/0.13/0.047/0.02
175[b]	13.6	2.1	0.50	0.3	1.0/0.15/0.037/0.02
186[b]	26.5	3.6	0.61	0.4	1.0/0.14/0.023/0.02
200[b]	30.8	3.7	0.53	0.45	1.0/0.12/0.017/0.02

[a] 98.5 mole % TD/D_2(1:100):1.5 mole % CH_4.
[b] Ethane observed at T $\geq$ 125°C. but in each case with a time dependent rate tending toward zero at higher doses.

In this investigation we observed that the more highly deuterated methanes and ethane formed by atomic and free-radical reactions between 150° and 200°C. disappear rapidly if the temperature of the reaction mixture is lowered and maintained at 75° to −196°C., and the rate of formation of CH_3D increases simultaneously.   Figure 1 shows that at 25°C. in a synthetic mixture initially composed of TD/D_2 (1:100):1.5% $CH_4/CD_4(23:1)$, CD_4 is converted with high efficiency to CHD_3 and that successive steps rapidly convert CHD_3 and CH_2D_2 to CH_3D until all detectable CD_4 and CHD_3 have been consumed and $G(CH_2D_2)$ approaches zero.   At this point $G(CH_3D)$ assumes the value characteristic of TD/D_2:1.5% CH_4 mixtures at 25° C.   All D atoms, introduced as CD_4, are accounted for as CH_3D and CH_2D_2.   The rate of disappearance of CD_4 is first order with respect to the CD_4 concentration, and the data of Figure 1 yield a pseudo first-order rate constant equal to 4.40×10^{-4} sec. $^{-1}$ at 25°C. (cf. Figure 2).   We observe the same value within a few percent at −78°C., and it is clear that an ionic chain reaction sequence which proceeds without thermal activation is responsible for destruction of the more highly deuterated methanes.

The majority of products in the range −196° to 125°C. are formed by reactions of ionic intermediates.   In irradiated 98.5% D_2 − 1.5% CH_4

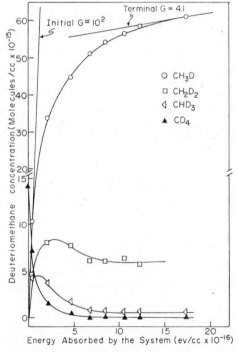

Figure   1. $TD/D_2(1:100):1.5\%$ $CH_4/CD_4(23:1)$ at   25°C.   Dose   rate   =   4.72 $\times 10^{12}$ e.v./cc.sec.

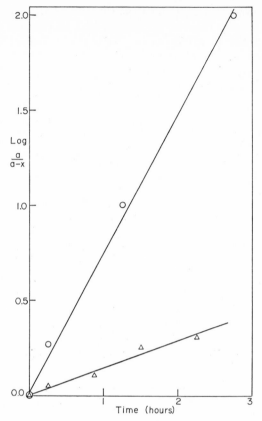

Figure 2. First-order plots for CD_4 and ND_3 consumption. ○—$\log\ [(CD_4)_0/(CD_4)]$ *vs. t, dose rate = 4.72 $\times$ 10^{12} e.v./cc.sec.* △— $\log\ [(ND_3)_0/(ND_3)]$ *vs. t, dose rate = 0.76 $\times$ 10^{10} e.v./cc.sec.*

mixtures one can estimate that 92–98% of the energy used to form ions is absorbed by D_2 (*4, 10, 23*). The predominant primary processes are:

$$D_2 \rightsquigarrow D_2{}^+ \tag{1}$$

$$D_2 \rightsquigarrow 2D\cdot \tag{2}$$

Substantial evidence has been presented for the reaction:

$$D_2{}^+ + D_2 \rightarrow D_3{}^+ + D\cdot \tag{3}$$

which proceeds with a rate constant equal to 1.4 $\times$ 10^{-9} cc./molecule sec. (*21*). It has been demonstrated (*1, 2, 7*) that $D_3{}^+$ reacts with CH_4 via

$$D_3{}^+ + CH_4 \rightarrow CH_4D^+ + D_2 \tag{4}$$

Table II.   Effects of Temperature and Additives in TD/D$_2$:CH$_4$/ CD$_4$ Mixtures

T, °C.	Additive[a]	$G(CH_3D)$[b]	$G(-CD_4)$[b]
25	none	1×10^2	1×10^2
25	Xe	5×10	5×10
25	C_2H_6	1.24[c]	0.0
25	NH_3	0.74[c]	0.0
-78	none	1×10^2	140
-78	Xe	1×10^2	1×10^2

[a] 97% TD/D$_2$(1:100):1.5% CH$_4$/CD$_4$(23:1):1.5% additive.
[b] Initial 100-e.v. yields.
[c] These figures merely reflect a difference in deuteron transfer efficiencies from D$_3$+ to NH$_3$ and C$_2$H$_6$ relative to that for CH$_4$; efficiency order is NH$_3$/C$_2$H$_6$/CH$_4$.

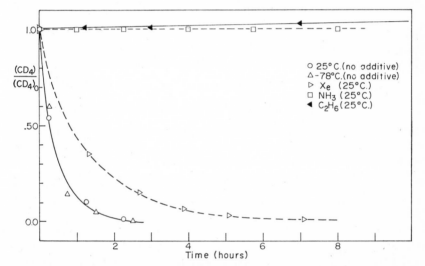

Figure 3.   Effects of temperature and proton scavenger additives in TD/ C$_2$:CH$_4$/CD$_4$.   Dose rate = 4.72 × 10^{12} e.v./cc.sec.

Thus, CH$_3$D may be formed via the proton transfer reaction:

$$CH_4D^+ + CH_4 \rightarrow CH_5^+ + CH_3D \tag{5}$$

and/or a neutralization step represented by Reaction 6,

$$CH_4D^+ + e(\text{or negative ion}) \rightarrow CH_3D + H\cdot \tag{6}$$

The following analysis indicates that neutralization is a negligible contributor.   As we have reported previously (*12*) and as indicated by Tables I and II and Figure 1, destruction of CD$_4$ and other methanes more highly deuterated than CH$_3$D is effected by an ionic chain reaction sequence which proceeds without thermal activation and which is strongly inhibited by small quantities of NH$_3$ and C$_2$H$_6$ (cf. Figure 3).

These observations indicate conclusively that the ionic sequence responsible is a proton and deuteron transfer sequence. Individual steps in this sequence may be expected to include the following:

$$CH_5^+ + CD_4 \rightarrow CH_4 + CHD_4^+ \qquad (7)$$

$$CHD_4^+ + CH_4 \rightarrow CHD_3 + CH_4D^+ \qquad (8)$$

$$CH_4D^+ + CH_4 \rightarrow CH_3D + CH_5^+ \qquad (5)$$

$$CH_5^+ + CHD_3 \rightarrow CH_2D_3^+ + CH_4 \qquad (9)$$

$$CH_2D_3^+ + CH_4 \rightarrow CH_4D^+ + CH_2D_\varepsilon \qquad (10)$$

etc., or in general, for the disappearance of CD_4, in particular,

$$CH_{5-i}D_i^+ + CD_4 \rightarrow CH_{4-i}D_i + CHD_4^+ \qquad (11)$$

where $i = 0, 1, 2, 3, 4$, the majority being CH_5^+ because the partially deuterated species react most frequently with the most abundant form, CH_4. Neutralization steps may be represented formally by:

$$CH_{5-i}D_i^+ + e(\text{or negative ion}) \rightarrow \text{neutral species} \qquad (12)$$

$$D_3^+ + e(\text{or negative ion}) \rightarrow \text{neutral species} \qquad (13)$$

Thus, we may write the pseudo first-order rate constant for disappearance of CD_4 as $k_{11}(CH_{5-i}D_i^+) = 4.40 \times 10^{-4}$ sec.$^{-1}$ Appropriate rate equations are

$$-d(CD_4)/dt = k_{11} (CH_{5-i}D_i^+) (CD_4) \qquad (I)$$

$$d(D_3^+)/dt = k_3 (D_2^+)(D_2) - k_4(D_3^+)(CH_4) - k_{13}(D_3^+)(e) \qquad (II)$$

$$d(CH_{5-i}D_i^+)/dt = k_4 (D_3^+)(CH_4) - k_{12}(CH_{5-i}D_i^+)(e) \qquad (III)$$

The W value for H_2 is 36.3 e.v./ion pair (28), which leads to an anticipated 100-e.v. yield of CH_3D equal to 2.8 molecules/100 e.v. in TD/D_2:-CH_4 if every D_3^+ ion reacts via Reaction 4. The temperature-independent (ionic) yield, $G(CH_3D) = 3.7 \pm 0.4$ molecule/100 e.v., arises partly from Reactions 3–5 and the remainder from methyl radicals formed by neutralization of CH_5^+ and by direct radiolysis of CH_4—the latter contribution not to exceed 0.2 molecule/100 e.v. which is $G(CH_3D)$ in the presence of NH_3 at $-78°$–$25°C$. We may reasonably assume, therefore, that a negligible fraction of D_3^+ ions is neutralized, and

$$d(D_3^+)/dt = k_3 (D_2^+) (D_2) - k_4 (D_3^+) (CH_4) \qquad (IIa)$$

Unquestionably, the rate of neutralization of D_2^+ is negligible, and we may equate the rates of formation of D_2^+ and D_3^+.

Now, $k_3(D_2^+)(D_2) = I/W = 1.28 \times 10^{11}$ ions/cc. sec. ($I = 4.72 \times 10^{12}$ e.v./cc. sec.). Steady-state treatment of I, IIa, and III yields $(CH_{5-i}D_i^+) = 3.6 \times 10^5/k_{12}^{1/2}$, and $k_{11}/k_{12}^{1/2} = 1.2 \times 10^{-9}$ cc./molecule-sec.)$^{1/2}$. Abramson and Futrell have measured the rate constant for the reaction, $CD_5^+ + CH_4 \rightarrow CD_4 + CH_4D^+$, in one of a series of experiments with a tandem mass spectrometer (9). Assuming that isotope effects are negligible, we may assign their value to k_{11} (3.3×10^{-11} cc./ molecule-sec.). On this basis we find that k_{12}, the neutralization rate constant for methanium ions, is equal to 7.6×10^{-4} cc./molecule-sec.

   Ionic Reactions in TD/D$_2$(1:10^5), 2.5% NH$_3$/ND$_3$/200:1) Mixtures. Munson and Field have estimated the rate constant of the reaction $ND_3H^+ + ND_3 \rightarrow ND_4^+ + ND_2H$ of the order 10^{-9} cc./molecule-sec. (*16*). Thus, measuring exchange rates in TD/D$_2$:NH$_3$/ND$_3$ mixtures permits a very rough estimate of the rate constant for neutralization of ammonium ions *in situ*. The anticipated reaction sequence is:

$$D_3^+ + NH_3 \rightarrow NH_3D^+ + D_2 \qquad (14)$$

$$NH_3D^+ + NH_3 \rightarrow NH_2D + NH_4^+ \qquad (15)$$

$$NH_{4-i}D_i^+ + ND_3 \rightarrow NH_{3-i}D_i^+ + ND_3H \qquad (16)$$

where $i = 0, 1, 2, 3$ with the majority of ammonium ions in NH_4^+ form, and

$$ND_3H^+ + NH_3 \rightarrow ND_2H + NH_3D^+ \qquad (17)$$

etc. and

$$NH_{4-i}D_i^+ + e \rightarrow \text{neutral species} \qquad (18)$$

The pseudo first-order rate constant (cf. Figure 2) is equal to $k_{16}(NH_{4-i}D_i^+) = 0.945 \times 10^{-4}$ sec.$^{-1}$ From the initial ND_3 concentration (3.45×10^{15} molecules/cc.) and the dose rate ($I = 0.76 \times 10^{10}$ e.v./cc. sec.) we find that $G(-ND_3) = 4.3 \times 10^3$ molecules/100 e.v. at zero dose and $25°C$. A kinetic treatment similar to that used above for the methane system yields $k_{16}/k_{18}^{1/2} = 6.6 \times 10^{-9}$ (cc./molecule sec.)$^{1/2}$.

   Employing Munson and Field's estimate of k_{16}, we find that the rate constant for neutralization of ammonium ions is roughly 10^{-2} cc./molecule sec. This value is, of course, extremely sensitive to the value of k_{16}, which we presently know only within an order of magnitude. Nevertheless, it is apparent that the efficiency of neutralization steps can be several orders of magnitude greater than estimates based upon earlier work (*6, 25*) in admittedly very different reaction systems. Even order of magnitude estimates of neutralization rate constants can be grossly unreliable in the absence of detailed understanding of the mechanisms for neutralization in a given radiolytic system. Assuming that neutralization efficiencies for ammonium and methanium ions in very similar systems are roughly equal, we find that $k_{16} = 1.8 \times 10^{-10}$ cc./molecule sec. for the step: $NH_4^+ + ND_3 \rightarrow NH_3 + ND_3H^+$.

   These results support the suggestion (*20*) that positive ion-molecule reactions can and do compete effectively with neutralization steps at pressures near 1 atm. It is, however, apparent that neutralization steps will compete quite effectively at dose rates greater than the relatively low ones used in this work. Since $G(-CD_4)$ and $G(-ND_3)$ are proportional to $I^{-1/2}$, neutralization will compete on an equal footing for methanium and ammonium ions at dose rates of the order of 10^{16} e.v./cc. sec. in otherwise identical reaction mixtures, and the chain character of the proton (deuteron) transfer sequence will, of course, vanish at dose rates of this order.

Effects of Temperature on Ionic Reactions in $TD/D_2:CH_4/CD_4$. Observation that the methanium ion proton (deuteron) transfer sequence fails to exhibit a temperature coefficient within experimental uncertainties leads unavoidably to the conclusion that none of the reactions from 1 to 12 requires thermal activation between $-78°$ and $25°C$. From Equations I, II, III, appropriate steady state assumptions, and representing both neutralization steps by k_{12}, we find that

$$E_{obs.} = E_4 + E_{11} \frac{k_{12}^{1/2}k_4(CH_4)(I/W)^{-1/2}[E_{12}/2 + E_4] + k_{12}E_{12}}{k_{12}^{1/2}k_4(CH_4)(I/W)^{-1/2} + k_{12}}$$

Now, since $I = 4.7 \times 10^{12}$ e.v./cc. sec., $(CH_4)_0 = 3.2 \times 10^{17}$ molecules/cc., $W = 36.3$ e.v./ion pair, and k_4 must exceed 10^{-14} cc./molecule sec., it is apparent that $E_{obs.} = E_{11} - E_{12}/2$ within experimental error. Essentially identical arguments lead to $E_{obs.} = E_5 - E_6/2 = 0$ in the $TD/D_2:$ CH_4 system between $-78°$ and $25°$ C. Subject to what would be a highly fortuitous possibility that the activation energy for neutralization is not zero and equal to half that for proton transfer in each case, it can be concluded that $E_{11} = E_{12} = E_5 = E_6 = 0$.

Ionic Reactions in $TD/D_2:$Ethane Mixtures. The data in Table III show that deuteron transfer occurs in irradiated mixtures of D_2 and ethane as well. Data are shown only for temperatures ($<25°C.$) at which ionic reactions clearly predominate. Analysis of data concerning thermal atomic and free-radical reactions at higher temperatures will be published elsewhere in the near future. The reaction of D_3^+ with ethane has been observed directly (1) and postulated (2) by other workers. Both groups have proposed that the sequence initiated by deuteron transfer to ethane proceeds as follows:

$$D_3^+ + C_2H_6 \rightarrow C_2H_6D^+) + D_2 \qquad (19)$$

$$\qquad\qquad \nearrow C_2H_5^+ + HD \qquad (20a)$$

$$(C_2H_6D^+) \rightarrow C_2H_4D^+ + H_2 \qquad (20b)$$

$$\qquad\qquad \searrow_M C_2H_6D^+ \qquad (20c)$$

Aquilante and Volpi's results (1) indicate that ethanium ions should be collisionally stabilized at pressures used in this work—i.e., $(k_{20a} + k_{20b})/k_{20c} = 3 \times 10^{16}$ molecules/cc., where M is ethane. They also observe that the anticipated ethanium ion-ethane proton transfer reaction is not significant. Our observations confirm the absence of proton transfer reactions between long-lived ions and ethane. A chain sequence analogous to that exhibited by methanium ions in methane does not occur. Such a sequence would rapidly destroy $C_2H_3D_3$ and $C_2H_4D_2$ in $TD/D_2:$ C_2H_6 mixtures and $C_2H_2D_4$ and $C_2H_3D_3$ in $TD/D_2:C_2H_5D$ mixtures.

Table III. Initial Deuteroethane Yields in TD/D₂: Ethane Systems

System	T, °C.	C_2H_5D	$C_2H_4D_2$	$C_2H_3D_3$	$C_2H_2D_4$	C_2D_6
I: 98.7% TD(D₂(1:100): 1.3% C₂H₆	−120	1.4	0.4		...	...
II: 98.5% TD/D₂(1:100): 1.5% C₂H₅D	−35	1.5	0.5		...	...
	25	1.4	0.2		...	...
	−30	...	2.5	0.6	0.1	...
	0	...	1.9	0.5	0.2	...
	25	...	1.6	0.5	0.1	...
III: 98.5% TD/D₂(1:-100):1.5% C₂H₆/C₂D₆ (28:1)	−78	2.5		0.06	...	0.00
IV: 97% TD/D₂(1:100):- 3% C₂H₆/NH₃ (1:10)	25	2.8	0.6	0.2	...	0.00
	−78	0.13	0.10	0.03	...	...
	25	0.34	0.07	0.04	...	...

G Values spans columns C_2H_5D through C_2D_6.

Such is not the case, and furthermore, the presence of NH_3 does not alter product ratios in favor of the more highly deuterated species as it does in the methane systems. The additional observation that C_2D_6 is untouched in TD/D₂ : C₂H₆/C₂D₆ mixtures (Table III, System III) makes the evidence against ethanium ion-ethane proton transfer conclusive.

Recent observations (*14, 15*) indicate that ethyl ions react with ethane via

$$C_2H_5^+ + C_2H_6 \rightarrow C_3H_7^+ + CH_4 \qquad (21)$$

followed by

$$C_3H_7^+ + C_2H_6 \rightarrow C_4H_9^+ + CH_4 \qquad (22)$$

We observe that G(propane) and G(butane) are negligible at 25°C. and below, and we must conclude that these reactions are not significant relative to competing steps (e.g., neutralization) under prevailing conditions in our work. The weight of available evidence suggests strongly that both ethanium and ethyl ions are important precursors of the deuteroethane products. Aquilante and Volpi report (*1*) that ethanium ions are removed by reaction(s) with ethane, but unfortunately they were not able to observe the product because of a high normal ethane mass spectral background at ethane pressures high enough to observe removal of ethanium ions. We suggest tentatively that ethanium ions and ethane undergo hydride ion transfer,

$$C_2H_6D^+ + C_2H_6 \rightarrow C_2H_5^+ + (C_2H_7D) \qquad (23)$$

$$(C_2H_7D) \begin{cases} \rightarrow C_2H_6 + HD & (23a) \\ \rightarrow C_2H_5D + H_2 & (23b) \end{cases}$$

and that ethyl ions are neutralized,

$$C_2H_5^+ + e \text{ (or negative ion)} \rightarrow (C_2H_5) \qquad (24)$$

and are either collisionally stabilized,

$$(C_2H_5) + M \rightarrow C_2H_5 \cdot \qquad (25)$$

or dissociate into ethylene and an H atom,

$$(C_2H_5) \rightarrow C_2H_4 + H \cdot \qquad (26)$$

C_2H_5D and $C_2H_4D_2$ may then be formed in the $TD/D_2 : C_2H_6$ system—e.g., via addition of D atoms,

$$C_2H_5 \cdot + D \cdot \xrightarrow{M} C_2H_5D \qquad (27)$$

and

$$C_2H_4 + D \cdot \xrightarrow{M} C_2H_4D \cdot \qquad (28)$$

followed by

$$C_2H_4D \cdot + D \cdot \xrightarrow{M} C_2H_4D_2 \qquad (29)$$

The observed ratios, $C_2H_5D/C_2H_4D_2$ in $TD/D_2 : C_2H_6$ and $C_2H_4D_2/C_2H_3D_3$ in $TD/D_2 : C_2H_5D$, are in every case greater than or equal to 3/1. Since one might reasonably expect Reaction 23b to produce C_2H_5D (in $TD/D_2 : C_2H_6$) at a rate roughly equal to the rate of formation of $C_2H_5{}^+$ ($k_{23b}/k_{23a} \simeq 3/1$), we estimate that no less than half of the ethyl ions are neutralized non-dissociatively. Alternatively, if k_{23b} were negligible, the over-all reaction would be

$$D_3{}^+ + C_2H_6 = D_2 + HD + C_2H_5{}^+,$$

requiring that at least two-thirds of the ethyl ions be neutralized without dissociation.

It seems prudent not to speculate on the source of ethane products containing three D atoms more than the reactant form, except, perhaps to suggest that direct radiolysis or energy transfer may produce precursors of these as well as minor portions of the other products.

Ionic Reactions in $TD/D_2(1,100), 1.5\%$ $CH_4/C_3D_8(50:1)$ Mixtures. The presence of a trace of propane-d_8 in $TD/D_2 : CH_4$ provides the following observations relevant to the fate of the intermediates $C_3D_8H^+$ and $C_3D_9{}^+$: (1) C_3D_8 is destroyed under indicated experimental conditions by a process which exhibits a pseudo first-order rate constant equal to 2.8×10^{-5} sec.$^{-1}$, and $G(-C_3D_8) = 5.6$ molecules/100 e.v.; (2) the only detectable initial products derived from C_3D_8 are C_2D_6, CD_4, and CHD_3; no protonated propanes and no higher hydrocarbons are observed; (3) C_2HD_5 is not formed initially but follows formation of C_2D_6 and is destroyed by a process which leads to formation of $C_2D_4H_2$; (4) the initial rates of formation of CD_3H and CD_4 are in the ratio of *ca.* 2/1; upon depletion of C_3D_8, CD_4 ceases to be produced, but net formation of CHD_3 continues.

There is no doubt (1, 6) that C_3D_8 readily accepts protons from methanium ions and deuterons from $D_3{}^+$. At $CH_4/C_3D_8 = 50/1$ the majority of propanium ions must be formed via the sequence,

$$D_3{}^+ + CH_4 \rightarrow CH_4D^+ + D_2 \qquad (4)$$

$$CH_4D^+ + CH_4 \rightarrow CH_3D + CH_5{}^+ \qquad (5)$$

$$CH_5{}^+ + C_3D_8 \rightarrow CH_4 + C_3D_8H^+ \qquad (30)$$

Aquilante and Volpi indicate (1) that propanium ions formed by proton transfer from $H_3{}^+$ are not collisionally stabilized at propane pressures as great as 0.3 mm. and that they decompose by elimination of hydrogen or a smaller saturated hydrocarbon to form an alkyl carbonium ion. Others (16, 19) have proposed one or the other of these fates for unstabilized propanium ions. Our observations can be rationalized within this framework by the following mechanisms:

$$C_3D_8H^+ \begin{cases} \nearrow C_2D_5{}^+ + CHD_3 & (31a) \\ \searrow C_2HD_4{}^+ + CD_4 & (31b) \end{cases}$$

$$C_3D_8H^+ \begin{cases} \nearrow C_3D_7{}^+ + HD & (32a) \\ \searrow C_3D_6H^+ + D_2 & (32b) \end{cases}$$

where $k_{32}/k_{31} \simeq 0.5$ according to Aquilante and Volpi (1). Step 31b can be ruled out because C_2HD_5 is not an initial product, but C_2D_6 will be formed by hydride ion transfer (1, 11) via

$$C_2D_5{}^+ + C_3D_8 \rightarrow C_2D_6 + C_3D_7{}^+ \qquad (33)$$

Similarly, Reaction 32b can be ruled out because C_3HD_7 is not a product. Secondary products, C_2HD_5 and $C_2H_2D_4$, may be formed by proton transfer reactions involving methanium ions, C_2D_6, and C_2HD_5. In addition, collisional stabilization of propanium ions cannot be ruled out at high pressures, and we have, in addition, no information bearing directly on possible reactions of propanium ions and propyl ions with CH_4 under our reaction conditions.

Finally, the mechanism is obviously not well enough understood to warrant an attempt to evaluate the rate constant of Reaction 30 from the measured value of $k_{30}(CH_5{}^+)$.

Acknowledgments

The authors are grateful to M. S. B. Munson, J. H. Futrell, and J. R. McNesby for samples of ND_3, C_3D_8, and C_2D_6, respectively. This work was partially supported by the U.S. Atomic Energy Commission, Contract No. At(11–1)-1116.

Literature Cited

(1) Aquilante, V., Volpi, G. G., *J. Chem. Phys.* **44**, 2307 (1966).
(2) Ausloos, P., Lias, S. G., *J. Chem. Phys.* **40**, 3599 (1964).
(3) Bell, J. A., Kistiakowsky, G. B., *J. Am. Chem. Soc.* **84**, 3417 (1962).
(4) Bethe, H. A., *Ann. Physik* **5**, 352 (1930).
(5) Derwish, G. A. W., Galli, A., Giardini-Guidoni, A., Volpi, G. G., *J. Chem. Phys.* **40**, 5 (1964).
(6) Doering, J. P., Mahan, B. H., *J. Chem. Phys.* **36**, 669 (1962).
(7) Dorfman, L. M., *Phys. Rev.* **95**, 393 (1954).
(8) Firestone, R. F., Lemr, C. F., Trudel, G. J., *J. Am. Chem. Soc.* **84**, 2279 (1962).
(9) Futrell, J. H., Abramson, F. P., ADVAN. CHEM. SER. **58**, 107 (1966).
(10) Klots, C. E., *J. Chem. Phys.* **39**, 1571 (1963).
(11) Lampe, F. W., Franklin, J. L., Field, F. H., *Progr. Reaction Kinetics* **1**, 87 (1961).
(12) Lawrence, R. H., Jr., Firestone, R. F., *J. Am. Chem. Soc.* **87**, 2288 (1965).
(13) Lind, S. C., "Radiation Chemistry of Gases," A.C.S. Monograph No. 151, Reinhold Corp., New York, 1961.
(14) Munson, M. S. B., Field, F. H., *J. Am. Chem. Soc.* **87**, 3294 (1965).
(15) Munson, M. S. B., Franklin, J. L., Field, F. H., *J. Phys. Chem.* **68**, 3098 (1964).
(16) Munson, M. S. B., Field, F. H., *J. Am. Chem. Soc.* **87**, 4242 (1965).
(17) Munson, M. S. B., Field, F. H., Franklin, J. L., *J. Am. Chem. Soc.* **85**, 3584 (1963).
(18) Quinn, E. I., Mohler, F. L., *J. Res. Natl. Bur. Std.* **65A**, 93 (1961).
(19) Ryan, K. R., Futrell, J. H., *J. Chem. Phys.* **42**, 824 (1965).
(20) Stevenson, D. P., *J. Phys. Chem.* **61**, 1453 (1957).
(21) Stevenson, D. P., Schissler, D. O., *J. Chem. Phys.* **23**, 1353 (1955).
(22) Stevenson, D. P., Schissler, D. O., "Chemical and Biological Action of Radiation," M. Haissinsky, Ed., Vol. V, Ch. IV, Academic Press, New York, 1961.
(23) Strickler, T. D., *J. Phys. Chem.* **67**, 825 (1963).
(24) Swallow, A. J., "Radiation Chemistry of Organic Compounds," Pergamon Press, New York, 1961.
(25) Takada, S., Dougal, A. A., *J. Appl. Phys.* **31**, 412 (1960).
(26) Tal'roze, V. L., *Pure Appl. Chem.* **5**, 455 (1962).
(27) Weiss, J., Bernstein, W., *Phys. Rev.* **98**, 1828 (1955).
(28) Weiss, J., Bernstein, W., *Phys. Rev.* **103**, 1253 (1956).
(29) Wexler, S., *J. Am. Chem. Soc.* **85**, 273 (1963).
(30) Whittle, E., Steacie, E. W. R., *J. Chem. Phys.* **21**, 993 (1953).

RECEIVED May 2, 1966. Based on a dissertation presented in partial fulfillment of requirements for the Ph.D. degree, The Ohio State University, 1965, by R. H. Lawrence, Jr., U.S.A.F., A.F.I.T. Program, 1961–1965.

Ion-Molecule Reactions in Flames

H. F. CALCOTE and D. E. JENSEN

AeroChem Research Laboratories, Inc., Princeton, N. J. 08540

Low energy ion-molecule reactions have been studied in flames at temperatures between 1000° and 4000°K. and pressures of 1 to 760 torr. Reactions of ions derived from hydrocarbons have been most widely investigated, and mechanisms developed account for most of the ions observed mass spectrometrically. Rate constants of many of the reactions can be determined. Emphasis is on the use of flames as media in which reaction rate coefficients can be measured. Flames provide environments in which reactions of such species as metallic and halide additive ions may also be studied; many interpretations of these studies, however, are at present speculative. Brief indications of the production, recombination, and diffusion of ions in flames are also provided.

Despite the widening theoretical and experimental interest in phenomena associated with ionization in gases which has been prompted in recent years by practical problems, few reliable rate constants for ion-molecule reactions at low energies are available. A flame provides an environment particularly suited to study such reactions since its pressure, temperature, and composition are easily controlled, and the average energies associated with individual molecules (a molecule at 2000°K. has an average translational energy of 0.26 e.v.) are low by general standards of mass spectrometry. Furthermore, the comparative simplicity of charged and uncharged species found in flames (some typical equilibrium flame compositions are given in Table I) makes it possible to interpret observed reaction rates in terms of fundamental parameters and to base estimates of unknown rate constants on more than empirical grounds. Flame temperatures vary typically from about 1000° to more than 4000°K; where possible, we refer our discussion of reaction rates to a temperature of 2000°K. The proportion of ions present in laboratory flames without metallic additives under such conditions may be between one part in 10^{13} and one part in 10^5.

Most information concerning ion-molecule reactions in flames has been obtained from mass spectrometric measurements, but some inferences have been drawn from results of other types of experiments

Table I. Typical Flame Temperatures and Equilibrium Compositions[a]

Flame Equivalence Ratio, ϕ[b]	$H_2/N_2/O_2$; ($N_2{:}O_2 = 3{:}1$) 1.75	H_2/Air 0.40	C_2H_2/O_2		C_2H_2/Air 1.9
			1.0	1.0	
Pressure, torr	760	40	20	1	760
Temperature, °K.	2250	1420	2840	2510	2239
[N₂]	0.46	0.73	—	—	0.62
[H₂O]	0.31	0.15	8.6×10^{-2}	7.5×10^{-2}	2.4×10^{-2}
[H₂]	0.23	1.1×10^{-6}	3.8×10^{-2}	3.7×10^{-2}	0.10
[H]	3.6×10^{-3}	—	0.11	0.13	2.2×10^{-3}
[OH]	7.3×10^{-4}	8.4×10^{-5}	7.6×10^{-2}	6.1×10^{-2}	7.9×10^{-5}
[O]	7.7×10^{-6}	1.8×10^{-6}	0.13	0.15	1.1×10^{-6}
[O₂]	4.3×10^{-6}	0.12	0.12	0.12	—
[CO]	—	—	0.33	0.32	0.25
[CO₂]	—	—	0.11	0.11	1.05×10^{-2}
[NO]	—	6.2×10^{-4}	—	—	9.2×10^{-6}
[CHO]	—	—	—	—	2.2×10^{-6}

[a] Concentrations are expressed as mole fractions. Species with concentrations $<10^{-6}$ are omitted.
[b] ϕ = (actual ratio of [fuel] to [O₂])/(ratio required for complete combustion to CO_2 and/or H_2O).

(e.g., from Langmuir probe studies). These techniques have been described in detail elsewhere (7, 8, 19). The most convenient experimental arrangement consists of a flat flame produced above a cylindrical burner containing tubes or grids which ensure uniform flow of gas across the burner. Such an arrangement provides an essentially one-dimensional system in which distance above the burner is a measure of reaction time, the linear gas flow rate being known (calculated from the unburned gas flow rate, the flame diameter, the temperature distribution, and the change in number of molecular species caused by chemical reaction).

We shall confine ourselves largely to a discussion of past and current experimental work on ion-molecule reactions in flames; much of the interpretation must, in the light of our present knowledge, remain highly speculative. Brief indications of the origins and decay mechanisms of ion concentrations are also included.

Hydrocarbon Flame Ions

Origin of Ions in Hydrocarbon Flames. Many ions, both positive and negative, are observed in hydrocarbon flames studied by mass spectrometric methods (9, 14, 26). Most of these are produced by ion-molecule reactions following the formation of primary ions from neutral species.

POSITIVE IONS. It is generally considered that positive ions in hydrocarbon flames are produced initially through the two reactions (11):

$$CH + O \rightarrow CHO^+ + e^- \qquad (1)$$

$$CH^* + C_2H_2 \rightarrow C_3H_3^+ + e^- \qquad (2)$$

where the free radical CH may be either in its ground state, electronically excited ($B^2\Sigma^-$ or $A^2\Delta$), or, possibly, vibrationally excited. Reaction 1, with CH in the ground state, is endothermic by 20 kcal./mole; the same reaction with CH in the $A^2\Delta$ state is exothermic by 58 kcal./mole. Nevertheless, the ground-state reaction probably dominates, because $n_{CH} \gg n_{CH*}$.

Reaction 2 has been invoked because $C_3H_3^+$ is apparently formed in a primary ionization step since the ion appears early in the flame front, its concentration maximizes in rich flames (this is true of no other positive ion observed), and it is present in the flame front in large concentrations (*9*).   However, not all the experimental evidence is consistent with this mechanism for producing $C_3H_3^+$; it might also be produced through an ion-molecule reaction, which will be considered below.

NEGATIVE IONS.   Negative ions in flames have been studied less widely than positive ions because they are present in much smaller concentrations; typically, $n_+/n_- \approx 100$.   The primary source of negative ions has been suggested (*20*) to be Reaction 3, comparable to Reaction 4 (*see* the section on flames with halogen additives).

$$e^- + H_2O \rightarrow OH^- + H \qquad (3)$$

$$e^- + HCl \rightarrow Cl^- + H \qquad (4)$$

The rate constant for Reaction 3, however, is far from well established. For example, an experimental value of k_3 can be estimated from the measured attachment cross-section data of Buchel'nikova (*4*) who observed a maximum cross-section $\sigma_{e, max} = 5 \times 10^{-18}$ cm.^{2} at 6.4 e.v. for electrons colliding with water molecules.   (The cross-section falls below 1×10^{-18} cm.^{2} at energies lower than 5 e.v.)   This suggests that

$$k_3 \approx v_e \sigma_e e^{-E/RT} \approx 10^7 \times 5 \times 10^{-18} e^{-147,000/RT}$$

or

$$k_3 \approx 10^{-26} \text{ cm.}^3 \text{ molecule}^{-1} \text{ sec.}^{-1} \text{ at } 2000°K.$$

where v_e is the mean electron velocity at 2000°K., and E is the energy threshold for Reaction 3.   This is an extremely small rate coefficient and would imply a surprisingly large temperature coefficient in the rate constant for the reverse of Reaction 3.

One might calculate a *maximum* value for k_2 by substituting for E the endothermicity of Reaction 3, which is 3.4 e.v.   This gives $k_3 \approx 5 \times 10^{-11} e^{-77,000/RT}$ cm.^{3} molecule^{-1} sec.$^{-1}$, or $k_3 \approx 10^{-19}$ cm.^{3} molecule^{-1} sec.$^{-1}$ at 2000°K.   Since the equilibrium constant for Reaction 3 is $k_3 \approx 5 \times 10^3 e^{-77,000/RT}$, the value of k_{-3} is $k_{-3} \approx 10^{-14}$ cm.^{3} molecule^{-1} sec.$^{-1}$. The resemblance between this value of k_{-3} and that of k_{-4} (estimated later in text) is noteworthy, in view of the formal similarity of Reactions 3 and 4, but further experimental work on these reactions is clearly necessary.

The above values of k_3 may be compared with that required to explain Green's results (*20*) (obtained from measurements on an atmospheric pressure $H_2/O_2/Ar$ flame at 2180°K. to which had been added 2.8% by volume of C_2H_2) in terms of Reaction 3.   Under steady-state conditions the rates of production and loss of negative ions are equal. (Steady-state conditions are those under which ion concentrations maximize. Since individual ion concentrations do not all maximize at exactly the same distance above the burner, the following calculations are by no means exact.) For the sake of argument, we assume the principal loss mechanism to be dissociative recombination between positive ions and OH^- and neglect charge transfer; the value of k_3 estimated will thus be a lower limiting value. The value of k_3 needed to explain Green's results is thus given by:

$$k_3 n_{e^-} \, n_{H_2O} \; = \; \alpha n_+ \, n_{OH^-}$$

Since under Green's conditions, $\alpha \approx 10^{-7}$ cm.^{3} molecule^{-1} sec.$^{-1}$ (unpublished experiments at AeroChem), $n_+ \approx n_{e^-} \approx 10^{11}$ cm.$^{-3}$, $n_{H_2O} \approx 3 \times 10^{17}$ cm.$^{-3}$, and $n_{OH^-} \approx 10^9$ cm.$^{-3}$, then $k_3 \approx 3 \times 10^{-16}$ cm.^{3} molecule^{-1} sec.$^{-1}$ This is some three orders of magnitude greater than the "maximum" value of k_3 calculated on the basis of Buchel'nikova's data. Therefore, dissociative attachment of electrons to water is too slow to account for the observed concentrations of negative ions.

Three-body attachment of electrons seems to provide a more attractive explanation. Several reactions are worthy of consideration:

$$e^- + O_2 + M \rightarrow O_2^- + M \tag{5}$$

$$k_5 \approx 3 \times 10^{-30} \text{ cm.}^6 \text{ molecule}^{-2} \text{ sec.}^{-1} \text{ at } 2000°K.$$

$$e^- + OH + M \rightarrow OH^- + M \tag{6}$$

$$k_6 \approx 10^{-30} \text{ cm.}^1 \text{ molecule}^{-2} \text{ sec.}^{-1} \text{ at } 2000°K.$$

$$e^- + O + M \rightarrow O^- + M \tag{7}$$

$$k_7 \text{ unknown, } \Delta H = -34 \text{ kcal./mole}$$

$$e^- + H_2O + H \rightarrow OH^- + H_2 \tag{8}$$

$$k_8 \text{ unknown, } \Delta H = -26 \text{ kcal./mole}$$

[The origin of k_5 and k_6 values is given later in the text.]

Attachment of electrons to O_2, Reaction 5, was eliminated by Green because O_2^- appeared far ahead of the flame front, which indicated that electron attachment occurred in the unburned gas rather than in the flame. However, in low pressure flames (where the spatial resolution is far better) O_2^- is observed in the flame front (see e.g., Figure 2).

A steady-state test similar to that described above can be applied to the three-body process; thus the value of k_6 required to explain Green's experimental data would be given by:

$$k_6 \approx \frac{\alpha n_+ n_{OH^-}}{n_e \cdot n_{OH} n_M}$$

Substituting the appropriate concentrations ($n_{OH} \approx 10^{15}$ cm.$^{-3}$) gives $k_6 \approx 10^{-31}$ cm.^{6} molecule^{-2} sec.$^{-1}$ This is less than the recommended value by one order of magnitude, and three-body attachment of electrons to OH thus appears to provide a reasonable reaction path; by comparison, Reactions 7 and 8 also seem reasonable.

In low pressure flames, however, the situation is less clear cut (*9*). For example, in stoichiometric acetylene-oxygen flames at 1.0 torr ($T = 2500°$K.) the value of k_6 required to explain the experimental data can be calculated by equating the rate of OH$^-$ formation at the steady state to the appropriate loss rate, which must include diffusion:

$$k_6 n_e n_{OH} n_M = \alpha n_+ n_{OH^-} + \tau_D^{-1} n_{OH^-}$$

where τ_D is the characteristic time for diffusion.   (τ_D^{-1} is given by $\dfrac{D_{OH^-}}{\Lambda^2}$, where D_{OH^-} is the diffusion coefficient, and Λ is a quantity characteristic of the experimental geometry.   For a cylinder, with height H and radius R, $\left(\dfrac{1}{\Lambda}\right)^2 = \left(\dfrac{\pi}{H}\right)^2 + \left(\dfrac{2.4}{R}\right)^2$. H is taken as the "thickness" of the ionized zone and R as the radius of the burner.)   Explanation of the experimental data in terms of three-body attachment to OH would therefore require $k_6 \approx 2 \times 10^{-29}$ cm.^{6} molecule^{-2} sec.$^{-1}$ ($n_{e^-} = n_+ = 2 \times 10^{10}$ cm.$^{-3}$; $n_{OH^-} = 2 \times 10^8$ cm.$^{-3}$; n_{OH} (equilibrium) $= 2 \times 10^{14}$ cm.$^{-3}$; $n_M = 4 \times 10^{15}$ cm.$^{-3}$; $D_{OH^-} \approx 1 \times 10^3$ cm,^{2} sec.$^{-1}$ (estimated as less than ambipolar diffusion coefficient (*9*)); $H \approx 10$ cm.; $R = 7.5$ cm.)   This is an order of magnitude larger than the recommended value of k_6 and suggests that some other reaction is important in the production of primary negative ions.

The following observations suggest that either C_2^- or C_2H^- is a primary ion:

(1) The negative ion concentrations all show very definite maxima on the fuel-rich side of stoichiometric flame composition.

(2) C_2^- or C_2H^- is one of the first ions to appear in the flame front.

(3) The C_2^- ion decays much more rapidly in the flame than does any other ion.

The work of Bleekrode and Nieuwpoort (*3*) suggests that at 1 torr in a stoichiometric C_2H_2/O_2 flame, $n_{C_2} \approx 10^{13}$ cm.$^{-3}$ The observed rate of production of negative ions would thus necessitate a three-body rate constant for attachment of electrons to C_2 of about 5×10^{-28} cm.^{6} molecule^{-2} sec.$^{-1}$ This seems somewhat high but is not altogether impossible.

Because of doubts about important rate constants in the above interpretations, other mechanisms have been considered (*9*); Reactions 9 and 10 are consistent with most of the experimental observations:

$$C_2H_2 + O \rightarrow C_2H_2O^* \qquad\qquad\qquad (9)$$

$$C_2H_2O^* + e^- \rightarrow C_2^- + H_2O \qquad \Delta H = -46 \text{ kcal./mole} \quad (10)$$

The reaction:

$$C_2H + e^- \rightarrow C_2^- + H \qquad \Delta H = +65 \text{ kcal./mole} \quad (11)$$

would also be attractive were it not for its high endothermicity.

Chemi-ionization reactions producing negative ions also remain possible—e.g.,

$$CH^* + HO_2 \rightarrow CHO^+ + OH^- \qquad \Delta H = -25 \text{ kcal./mole} \qquad (12)$$

and

$$CH^* + O_2 \rightarrow CHO^+ + O^- \qquad \Delta H = -5 \text{ kcal./mole} \qquad (13)$$

Positive Ion-Molecule Reactions. Some of the important ions identified in hydrocarbon/air or oxygen combustion are presented in Table II. With the exception of CHO^+ and possibly $C_3H_3^+$, all the ions are produced in ion-molecule reactions.

Table II. Some Important Ions in Hydrocarbon Combustion

		1-atm. Flames				
$Mass^a$	Identity	Sugden et al. (19)	van Tiggelen et al. (12, 39)	Low Pressure Flames (7, 9)	O-Atom Reaction (15)	Shock Waves (18)
15	CH_3^+	X	X	X	X	...
19	H_3O^+	X	X	X	X	X
26	$C_2H_2^+$, CN^+	X	...	...	...	...
27	$C_2H_3^+$	...	...	...	X	X
29	CHO^+	X	X	X	X	...
31	CH_3O^+	X	X	X	X	X
33	CH_5O^+, HO_2^+	X	X	X	X	X
39	$C_3H_3^+$	X	X	X	X	X
43	$C_2H_3O^+$, $C_3H_7^+$	X	X	X	X	X
45	$C_2H_5O^+$, CHO_2^+	X	b	X	X	...
47	$C_2H_7O^+$, $CH_3O_2^+$	X	X	...	...	...
49	$CH_5O_2^+$	X	X	X	...	...
53	C_3HO^+, $C_4H_5^+$	X	...	X	X	...
61	$C_2H_5O_2^+$	X	...	...	...	...

^{a} Green and Sugden (19) identify masses 33, 43, 45, and 53 as input ions—i.e., those produced in the sampling systems; other ions are natural flame ions, except mass 15 which could not be classified.
^{b} Only observed when HBr added (12).

RATE COEFFICIENTS FROM FLAME EXPERIMENTS. The most dominant ion, H_3O^+ (*see* Figure 1), is produced by (11):

$$CHO^+ + H_2O \rightarrow H_3O^+ + CO \qquad (14)$$

The rate coefficient for Reaction 14 can be estimated via a steady-state analysis when the major loss mechanism (as at 760 torr) is the dissociative recombination

$$H_3O^+ + e^- \rightarrow \text{Products} \qquad (15)$$

since the rate constant for this reaction has been determined in flames by a number of investigators and is $\alpha = 2.4 \pm 0.4 \times 10^{-7}$ cm.^{3} molecule^{-1} sec.$^{-1}$, independent of both pressure and temperature (11). For low pressure flames, diffusion must also be included, and at the steady state

$$k_{14}n_{CHO^+} n_{H_2O} = \alpha n_{H_3O^+} n_{e^-} + \tau_D^{-1} n_{H_3O^+}$$

When $n_{e^-} = n_{H_3O^+}$ (i.e., negative ions are present in negligible concentrations) and $\alpha_e\text{-}n_{H_3O^+}n_{e^-} \gg \alpha_-n_{H_3O^+}n_-$, which is the usual situation,

$$k_{14} = \frac{\alpha(n_{H_3O^+}{}^{max})^2 + \tau_D{}^{-1}n_{H_3O^+}}{n_{H_2O}n_{CHO^+}}$$

The appropriate concentrations (from Figure 1 at low pressures and from the data of Green and Sugden (*19*) at 1 atm.) are given in units of molecules/cm.[3] below.

	2 torr (Figure 1)	760 torr (Green and Sugden)
Maximum H_3O^+ concentration, $n_{H_3O^+}{}^{max}$	3×10^{10}	2×10^{11}
Measured n_{CHO^+}	1.5×10^7	5×10^5
Equilibrium n_{H_2O}	5.8×10^{14}	1.9×10^{18}

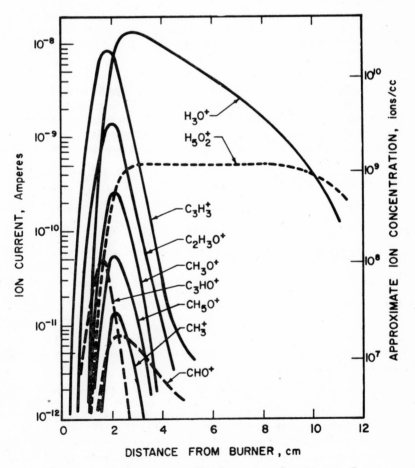

Figure 1.   Positive ion profiles in an acetylene/oxygen flame

Pressure = 2 torr; total flow = 70 cc./sec. at STP; equivalence ratio = 1.0; burner diameter = 15 cm.; from Ref. 9.

The results show that at 2 torr, $k_{14} = 2.5 \times 10^{-8}$ and at 760 torr $k_{14} = 1.0 \times 10^{-8}$ cm.^{3} molecule^{-1} sec.$^{-1}$ This is reasonably good agreement in view of the possible errors. Furthermore, the values of k_{14} obtained are consistent with earlier estimates based on comparisons with similar reactions (*10, 19*). Our purpose in presenting it here is to illustrate the potential use of flames in estimating more accurate rate constants for reactions like Reaction 14. Of course, the influence of diffusion must always be accounted for in such estimations; diffusion is particularly important at low pressures and for small ion concentrations. (It is often advantageous to work at low pressures because the spatial resolution is much better than at 1 atm. At low pressures most measurements are made in or close to the reaction zone itself. At high pressures, where the reaction zone is thinner, measurements are made both in the reaction zone and in the burned gases.)

REACTIONS OF CHO$^+$ WITH NEUTRAL MOLECULES. Ions of masses 31, 33, and 45 have been demonstrated to be possible products of reactions between CHO$^+$ and neutral molecules, for they are produced when CH$_2$O, CH$_3$OH, and CH$_3$CHO are added to a "cold" ($T_{max} \approx 600°$K.) chemiionization system. This system consists of an atomic oxygen hydrocarbon diffusion flame produced when oxygen atoms formed in a microwave discharge cavity flow into ethylene at 1–10 torr. Adding CH$_2$O, CH$_3$OH, and CH$_3$CHO to the ethylene results in pronounced increases in concentrations of ions of masses 31, 33, and 45, respectively (*9*). In this system, $n_{CHO^+} > n_{H_3O^+}$, and thus the following reactions seem reasonable.

$$\Delta H, \text{ kcal./mole}$$

$$CHO^+ + CH_2O \rightarrow CH_2OH^+ + CO \qquad -41 \qquad (16)$$

$$CHO^+ + CH_3OH \rightarrow CH_3OH_2^+ + CO \qquad -62 \qquad (17)$$

$$CHO^+ + CH_3CHO \rightarrow CH_3CHOH^+ + CO \qquad -4.5 \qquad (18)$$

Mass 43 probably results from the reaction:

$$CHO^+ + C_2H_2O \rightarrow C_2H_3O^+ + CO \qquad \Delta H = -32 \text{ kcal./mole} \qquad (19)$$

C$_2$H$_2$O is expected to be formed in the flame (*13, 21*) via

$$C_2H_2 + O \rightarrow C_2H_2O \qquad (20)$$

Acetylene is present in most hydrocarbon flames (*16*). Mass 15 might be produced via

$$CH_3OH_2^+ \rightarrow CH_3^+ + H O \qquad \Delta H = +62 \text{ kcal./mole} \qquad (21)$$

which apparently occurs in mass spectrometers, the necessary energy coming from the formation of CH$_3$OH$_2^+$ via Reaction (17).

DEPENDENCE OF FLAME SPECIES CONCENTRATIONS UPON ADDITIVE CONCENTRATIONS. A method of determining the dependence of various ionic, neutral molecule, and excited species concentrations on the concentration of hydrocarbon added to a hydrogen/oxygen or hydrogen/air flame (based on a principle similar to that of flame ionization detectors used in gas chromatography (*35*)) has been developed.   Flame ionization detectors measure *rates of production* of electrons directly.   A linear increase in rate of electron production with increase in hydrocarbon concentration in these detectors is observed over a very wide range of hydrocarbon concentrations.   Green and Sugden (*19*) observed the *steady-state concentrations* of various positive ions obtained when acetylene is added in volume proportions of 0.3–3% to a hydrogen/air flame at 1 atm.   These data have been interpreted (*1, 11, 19*) in terms of ion-molecule reactions occurring in the flame.   Miller (*28*) has recently made even more extensive measurements, adding either acetylene or ethylene to a 4-torr hydrogen/oxygen flame (equivalence ratio = 0.5).   Some of the results are summarized in Table III, where the order of dependence, x, of n_+ on [additive] is reported; $n_+ \propto$ [additive]^x.

Different dependencies are obtained at the two pressures and for the different flames.   First, consider the difference owing to pressure change in the light of the linear dependence of ion formation rate on additive concentration that is obtained in gas chromatographic experiments. It has been demonstrated that at high pressures the principal ion loss mechanism is dissociative recombination.   Thus, with $n_+ = n_{e^-}$, we can write

$$n_{C_2H_2} \propto \alpha n_+^2$$

$$n_+ \propto \sqrt{\frac{n_{C_2H_2}}{\alpha}} \propto n_{C_2H_2}^{0.5}$$

as observed.   At the lower pressures and at small ion concentrations where diffusion dominates, we have

$$n_{C_2H_2} \propto -\left(\frac{D_a}{\Lambda^2}\right) n_+$$

or

$$n_+ \propto -\left(\frac{\Lambda^2}{D_a}\right) n_{C_2H_2} \propto n_{C_2H_2}^{1.0}$$

as observed (D_a = ambipolar diffusion coefficient).   The other exponential concentration dependencies have yet to be explained in a completely satisfactory manner although they have provided information relevant to discussions of possible mechanisms.   (In interpretations of the 760 torr results, it was assumed that $n_{CH*} \propto n_{C_2H_2}$, which is shown to be wrong, at least at low pressures.)   Most of these discussions invoked only a few simultaneous reactions and neglected the effects of diffusion both out of the flame and parallel with the flow; more detailed analyses are apparently required to unravel the data.

ORIGIN OF $C_3H_3^+$.   If $C_3H_3^+$ is rejected as a primary ion, (*18, 28*) an ion-molecule reaction which explains its rather unusual behavior must be found.   Miller has recently studied this problem (*28*) and concludes that this ion is formed in a proton transfer and/or ion-molecule (CH^+

transfer) reaction involving C_3H_2 or C_2H_2. Furthermore, he concludes that the mechanism is different when C_2H_4 rather than C_2H_2 is added to a hydrogen/oxygen flame. Several of his conclusions, however, are based upon simple interpretations of the data in Table III, which failed to include effects of diffusion or simultaneous reactions.

Table III. Dependence of Observed Concentrations on Hydrocarbon Additives in Hydrogen/Air or Oxygen Flames

Additive	C_2H_2	C_2H_2	C_2H_4
Oxidizer	Air	Oxygen	Oxygen
Pressure, torr	760	4	4
		Order of Dependence[a]	
Total Ions	0.5	1.0	1.0
CH*	...	2.0	2.0
C_2H_2[b]	...	...	1.0
H_3O^+	0.5	1.0	1.0
CHO^+	1.0	1.0	...
CH_3O^+	1.5	2.5	3.5
CH_5O^+	...	2.0	2.5
$C_3H_3^+$	2.0	2.0	3.5
$C_2H_3O^+$	...	1.0	1.5
$C_2H_5O^+$	...	...	2.0

[a] From slope log n_{max} vs. log $n_{hydrocarbon\ added}$; uncertainty in slopes ±0.1.
[b] From small sampling probes

The mechanism originally proposed (10) for $C_3H_3^+$ formation:

$$H_3O^+ + C_3H_2 \rightarrow C_3H_3^+ + H_2O \qquad \Delta H = -40 \text{ kcal./mole} \quad (22)$$

or

$$CHO^+ + C_3H_2 \rightarrow C_3H_3^+ + CO \qquad \Delta H = -95 \text{ kcal./mole} \quad (23)$$

was rejected at the Ninth Symposium on Combustion (see Discussion of Ref. 19) on the basis that C_3H_2 has not been identified in flames. However, it may be present; it is difficult to suggest a good way to identify this radical. Thus, Reactions 22 and 23 still remain possible (28).

The second mechanism, proposed by Green and Sugden (19), involves the equilibria

$$H_3O^+ + CH_2O \rightleftharpoons CH_3O^+ + H_2O \qquad \Delta H = +41 \text{ kcal./mole} \quad (24)$$

and

$$CH_3O^+ + C_2H_2 \rightleftharpoons C_3H_3^+ + H_2O \qquad \Delta H = -64 \text{ kcal./mole} \quad (25)$$

and has been rejected as being inconsistent with the orders of ion dependence in Table III and with the concentrations of reactants observed and required for reasonable rate constants (11, 28).

The reaction:

$$CHO^+ + C_2H_2 \rightarrow C_3H_3^+ + O \qquad \Delta H = 43 \text{ kcal./mole} \quad (26)$$

in which CH^+ is transferred, has recently been suggested by Glass et al. (17), and similar reactions have been discussed in detail by Miller (28).

Miller suggests that for C_2H_2 addition to an H_2/O_2 flame the dominant reaction producing $C_3H_3{}^+$ may be:

$$C_2H_3O^+ + C_2H_2 \rightarrow C_3H_3{}^+ + CO + H_2 \qquad \Delta H = 8 \text{ kcal./mole} \qquad (27)$$

while for C_2H_4 addition the dominant reaction may be

$$CH_5O^+ + C_2H_2 \rightarrow C_3H_3{}^+ + H_2O + H_2 \qquad \Delta H = 10 \text{ kcal./mole} \qquad (28)$$

In a lean acetylene/oxygen flame, $C_2H_3O^+$ is, in fact, the dominant ion, its concentration exceeding even the maximum H_3O^+ concentration (9). It is presumably produced by Reaction 19.

In summary, the question of the mechanism of formation of $C_3H_3{}^+$ in flames is still open; in fact, several of the reactions discussed may well occur simultaneously in some flames. Probably, past interpretations have been oversimplified, and it is now time to consider simultaneous contributions from various reactions.

ION ADDITION. Thus far, formation of most of the ions in Table II has been accounted for. Occurrence of the larger ions is not difficult to explain—e.g., addition of H_2O to ions of masses 19, 29, 31, and 43 will give ions of masses 37, 47, 49, and 61, respectively. Other larger ions can be expected because they are usually formed in exothermic reactions of smaller ions; once a hydrocarbon ion is produced, larger ions are readily formed by:

$$R_1{}^+ + R_2 \rightarrow R_1R_2{}^+ \qquad (29)$$

In fact, such polymerization reactions may play an important role in carbon formation in flames (26).

DECAY OF SECONDARY ION CONCENTRATIONS. The fate of the secondary ions must now be considered. Miller (28) has observed that for C_2H_4/O_2 and C_2H_2/O_2 flames at 2 and 4 torr the rates of decay of all secondary ions, including $C_3H_3{}^+$, are approximately the same (*see*, for example, Figure 1). The slow decay of the primary ion CHO^+, paralleling that of H_3O^+, has been attributed (11) to establishment of equilibrium for Reaction 14.

$$CHO^+ + H_2O \rightleftharpoons H_3O^+ + CO \qquad (14)$$

Miller interprets the constant decay rate of the secondary ions as being caused by all of these ions reacting with the same oxidative species (O, OH, O_2) in a set of reactions having the same bimolecular rate coefficient (corrected for diffusion) of $k = (4 \pm 2) \times 10^{-11} \text{ cm.}^3 \text{ molecule}^{-1} \text{ sec.}^{-1}$ Although this explanation is consistent with the data, it is somewhat disquieting to find that so many reactions must have the same rate constant. In view of the similarity of the curves in Figure 1, it seems reasonable to seek an explanation in terms of rapid equilibration among all the species with one reaction leading to H_3O^+, this last ion then being lost from the system via dissociative recombination (Reaction 15) or ambipolar diffusion. The fact that these secondary ions all decay faster than H_3O^+ (which, as we have already demonstrated, decays by ambipolar diffusion in this set of experiments) is proof that they decay to

H_3O^+ and are not lost by diffusion or recombination. If they were lost by dissociative recombination, the recombination coefficient would have to be too large; $\alpha > 3 \times 10^{-6}$ cm.^{3} molecule^{-1} sec.$^{-1}$ would be required.

The following reactions have been suggested (9) to account for the oxidation of the flame ions

$$\Delta H, \text{kcal./mole}$$

$$C_3H_3^+ + O_2 \rightarrow C_2H_3O^+ + CO \qquad -114 \qquad (30)$$

$$C_3H_3^+ + O \rightarrow CHO^+ + C_2H_2 \qquad -43 \qquad \text{Reverse (26)}$$

$$C_2H_3O^+ + O \rightarrow CH_3O^+ + CO \qquad -45 \qquad (31)$$

$$C_2H_3O^+ + OH \rightarrow CH_3O^+ + CHO \qquad -49 \qquad (32)$$

$$CH_3O^+ + O \rightarrow H_3O^+ + CO \qquad -157 \qquad (33)$$

and other similar reactions are possible, e.g., Reaction 34.

$$C_2H_3O^+ + CH_2O \rightarrow C_2H_5O^+ + CO \qquad -2 \qquad (34)$$

Note that all the ions involved have already been produced by previous reactions and that apart from those of Reactions 30 and 33 the heats of reaction are small. Thus, with these reactions and similar ones, there is no reason why equilibria should not be maintained. Again, the need to treat a large number of reactions simultaneously to explain the results is stressed. A computer study of such a reaction scheme is now under way at AeroChem.

Negative Ion-Molecule Reactions. The negative ions which have been observed in flames are listed in Table IV. An example of negative ion profiles, showing their relationship to positive ion profiles, is given in Figure 2. As far as reactions of these ions are concerned, however, few quantitative data are yet available; negative ion studies are in their infancy. Our present object is to develop a qualitative picture of negative ion reactions in flames; experiments designed to produce rate coefficients can be suggested in the light of such a picture. Eventually, the flame should be a very useful medium in which negative ion reactions can be studied over broad ranges of pressure and temperature. In this section we outline the phenomena which must be investigated in more detail in the future.

It has already been shown that different problems can arise at 1 atm. and at low pressures. One of the more interesting observations is that at 1–2 torr in C_2H_2/O_2 and C_2H_4/O_2 flames large concentrations of C_2^- are present, and no C_2H^- is observed (9); yet if the pressure is increased to 10 torr, only C_2H^- is observed (compare Figures 3 and 4). In addition, in 1-atm. flames (20) and in atomic flames at 1–10 torr and at low temperatures C_2H^- predominates (29). C_2^- decays more rapidly than does any other ion while C_2H^- decays at a rate comparable to the decay rates of other ions (cf. Figures 2, 3, and 4). These observations are consistent with C_2^- as a primary ion which produces C_2H^- through the exothermic three-body process:

$$C_2^- + H + M \rightarrow C_2H^- + M \qquad \Delta H = -140 \text{ kcal./mole} \qquad (35)$$

Thus, C_2H^- would be strongly favored at higher pressures but would be

Table IV. Negative Ions Identified in Flames[e]

Mass	Identity	Stoic. O_2[a]	Stoic. O_2/N_2[b]	2.8% in H_2/O_2[c]	Atomic O[d]	Methane[b] Stoic. O_2/N_2	Neopentane[b] Stoic. O_2/N_2
		Acetylene Flames					
	Pressure, torr	6	760	760	1–10	760	760
12	C^-	5	...	...	...	...	...
15	CH_3^-	...	15	...	...	3	...
16	O^-	1	14	...	7	2	11
17	OH^-	2	8	8	6	1	5
24	C_2^-	3	12	5	8	...	...
25	C_2H^-	...	1	2	3	...	4
26	CN^-	...	11	...	4	...	8
32	O_2^-	4	6	3	5	7	6
36	C_3^-	8	...	7	...	...	...
41	C_2OH^-	...	9	...	...	...	...
42	$C_2OH_2^-$	...	4	...	2(CNO)	...	7
43	$C_2OH_3^-$	...	3	...	...	8	10
45	CO_2H^-	...	...	1	...	...	...
46	CH_2O_2 -^{13}C isotope, mass 45	...	2	...	1(NO$_2$)	6	2
47	$CO_2H_3^-$	...	13	...	...	...	9
49	C_4H^-	...	...	9	...	...	...
50	$O_3H_2^-$, $C_4H_2^-$	...	...	...	...	...	...
53	C_3HO^-	...	...	...	...	...	12
60	$C_2O_2H_4^-$, CO_3^-, C_5^-	...	10	...	...	...	...
62	$CO_3H_2^-$, $C_2O_2H_6^-$, $C_5H_2^-$	7	5	...	...	4	1
63	$CO_2H \cdot H_2O^-$, $C_5H_3^-$	...	7	4	...	5	3
73	C_6H^-	...	...	6	...	...	...
80	$CO_2(H_2O)_2^-$	6	...	...	...	...	...

[a] Ref. 9.
[b] Ref. 14; O_2/N_2 mixture contains 70% N_2.
[c] Ref. 20; 2.8 vol. % C_2H_2 in $H_2/O_2/Ar$ = 3.8/1.0/7.1 flame. Found C_mH^- to $m = 7$, and $C_mH_2^-$ $C_mH_3^-$ to $m = 3$.
[d] Ref. 29.
[e] Numbers indicate the order of decreasing maximum concentrations; the ion against which No. 1 appears occurs in the highest concentration, etc. Maxima usually do not occur at the same position in the flame.

formed relatively slowly at low pressures where the three-body reactions would not be able to compete with two-body reactions.

Another reaction which could produce C_2H^- from C_2^- is

$$C_2^- + C_2H_2 \rightarrow C_2H^- + C_2H \qquad \Delta H = -32 \text{ kcal./mole} \qquad (36)$$

In fact, extraction of a hydrogen atom from almost any hydrocarbon would be possible.   Alternative reactions might be:

ΔH, kcal./mole

$C_2^- + H_2$	$\rightarrow C_2H^- + H$	-39	(37)
$C_2^- + OH$	$\rightarrow C_2H^- + O$	-41	(38)
$C_2^- + H_2O$	$\rightarrow C_2H^- + OH$	-25	(39)

Other ions might be produced from C_2^- via the following reactions, some of which may rapidly reach equilibrium:

ΔH, kcal./mole

$C_2^- + OH$	$\rightarrow O^- + C_2H$	4.6	(40)
$C_2^- + OH$	$\rightarrow OH^- + C_2$	30	(41)
$C_2^- + H_2O$	$\rightarrow OH^- + C_2H$	14	(42)
$C_2^- + O$	$\rightarrow O^- + C_2$	37	(43)
$C_2^- + O$	$\rightarrow C^- + CO$	-69	(44)

It seems reasonable to suppose that masses 16 and 17, O^- and OH^-, are produced principally by Reactions 40 and 42 while mass 12, C^-, is produced by Reaction 44.

Some of the other ions in Table IV might be produced via:

ΔH, kcal./mole

$O_2^- + H$	$\rightarrow O^- + OH$	-71	(45)
$O^- + C_2H_2$	$\rightarrow OH^- + C_2H$	-2.3	(46)
$C_2H^- + OH$	$\rightarrow OH^- + C_2H$	-14	(47)
$C_2H^- + H_2O$	$\rightarrow C_2H \cdot H_2O^-$		(48)
$OH^- + CHO$	$\rightarrow CHO_2^- + H$		(49)
$O^- + CH_2O$	$\rightarrow CH_2O_2^-$		(50)
$OH^- + CH_2O$	$\rightarrow CH_3O_2^-$		(51)
$O_2^- + H_2O$	$\rightarrow H_2O_3^-$		(52)
$O_2^- + CH_2O$	$\rightarrow CH_2O_3^-$		(53)
$CHO_2^- + H_2O$	$\rightarrow CHO_2 \cdot H_2O^-$		(54)

Reactions 48–54 are simple attachments of ions to electronegative species, forming ions for which the heats of formation are unknown. The ions CHO_2^- (mass 45) and $CHO_2 \cdot H_2O^-$ (mass 63) are evidently not genuine flame ions in Green's system (20); they are produced in the sampling system.   Nevertheless, under other conditions they might well be produced in the flame itself.

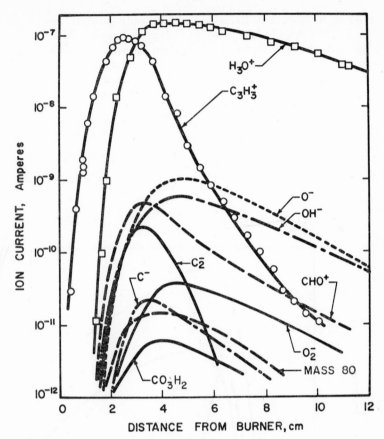

*Figure 2.   Positive and negative ion profiles in an acetylene/
oxygen flame*

*Pressure = 1.0 torr; total flow = 70 cc./sec. at STP; equivalence ratio =
1.0; burner diameter = 15 cm.; from Ref. 9.*

Thus, there is no great difficulty in accounting for each of the ions
in Table IV; the problem which remains is that of characterizing the
rates and equilibrium constants of the various simultaneous reactions.

As expected, the addition to the flame of the electronegative species
Cl (from HCl) or CN (from CH_3CN) produces Cl^- or CN^-. At low
pressures, the total negative ion population may be increased (*9*) while
at 1 atm. all the negative ions can be replaced by Cl^- (*14*). Thus, both
direct attachment and charge transfer are involved.

Nonhydrocarbon Flame Ions

Origin of Ions in Nonhydrocarbon Flames.   Of flames which
do not contain hydrocarbons, only cyanogen/oxygen flames have so far
been found to contain levels of "natural" ionization comparable with those

observed in hydrocarbon flames (5).   The only positive ion present in significant quantities in low pressure cyanogen flames is NO$^+$ (a marked contrast with the situation in hydrocarbon flames).   Bulewicz and Padley (5) have demonstrated that levels of ionization achieved in cyanogen flames are not consistent with thermal ionization and have suggested that one or more of the following energetically feasible reactions might result in primary ionization.

$$NO + N + N \rightarrow NO^+ + e^- + N_2 \qquad \Delta H = -12 \text{ kcal./mole} \qquad (55)$$

$$CN + O + O \rightarrow NO^+ + CO + e^- \qquad \Delta H = -6 \text{ kcal./mole} \qquad (56)$$

$$NO + C + O \rightarrow CO + NO^+ + e^- \qquad \Delta H = -42 \text{ kcal./mole} \qquad (57)$$

The reaction

$$N + O \rightarrow NO^+ + e^- \qquad \Delta H = +67 \text{ kcal./mole} \qquad (58)$$

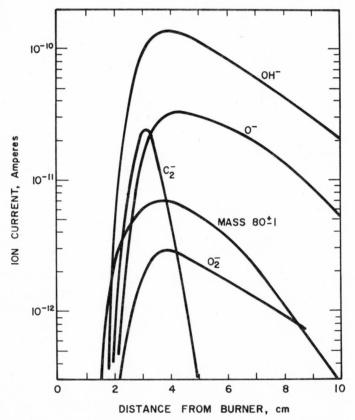

Figure 3.   Negative ion profiles in an ethylene/oxygen flame at 2 torr

Equivalence ratio = 1.0; total flow = 70 cc./sec. at STP; burner diameter = 15 cm.; unpublished work of W. J. Miller.

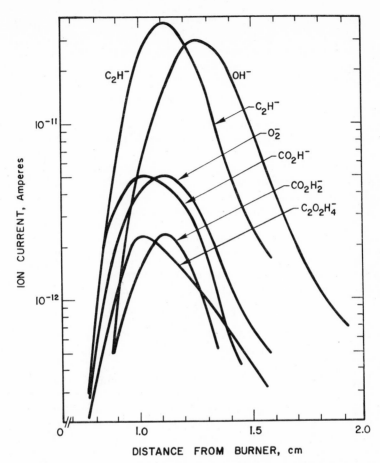

*Figure 4.   Negative ion profiles in an ethylene/oxygen flame at
10 torr*

*Equivalence ratio = 1.0;   total flow = 52 cc./sec. at STP;   burner
diameter = 7.5 cm.;   unpublished work of W. J. Miller.*

(analogous to $CH + O \rightarrow CHO^+ + e^-$) apparently accounts for only a
small proportion of ionization even in hot ($\sim$4000°K.) cyanogen flames.
Ionization in other flames (e.g., hydrogen/oxygen/nitrogen flames)
appears to stem almost entirely from the presence of hydrocarbon impurities; such reactions as (27):

$$H + H + OH \rightarrow H_3O^+ + e^- \qquad \Delta H = +27 \text{ kcal./mole} \qquad (59)$$

are no longer considered to make important contributions (*see* Discussion
of Ref. 5).   The origin of ions observed in ammonia/oxygen flames also
remains a matter for conjecture (*12*).

Ion-Molecule Reactions in Nonhydrocarbon Flames. Ion-
molecule reactions which play important parts in flame ionization phe-

nomena in nonhydrocarbon flames fall into three broad categories: (1) proton-transfer, (2) collisional detachment, and (3) dissociative charge transfer. Examples of such processes are considered below.

PROTON TRANSFER REACTIONS. De Jaegere, Deckers, and van Tiggelen (12) have observed that the equilibrium

$$NH_4^+ + H_2O \rightleftarrows NH_3 + H_3O^+ \qquad (60)$$

is rapidly established in ammonia/oxygen flames at a pressure of about 100 torr. Lack of experimental data makes it difficult to estimate the rate constant of this reaction at present.

COLLISIONAL DETACHMENT. Reactions of negative ions in flames not containing hydrocarbons have not been widely studied, although OH^- ion formation is important in flames containing high electron concentrations. The rate constant k_{61} of the reaction

$$OH^- + M \rightarrow OH + e^- + M \qquad K_{61} = \frac{k_{61}}{k_{-61}} \qquad (61)$$

(where k_{-61} is the rate constant of the reverse reaction) has not been measured, but comparison with results for the related reaction

$$O_2 + e^- + M \rightarrow O_2^- + M \qquad (62)$$

obtained by Pack and Phelps (30) suggests that k_{-61} cannot be far away from 10^{-30} cm.^{6} molecule^{-2} sec.$^{-1}$ at 2000°K. If the electron affinity of OH is taken to have its generally accepted value of 41 kcal./mole, K_{61} (calculated) $= 9 \times 10^{20} e^{-41,000/RT}$ molecule cm.$^{-3}$ at 2000°K., and k_{61} is thus $\sim 10^{-9} e^{-41,000/RT}$ cm.^{3} molecule^{-1} sec.$^{-1}$ The pre-exponential factor in k_{61} is approximately an order of magnitude higher than the neutral particle collision frequency. Reaction 61 is rather slow ($k_{61} < 10^{-13}$ cm.^{3} molecule^{-1} sec.$^{-1}$), and equilibrium between $[OH^-]$ and $[e^-]$ in flames may well be established more rapidly through

$$OH^- + H_2 \rightleftarrows H_2O + H + e^- \qquad \Delta H = +26 \text{ kcal./mole} \quad (63)$$

than through Reaction 61.

DISSOCIATIVE CHARGE TRANSFER. Knewstubb and Sugden (27) have observed mass spectrometrically that NO^+ ions are formed when 1% of NO is supplied to the unburned gases of an atmospheric-pressure $H_2/O_2/N_2$ flame at 2300°K. These authors originally suggested that their results could be accounted for in terms of the dissociative charge transfer

$$NO + H_3O^+ \rightarrow NO^+ + H_2O + H \qquad \Delta H = +68 \text{ kcal./mole} \quad (64)$$

but later rejected this explanation (see Discussion of Ref. 5); the reaction would need to have a very high pre-exponential factor ($\sim 10^{-7}$) to explain the observed rate of NO^+ production. The mechanism of formation of NO^+ ions under these conditions remains uncertain, although charge exchange with hydrocarbon ions present as impurities is a possibility.

Metallic Additives

For many metals, adding a small proportion ($\sim$1 part in 10^6) of metallic compound to an acetylene/air flame (or to an hydrogen/oxygen/-nitrogen flame to whose unburned gases has been added 1 vol. % C_2H_2) at atmospheric pressure results in an above-equilibrium concentration of electrons in the burned gases (6). The equilibrium value of n_{e^-}, $n_{e^-, \text{eq.}}$, for a metal Me is given by the Saha equation:

$$\log_{10}\left\{\frac{n_{\text{Me}^+}n_{e^-}}{n_{\text{Me}}}\right\} = \frac{-5050V}{T} + \frac{3}{2}\log_{10} T + 15.37 + \log_{10}\{g(T)\}$$

where V is the ionization potential in e.v., and $g(T)$ is a term accounting for electronic partition functions of Me^+, Me, and e^-. For many metals (e.g., Pb, Cr, Mn), $n_{e^-}/n_{e^-, \text{eq.}}$, $\sim$ 10 under the above conditions (6, 24). These observations have been interpreted in terms of a rapid charge transfer reaction

or
$$H_3O^+ + Me \begin{cases} \nearrow Me^+ + H_2O + H & (65) \\ \searrow Me^+ + H_2 + OH & (66) \end{cases}$$

The rate constants of these reactions are difficult to measure since the charge transfer is usually completed within a short distance of the reaction zone. Soundy and Williams (34) have nevertheless been able to obtain preliminary values for the rate constants, selected values of which appear in Table V. Although the order of magnitude of these

Table V.   Rate Constants of the Reaction
Me + H_3O^+ → Me^+ + Products

Metal, Me	ΔH(kcal./mole)	$k_{65}(10^{-10}$ cm.^{3} molecule^{-1} sec.$^{-1}$)
Pb	+26	10
Mn	+26	8.5
Cr	+11	8.0
Li	−21	7.5
Zn	+71	1.0

rate constants seems reasonable for reactions of this type, the pattern of results is somewhat puzzling; for example, it is surprising that the exother-

$$Li + H_3O^+ \rightarrow Li^+ + Products \qquad (67)$$

mal reaction appears to be slower than the endothermal process

$$Mn + H_3O^+ \rightarrow Mn^+ + Products \qquad (68)$$

However, the fact that lithium hydroxide formation was ignored when k_{65} for Li was calculated might account for the low observed value for this metal. Again, both $n_{e^-}/n_{e^-, \text{eq.}}$ and k_{65} appear to achieve maximum values for metals with ionization potentials of about 170 kcal./mole whereas the energy available from the reaction

$$H_3O^+ + e^- \rightarrow H_2O + H \qquad (15)$$

is only about 143 kcal./mole.   (The values of ΔH, the heat change of Reaction 65, listed are based on Tal'roze and Frankevich's (38) rather reliable value for the proton affinity of water (168 kcal./mole).)   Furthermore, recent preliminary mass spectrometric studies of Hayhurst and Sugden (22) suggest that the rate of production of sodium ions in the reaction zone of an $H_2/O_2/N_2$ flame to which sodium and 1% acetylene have been added exceeds the rate of disappearance of H_3O^+.   The possibilities that ions other than H_3O^+ contribute to charge exchange or even that the observed ionization levels stem from "hot-electron" reactions (22, 40):

$$Me + e^{-*} \rightarrow Me^+ + 2e^- \tag{69}$$

therefore cannot be ruled out at present.   At low pressures ($\sim$3 torr) metallic ions are produced only slowly in flames containing hydrocarbons, and at high pressures ($\sim$1 atm.) ions are generated too fast to measure isothermal rates accurately.   Further work at intermediate pressures might well resolve the questions raised above.

Replacing H_3O^+ (or other polynuclear) ions by such species as Na^+ and K^+ has important consequences in rocket exhaust analyses (32). The subsequent recombination reaction (25):

$$Na^+ + e^- + M \rightarrow Na + M \qquad (k \sim 1.5 \times 10^{-20}\,T^{-2}) \tag{70}$$

provides for a considerably slower rate of electron concentration decay than does Reaction 15, for which $k = 2.4 \times 10^{-7}$ cm.^{3} molecule^{-1} sec.$^{-1}$

Another type of charge exchange reaction proposed recently is (33) Reaction 71.

$$Na + SrOH^+ \rightarrow Na^+ + SrOH \qquad \Delta H \sim 0 \text{ kcal./mole} \tag{71}$$

Sugden and Schofield (33) suggest that this reaction (with a rate constant $\sim$10^{-8} cm.^{3} molecule^{-1} sec.$^{-1}$) can account for the boost in ionization of sodium observed when strontium salts are supplied to flames containing sodium.   There is evidence (24, 33, 36) which strongly suggests that equilibrium ionization of strontium in flames is rapidly established via

$$SrO + H \rightleftarrows SrOH^+ + e^- \tag{72}$$

and/or

$$Sr + OH \rightleftarrows SrOH^+ + e^- \tag{73}$$

and the ion-molecule reaction

$$SrOH^+ + H \rightarrow Sr^+ + H_2O \tag{74}$$

Reactions like (71), even if not precisely thermoneutral, are likely to be much faster than charge transfers involving atomic species alone, such as

$$Na^+ + K \rightarrow K^+ + Na \tag{75}$$

Excess energy in Reaction (75) would not be readily accommodated in the translational degrees of freedom available.

Hayhurst and Sugden (*22*) have shown that the reactions:

$$LiH_2O^+ + M \rightarrow Li^+ + H_2O + M \qquad \Delta H \sim +50 \text{ kcal./mole} \qquad (76)$$

$$NaH_2O^+ + M \rightarrow Na^+ + H_2O + M \qquad \Delta H \sim +35 \text{ kcal./mole} \qquad (77)$$

$$KH_2O^+ + M \rightarrow K^+ + H_2O + M \qquad \Delta H \sim +20 \text{ kcal./mole} \qquad (78)$$

reach equilibrium rapidly (within about 10^{-4} sec.) in flames at about 2000°K. One is therefore able to guess roughly a lower limit to the rate constant of Reaction 76 (the most endothermal and therefore probably the slowest of the three), which is $k_5 \sim 10^{-14}$ cm.^{3} molecule^{-1} sec.$^{-1}$ at 2000°K. This would correspond to a pre-exponential factor in k_{76} somewhat greater than 10^{-9} cm.^{3} molecule^{-1} sec.$^{-1}$, which would not be unreasonable. Reactions (76–78) and subsequent recombination reactions, such as

$$LiH_2O^+ + e^- \rightarrow Li + H_2O \qquad (79)$$

are worthy of further kinetic study.

Flames with Halogen Additives

The reactions

$$H + Cl^- \underset{k_{-4}}{\overset{k_4}{\rightleftarrows}} HCl + e^- \qquad K_4 = \frac{k_4}{k_{-4}} \qquad (4)$$

are of theoretical interest and practical importance. When a small proportion (0.1% by volume) of chlorine is added to an $H_2/O_2/N_2$ flame containing about 1 part per million of sodium, the electron concentration close to the reaction zone increases (*23, 31, 37*). This is at first somewhat surprising since adding chlorine might be expected to result in a lower value of n_{e^-} because of both sodium chloride formation and attachment of electrons to Cl. The effect has been explained by Padley, Page, and Sugden (*31*) in terms of three rapidly balanced equilibria:

$$Na + Cl \rightleftarrows Na^+ + Cl^- \qquad (80)$$

$$H + Cl^- \rightleftarrows HCl + e^- \qquad \text{Reverse} \quad (4)$$

and

$$HCl + H \rightleftarrows H_2 + Cl \qquad (81)$$

The net effect is to establish the equilibrium:

$$Na + H + H \rightleftarrows Na^+ + e^- + H_2 \qquad (82)$$

and thus to catalyze the ionization of sodium (which, in the absence of chlorine, proceeds slowly). Further addition of chlorine ($\sim$1 mole %) results finally in the expected decrease in n_{e^-} as NaCl formation and electron attachment to Cl overwhelm the catalytic effect. Similar phenomena are observed for other alkali metals and halogens (*23, 37*).

Consideration of work by Buchel'nikova (4) on the dissociative attachment of electrons to HCl leads to the conclusion that k_4 is given approximately by $k_4 \sim 10^{-10} e^{-20,000/RT}$ cm.^{3} molecule^{-1} sec.$^{-1}$ Since $K_{-4} \sim 2 \times 10^{-3} e^{18,000/RT}$ at 2000°K., $k_{-4} \sim 10^{-13}$ cm.^{3} molecule^{-1} sec.$^{-1}$ This is considerably smaller than rate constants for other exothermal ion-molecule reactions, which probably reflects the importance of participation of molecular vibrational energy in such reactions. Remember, however, that the uncertainty in k_4 is probably at least an order of magnitude.

The practical importance of Reaction 4 stems from the fact that HCl in rocket exhausts behaves as an electron scavenger, rapidly reducing electron concentrations. This fact, together with the above discussion, emphasizes the need for a more thorough investigation of the values of k_4 and k_{-4}. Detachment of electrons from Cl$^-$ through

$$\text{Cl}^- + \text{M} \rightarrow \text{Cl} + e^- + \text{M} \tag{83}$$

or through

$$\text{Cl}^- + \text{H}_2 \rightarrow \text{HCl} + \text{H} + e^- \tag{84}$$

also deserves attention.

Summary

Flames, either with or without metallic additives, are rich in ion-molecule reactions of both positive and negative ions. The use of flames as media in which these reactions may be studied over broad ranges of temperature and pressure is in its infancy. Most of the phenomena observed can be explained qualitatively, and some quantitative results have been obtained.

Table VI.   Rate Constants for Ion-Molecule Reactions in Flames

	$\Delta H (kcal./mole)$	$k (cm.^3 \ molecule^{-1} sec.^{-1})$
$\text{CHO}^+ + \text{H}_2\text{O} \rightarrow \text{H}_3\text{O}^+ + \text{CO}$	$-34,000$	10^{-8}
$\text{OH}^- + \text{M} \rightarrow \text{OH} + e^- + \text{M}$	$+41,000$	$10^{-9}e^{-41,000/RT}$
$\text{OH}^- + \text{H} \rightarrow \text{H}_2\text{O} + e^-$	$-77,000$	$\sim 10^{-14}(?)$
$\text{Cl}^- + \text{H} \rightarrow \text{HCl} + e^-$	$-18,000$	$\sim 10^{-13}$
$\text{H}_3\text{O}^+ + \text{Pb} \rightarrow \text{Pb}^+ + \text{H}_2\text{O} + \text{H}$	$+26,000$	$\sim 10^{-9}$
$\text{H}_3\text{O}^+ + \text{Li} \rightarrow \text{Li}^+ + \text{H}_2\text{O} + \text{H}$	$-21,000$	$7.5 \times 10^{-10}(?)$
$\text{LiH}_2\text{O}^+ + \text{M} \rightarrow \text{Li}^+ + \text{H}_2\text{O} + \text{M}$	$\sim +50,000$	$10^{-9}e^{-50,000/RT}$
$\text{SrOH}^+ + \text{Na} \rightarrow \text{Na}^+ + \text{SrOH}$	~ 0	$\sim 10^{-8}$

Some of the rate constants discussed above are summarized in Table VI. The uncertainties (often very large) in these rate constants have already been indicated. Most of the rate constants have pre-exponential factors somewhat greater than the corresponding factors for neutral species reactions, which agrees with theory. At 2000°K. for two molecules each of mass 20 atomic units and a collision cross-section of 15 A^2. simple bimolecular collision theory gives a pre-exponential factor of 3×10^{-10} cm.^{3} molecule^{-1} sec.$^{-1}$

Acknowledgments

The preparation of this paper was supported by the Office of Naval Research under Contract Nonr-3809(00).   The authors are grateful to W. J. Miller for permission to use his as yet unpublished data in Figures 3 and 4.

Appendix

The thermodynamic data used to calculate the heats of reaction are in many cases not well known.   Values used in this paper are based on compilations in Refs. *9* and *11* and a compilation by Bernecker and Long (*2*).   Some of the more important values are summarized for the convenience of the reader below.

Thermodynamic Data

Species	ΔH_f, kcal./mole
CH	143
$CH(A^2\Delta)$	209
CH_2O	-28
H_3O^+	140
CHO^+	222
CH_3O^+	212
CH_5O^+	136
CHO_2^+	166
$C_2H_3O^+$	172
$C_3H_3^+$	260
Cl^-	-54.3
OH^-	-32.0
O_2^-	-10.6
O^-	25.3
C_2^-	126
C^-	142
C_2H^-	35

Literature Cited

(1) Bascombe, K. N., Green, J. A., Sugden, T. M., *Advan. Mass Spectrometry* **2**, 66 (1963).
(2) Bernecker, R. R., Long, F. A., *J. Phys. Chem.* **65**, 1565 (1961).
(3) Bleekrode, R., Nieuwpoort, W. C., *J. Chem. Phys.* **43**, 3680 (1965).
(4) Buchel'nikova, I. S., *J. Expt. Theoret. Phys.* (*U.S.S.R.*) **35**, 1119 (1958).
(5) Bulewicz, E. M. and Padley, P. J., *Symp. Combust., 9th, Cornell Univ., Ithaca, N. Y., 1962*, 647 (1963).
(6) Bulewicz, E. M., and Padley, P. J., *Combust. Flame* **5**, 331 (1961).
(7) Calcote, H. F., *Symp. Combust., 9th Cornell Univ., Ithaca, N. Y., 1962*, 622 (1963).
(8) Calcote, H. F., Reuter, J. L., *J. Chem. Phys.* **38**, 310 (1963).
(9) Calcote, H. F., Kurzius, S. C., Miller, W. J., *Symp. Combust., 10th, Univ. Cambridge, Cambridge, Engl., 1964*, 605 (1965).
(10) Calcote, H. F., *Symp. Combust., 8th, Pasadena, Calif., 1960*, 184 (1962).
(11) Calcote, H. F., 26th Meeting of AGARD Propulsion and Energetics Panel, Pisa, Italy, September 1965, in press.
(12) De Jaegere, S., Deckers, J., van Tiggelen, A., *Symp. Combust., 8th, Pasadena, Calif., 1960*, 155 (1962).
(13) Fenimore, C. P., Jones, G. W., *J. Chem. Phys.* **39**, 1514 (1963).
(14) Feugier, A., van Tiggelen, A., *Symp. Combust., 10th, Univ. Cambridge, Cambridge, Engl., 1964*, 621 (1965).

314   ION-MOLECULE REACTIONS IN THE GAS PHASE

(15) Fontijn, A., Miller, W. J., Hogan, J. M., *Ibid.*, p. 545.
(16) Fristrom, R. M. and Westenberg, A. A., "Flame Structure," McGraw-Hill Book Co., New York, 1965.
(17) Glass, G. P., Kistiakowsky, G. B., Michael, J. V., Niki, H., *Symp. Combust. 10th, Univ. Cambridge, Cambridge, Engl., 1964*, 513 (1965).
(18) Glass, G. P., Kistiakowsky, G. B., Michael, J. V., Niki, H., *J. Chem. Phys.* **42,** 608 (1965).
(19) Green, J. A., Sugden, T. M., *Symp. Combust. 9th, Cornell Univ., Ithaca, N. Y., 1962*, 607 (1963).
(20) Green, J. A., 26th Meeting of AGARD Propulsion and Energetics Panel, Pisa, Italy, September 1965.
(21) Haller, I., Pimentel, G. C., *J. Am. Chem. Soc.* **84,** 2855 (1962).
(22) Hayhurst, A. N., Sugden, T. M., IUPAC Meeting on Plasmas, Moscow, 1965.
(23) Hayhurst, A. N., PhD Dissertation, University of Cambridge, Cambridge, England, 1964.
(24) Jensen, D. E., PhD Dissertation, University of Cambridge, Cambridge, England, 1965.
(25) Jensen, D. E., Padley, P. J., *Symp. Combust. 11th, 1966*, in press.
(26) Knewstubb, P. F., Sugden, T. M., *Symp. Combust., 7th, London Oxford, 1958*, 247 (1959).
(27) Knewstubb, P. F., Sugden, T. M., *Proc. Roy. Soc.* **A255,** 520 (1960).
(28) Miller, W. J., *Symp. Combust. 11th, 1966*, in press.
(29) Miller, W. J., Fontijn, A., *Nature* **204,** 679 (1964).
(30) Pack, J. L., Phelps, A. V., *J. Chem. Phys.* **44,** 1870 (1966).
(31) Padley, P. J., Page, F. M., Sugden, T. M., *Trans. Faraday Soc.* **57,** 1552 (1961).
(32) Pergament, H. S. and Calcote, H. F., *Symp. Combust. 11th, 1966*, in press.
(33) Schofield, K., Sugden, T. M., *Symp. Combust. 10th, Univ. Cambridge, Cambridge, Engl., 1964*, 589 (1965).
(34) Soundy, R. G., Williams, H., 26th Meeting of AGARD Propulsion and Energetics Panel, Pisa, Italy, September 1965.
(35) Sternberg, J. C., Galloway, W. S. and Jones, D. T. L., "Gas Chromatography," N. Brenner, J. E. Cullen, and M. D. Weiss, eds., p. 231, Academic Press, New York, 1962.
(36) Sugden, T. M., Wheeler, R. C., *Discuss. Faraday Soc.* **19,** 76 (1955).
(37) Sugden, T. M., 26th Meeting of AGARD Propulsion and Energetics Panel, Pisa, Italy, September 1965.
(38) Tal'roze, V. L., Frankevich, E. L., *Dokl. Akad. Nauk SSSR* **111,** 376 (1956).
(39) van Tiggelen, A., Progress in Astronautics and Aeronautics **12,** 165 (1963).
(40) von Engel, A. and Cozens, J. R., 26th Meeting of AGARD Propulsion and Energetics Panel, Pisa, Italy, September 1965.

RECEIVED May 23, 1966.

Mass Spectrometric Studies of Ion-Molecule Reactions in Gas Discharges

M. M. SHAHIN

Xerox Corp., Rochester, N. Y.

Mass spectrometric studies of the ionic species which arrive at the cathode of both glow and corona discharges yield useful information regarding ion-molecule reactions which occur within these systems. Glow discharges have been used to study endothermic reactions, and their usefulness and limitations have been demonstrated by studies of the dissociative charge transfer reactions: $Ar^+ + N_2 \rightarrow N^+ + N + Ar$; $N_2^+ + N_2 \rightarrow N^+ + N + N_2$; $N_2^+ + O_2 \rightarrow O^+ + O + N_2$. Exothermic reactions have been studied by low pressure corona (or Townsend) discharges in nitrogen containing trace quantities of water vapor. Kinetic analysis of the data in this system yields values of the cross-sections for a number of intermediate processes which lead to the formation of hydrated proton clusters of the type $(H_2O)_n H^+$ where $n = 1, 2$, etc.

Mass spectrometric studies of electrical discharges have been carried out during recent years to determine the nature of the charge carriers responsible for various discharge properties (*5, 12, 13*). Such properties as ion mobility, ion electrode interactions, emission of radiation, or the production of neutral chemical by-products in the discharge are all influenced by the exact nature of the ionic species in the discharge. Studies of these systems are often complicated, however, by the fact that the primary ionic species, which are generally formed by direct electron bombardment on neutral gas molecules, may undergo processes in which their identity may be lost before they are observed in the mass spectrometer. It is therefore of great interest to learn not only the identity of the final charge carriers in these systems but also to trace their possible precursors to understand both the properties of the discharge and to unravel the mechanisms of the chemical reactions which cause the neutral by-products.

Two main processes—simple charge exchange and ion-molecule reactions—substantially alter the properties of the discharge. The simple charge exchange processes occur between the ionic species and either the parent neutral molecule or the impurity species. In the latter case the identity of the ion is completely changed while the former will influence both the mobility of the ion and its energy distribution within the system and produces highly energetic neutral species as side products. These energetic species may then dissociate and partly become the precursors of various neutral free-radical reactions prevailing in the discharge. The processes designated as ion-molecule reactions, on the other hand, not only change the nature of the charge carriers but are direct precursors of at least part of the neutral discharge products. These reactions are particularly interesting since they are some of the fastest known and provide opportunities to study the influence of Coulombic forces on chemical reactions.

Using gas discharges to study ion-molecule reactions is particularly restricted owing to the simultaneous occurrence within the system of other gaseous electronics processes which tend to obscure the processes of interest. Such investigations are therefore intended primarily to provide a better understanding of the phenomena occurring within the discharge; the information they give on ion-molecule reactions is only incidental. To minimize the restrictions dictated by this inherent complexity, it is customary to choose a discharge in which the electrical properties are well understood. This facilitates treatment of the data as a function of the electric field in the discharge. Furthermore, because of the wide range of pressures used in discharge studies, minute quantities (p.p.m.) of reactive impurity gases could easily compete for the reactant ions. To eliminate such undesirable side reactions, exceptional precautions are necessary to remove trace quantities of impurities. Such a system then, at sufficiently high pressures, would allow one to study slow ion-molecule reactions which are inaccessible by other methods. In studying fast reactions, on the other hand, the lower limit of the discharge reactions may still allow not only secondary ionic products to appear, but the tertiary and quaternary species may also be detected in abundance at the mass spectrometer. A detailed study of such a system may be difficult experimentally. Other serious complications, such as electron-ion recombination and selective ion diffusion could confuse the results in discharge systems. By judiciously choosing the type of discharge however, the contribution of some of these processes could be made negligible.

A further consequence of the specific characteristics of the discharge systems is the difficulty of determining meaningful rate constants for the specific reactions. This is mainly caused by the complex dependence of rate constants on ionic velocities and the variation of the latter, not only in the presence of electric fields which are generally variable within the discharge but also the drastic modification of ion velocities by both resonance charge exchange processes and elastic scattering. Therefore, one must specify reactions by measuring their respective cross-sections as functions of average ion energy.

Finally, a quantitative study of these systems is subject to the general limitations when mass spectrometers are used to sample the intermediate species from a system. No attempts have been made here to correct the data for possible mass dependence of the species emerging from the sampling port. However, in systems where adiabatic expansion of the gas is suspected to give rise to the formation of ionic aggregates just outside the sampling port, the concentration of the particular gaseous component responsible for such clusters is reduced sufficiently so that the probability of encounters to form such aggregates is made negligible (*6, 13*).

Suitable Discharge Systems

The choice of a particular type of gas discharge for quantitative studies of ion-molecule reactions is essential if useful information is to be obtained from ion abundance measurements. Generally, two types of systems have been used to study ion-molecule reactions. The pulsed "afterglow" technique has been used successfully by Fite *et al.* (*3*) and Sayers *et al.* (*1*) to obtain information on several exothermic reactions including simple charge transfer processes important in upper atmosphere chemistry. The use of a continuous d.c. discharge was initiated in our laboratories and has been successful in both exothermic and endothermic ion-molecule reactions which occur widely within these systems.

Several types of continuous discharges are easily available in the laboratory. These are radio frequency, Townsend, coronas, glows (normal and abnormal), and arcs. Each system possesses special characteristics which in effect govern the motion of charged particles between the electrodes, and apart from a few special cases the systems are too complex to lend themselves to simple analytical description for studying ion-molecule reactions. Here, two of the latter systems—namely, coronas and glows—will be treated in detail in order to demonstrate their feasibility for studying both exothermic and endothermic reactions.

Experimental

Detailed experimental procedures for producing glow (*12*) and corona (*13*) discharges have already been given. The apparatus used for corona discharges is shown in Figure 1. For glow discharges two plane parallel nickel electrodes are used within a glass envelope of 3–4 cm. diameter while for corona discharge studies a coaxial geometry with a fine anode wire provided the most stability. Briefly, the ionic species are sampled continuously through a small orifice in the cathode, and the abundances of various ionic species are determined by means of a quadrapole mass spectrometer under varying discharge conditions. Differential pumping techniques are used to extend the studies of discharge systems up to pressures of 1 atmosphere. The flow through the discharge tube is generally maintained at a high level to reduce or completely remove any observable effect caused by the neutral products of the discharge. The flow rate thus ranges from a few atm.-ml./min. for glow discharges which are maintained at pressures of less than 0.5 torr to 200 atm.-ml./min. for corona discharges at 1 atmosphere pressure. The flow conditions through the nozzle were usually chosen to be "viscous" or close to the "slip" region by varying nozzle diameters from 10 to 100 microns over pressure ranges of atmospheric to tenths of millimeters. Nozzles which permit "molecular flow" conditions at sufficient intensities are now becoming available, and experiments with these nozzles are in progress. The mass spectrometer electron gun assembly serves as an independent ionizing source for monitoring the composition of the discharge gas when ions are not extracted from the discharge systems.

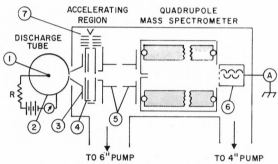

Figure 1. Schematic diagram of the apparatus

(1) anode wire, (2) cylindrical cathode, (3) extraction electrode, (4) mass spectrometer ion source, (5) focusing electrodes, (6) multiplier detector, (7) electron gun assembly

In glow discharges the choice of the gas composition is often critical if interference from side reactions is to be minimized. Measurements of the cathode fall potential and the length of the cathode dark space in glow discharges are carried out in individual experiments while the discharges are in operation. Changes in the ion energy distribution (*see* below) are brought about by variation of the cathode fall potentials by increasing current densities of the discharges. These changes influence the degree of ion-molecule reaction and appear as variations of relative ionic abundances in the mass spectrometer.

In corona (or Townsend) discharges it is often desirable to work at pressures below 100 torr to limit both the extent of the reaction, which may involve several consecutive steps, and any impurity interference. In any series of experiments pertaining to a particular study, the total pressures of the discharge and the voltage are usually varied while the concentration of the minor component is kept constant. In systems where the concentration of the electronegative gas (e.g., oxygen), is low it may be necessary to use an external source of ionization through the use of a weak radioactive source, for example, to stabilize the corona discharge.

Use of Glow Discharges

One of the commonest forms of gas discharges is a glow discharge which is formed at gas pressures of a few tenths to several millimeters of mercury and is characterized by the presence of a well defined dark space region before the cathode and separated from the rest of the discharge by a distinct glow region called the "negative glow." If ion abundance is measured at the cathode of the discharge, the arrival of ions at the mass spectrometer will be governed by the well established properties of the dark space. A model which quantitatively explained the general features of the cathode dark space was originally proposed by Little and VonEngel (7) and was later highly successful in describing the energy distribution of the ions arriving at the cathode as determined experimentally by Davis and Vanderslice (2). This model will be used here to help identify ion-molecule reactions which may be occurring within this region of the discharge. The general features of the model are as follows:

(1) Ions arriving at the cathode originate in the negative glow where the electric field is zero or the very low field region just before the glow, with near thermal energies.

(2) The energy distribution of the ions within the dark space is primarily governed by charge transfer processes in which the ions lose all their energy gained from the field—i.e., the newly formed ions begin their motion from thermal energies and travel through the field. These types of collisions are probably dominated by symmetrical charge transfer in which an energetic ion interacts with its parent neutral particle, producing a fast neutral and an identical ion with essentially zero energy. Symmetrical charge transfer process of this type for which ΔE of reaction is zero are characterized by large cross-sections compared with unsymmetrical charge transfer processes.

Elastic scattering within the dark space is generally assumed (7) not to affect the energy distribution of the ions seriously. This is apparently caused by the low scattering angles involved which result in little or no momentum transfer.

(3) Ions moving toward the cathode pass through an intense longitudinal field which tends to reduce their lateral diffusion. Thus, the path of the ions may be regarded as beam-like.

(4) The low concentration and high energy of the electrons in this region reduces the probability of ion-electron recombination processes.

(5) The electric field decreases linearly from the cathode to the edge of the negative glow as determined experimentally (14).

The above model predicts the experimental findings (2) that ions reaching the cathode possess a wide distribution of energy extending from thermal to that corresponding to the entire cathode fall potential. These ions, therefore, should be able to undergo various endothermic and exothermic ion-molecule reactions, limited only by threshold energy conditions if any, neutral particle density, and the variation of the cross-section of the reaction with ionic energy. Mass spectral data of the relative abundances of the ions at the cathode and their changes with discharge conditions should reflect the effect of those ion-molecule reactions which may occur within this region of the discharge.

Theory. The requirement of a threshold energy for an endothermic ion-molecule reaction can be used together with the described model to calculate the exact position within the dark space where an ion can undergo reaction having gained from the field at least the necessary amount of energy.   Exothermic reactions, on the other hand, occur both within the negative glow and throughout the dark space and therefore are not easy to calculate.

If at any point x (Figure 2) away from the cathode but within the dark space $\delta N_{(E,x)}$ denotes the number of ions per unit volume with energy between E and $E + dE$, such that $E > E_o$, the threshold energy for the reaction, then as the ions move toward the cathode, the total amount of a bimolecular reaction they will undergo with neutral reactant species of density ρ, to yield N_S secondary ions per cc. at the cathode is given by:

$$N_S = \rho \int_{x_{max}}^{o} dx \int_{E_o}^{E_{max}} Q_{(E)} \cdot \delta N_{(E,x)} \cdot dE \qquad (1)$$

where $Q_{(E)}$ is the reaction cross-section which is a function of energy, E_{max} corresponds to the maximum energy of the ion and is a function of x.   The value of x_{max} depends both on the total cathode fall potential V_c and the threshold energy of the reaction E_o since it denotes the distance that an ion, starting from the edge of the glow, should travel toward the cathode before it has gained the minimum energy for the reaction. The energy distribution function $\delta N_{(E,x)}$ is derived as follows, using the model previously described.

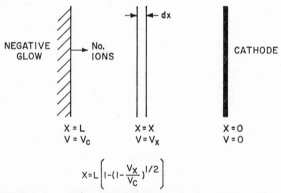

Figure 2.   Schematic diagram of the model of the cathode dark space.   Concentration of the ions is denoted by N_o

If the cross-section for charge transfer is denoted by σ and the total number of ions/cc. which start from the negative glow, N_o remains constant (Figure 2) throughout the dark space, then the number of collisions that occur within a distance dx at any point x in the dark space would be (σP_o). $N_o dx$, where P_o is the density of the neutral particles.   The number of these ions which eventually arrive at the cathode without further collision and having acquired the potential drop V_x (or an energy $E_x = eV_x$), assuming an exponential law, will therefore be given by:

$$dN = (\sigma P_o) \cdot N_o \cdot dx \cdot e^{-\sigma P_o x}$$

Substituting for x from the linear field relationship (14),

$$x = L[1 - (1 - V_x/V_c)^{1/2}] \tag{2}$$

where L is the length of the cathode dark space, and V_c is the cathode fall potential. One obtains after simplifying for $L \gg 1/(\sigma P_o)$,

$$dN = \frac{N_o L(\sigma P_o)}{2V_c} \cdot \exp\left[\frac{-L(\sigma P_o)}{2V_c} \cdot V_x\right] \cdot d(V_x) \tag{3}$$

In this derivation σ, the charge transfer cross-section is assumed to remain constant within the energy range applicable. Equation 3 describes the energy distribution of the ions at the cathode, and its general form has been substantiated experimentally (2).

To obtain the energy distribution at any point x within the dark space, L is replaced by $L - x$ and V_c by $V_c - V_x = V_c\left(\dfrac{L - x}{L}\right)^2$ in Equation 3. It therefore follows:

$$\delta N_{(E,x)} = \frac{N_o L^2(\sigma P_o)}{2(L - x)V_c} \cdot \exp\left[\frac{-L^2(\sigma P_o)V_x}{2(L - x)V_c}\right] \cdot d(V_x) \tag{4}$$

where the ion energy $E = eV_x$. Equation 4 is applicable again for all cases where $(L - x) \gg 1/(\sigma P_o)$ and will be true for most endothermic reactions in which the ion moves a considerable distance from the edge of the glow before it can acquire the minimum energy necessary for the reaction.

The measured values of L and V_c together with known values of σ are used in Equation 4, and subsequently the function $\delta N_{(E,x)}$ is used in Equation 1 to obtain information concerning the function $Q_{(E)}$. The limits of integrations of Equation 1 are $x_{max} = L[1 - (E_o/V_c)^{1/2}]$ as determined by threshold requirement of the reaction and $E_{max} = V_c\left(\dfrac{L - x}{L}\right)^2$. The function $Q_{(E)}$ can be evaluated either by a deconvolution or curve fitting technique.

Average Ionic Energy. The experimental data N_S/N_o could also be used in Equation 1 and without integrating $Q_{(E)}$ over the energy range, to obtain a weighted average cross-section. This cross-section could then be used along with a weighted average ionic energy which can be calculated by Equation 5.

$$\overline{E}_{av} = \int_{x_{max}}^{x=o} dx \cdot \int_{V_x=E_o/e}^{V_x=E_{max}/e} eV_x \cdot \delta N_{(E,x)} \cdot dE \bigg/ \int_{x_{max}}^{x=o} dx \cdot \int_{V_x=E_o/e}^{V_x E_{max}/e} \delta N_{(E,x)} \tag{5}$$

Such average calculations are relatively simple and reasonably accurate where the variation of $Q_{(E)}$ with E is not too large. However, where the cross-section may vary over 2–3 orders of magnitude, its usefulness will be limited.

Reaction Time. For certain reactions in which the function $Q_{(E)}$ varies inversely with the ionic velocity, it may be useful to derive a rate constant by calculating the total reaction time during the passage of the ion from the edge of the glow to the cathode. In such calculations (*12*), only segments of the total distance in which the ion possesses energy above the threshold energy are considered, and the reaction time is calculated using the average velocity of the ion during the passage of this distance. The velocity of the ion would be considered thermal again when it will subsequently undergo charge transfer. For these cases, the data will be treated in a manner similar to the conventional forms used in studying ion-molecule reactions in mass spectrometer ion sources to obtain a rate constant for the specific reaction.

Results. A general type of ion-molecule reaction which lends itself easily to study in the cathode region of a glow discharge is endothermic dissociative charge transfer, which requires a minimum threshold energy. Several such reactions involving the rare gas ions have recently received attention both theoretically (*8, 9*) and experimentally (*4, 10*) and provide an example for comparison of the results from the glow discharge work with those from more conventional systems. Below, three ex-

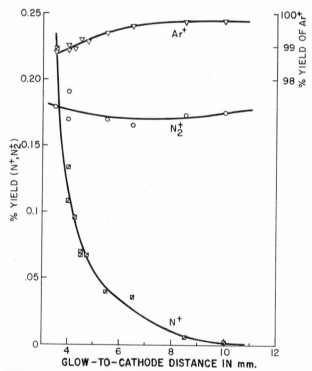

Figure 3.   Glow discharge in a mixture of 99% argon and 1% nitrogen

Pressure = 0.3 mm Hg; nickel cathode; % yield refers to %
total ions observed

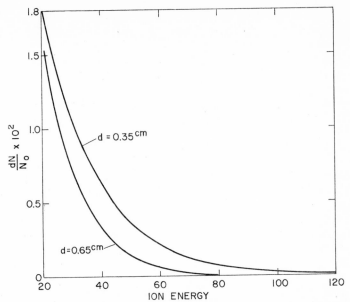

Figure 4.   Calculated energy distribution of the argon ions at the cathode of a glow discharge in a mixture of 99% argon and 1% nitrogen for two different optically measured cathode dark space lengths

Ion energies are given in lab. scale in e.v.

amples of dissociative charge transfer processes involving atomic and molecular ions are described, and where available comparison with other experimental work is given.

REACTION OF ENERGETIC ATOMIC IONS WITH MOLECULAR SPECIES. $Ar^+ + N_2 \to N^+ + N + Ar$ ($\Delta H = 8.54$ e.v.).   The dissociative charge transfer of argon ion with molecular nitrogen has been studied in a glow discharge in argon containing 1% nitrogen as a reactive component. The results of the measured relative abundances of the various ions which arrived at the cathode are plotted in Figure 3 against the optically measured length of the cathode dark space.   This parameter is used here to reflect the change in the ion energy distribution within the dark space for various experiments since it generally decreases (15) with increase in the cathode fall potential for an "abnormal" glow discharge and therefore is related to E/P, the pressure reduced field strength within the dark space.   The data in Figure 3 indicate that as the average ion energy is increased, the yield of N^+ ions is rapidly increased at the expense of Ar^+ ions and exceeds the yield of N_2^+ ions.   On the other hand, the yield of N_2^+ ions remains almost unchanged throughout these experiments.   It appears that the most probable reaction for the production of N^+ ion is $Ar^+ + N_2 \to N^+ + N + Ar$, with other possible mechanisms contributing negligibly to the measured yield.   On this basis, it is possible to treat the data and to obtain a cross-section for this reaction.

To illustrate the ion energy distribution above the threshold energy of the reaction, calculations are made according to Equation 3 for two cathode dark space lengths and are given in Figure 4. The variations among similar distribution curves representing points through the dark space will affect the ionic yield especially if the cross-section for the reaction

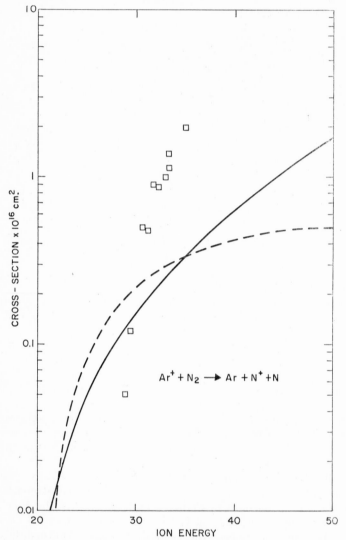

Figure 5. Cross-section for the reaction $Ar^+ + N_2 \rightarrow Ar + N^+ + N$

Data points are calculated as weighted average values; solid line is the cross-section function best fitted to the experimental data; broken line represents the results of Maier (10). Ion energies are given in lab. scale in e.v.

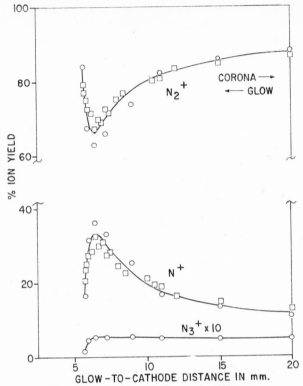

Figure 6.   Glow discharge in nitrogen

*Pressure = 0.3 mm Hg; nickel cathode; ions are sampled
from the cathode; % yield refers to % total ions observed.
At very low discharge currents the distinct glow in front of
the cathode disappears, and a continuous glow (corona) is
obtained throughout the discharge tube*

depends critically on the energy of the reactant ion. The data thus
treated are shown in Figure 5 in two forms: (a) as a weighted average
cross-section for a median energy, representative of a particular distribution (Equation 5), and (b) as an unfolded function ($Q_{(E)}$ as in
Equation 1) representing the variation of the cross-section with energy
over the range significantly covered by the distribution.   The form of this
function is obtained through curve fitting techniques covering the energy
distribution of the ions within each data point.   It is interesting to note
that this function closely resembles the measured cross-section for this
reaction by Maier (10) both in the general form and the absolute magnitude.   Thus, the method which is based on the model given above can
clearly be taken as generally sound and would be expected to yield reasonable results, provided that the ionic yield data could unambiguously be
assigned to a particular reaction.   To ensure such a condition, the system
should be chosen so that other contributions to the product yield are
negligible.

REACTION OF MOLECULAR IONS WITH MOLECULAR SPECIES. (a) $N_2^+ + N_2 \rightarrow N^+ + N + N_2$, ($\Delta H = 8.7$ e.v.). In a system of pure nitrogen, the ionic abundance at the cathode depends strongly on the discharge conditions. The yields of various ions N^+, N_2^+, and N_3^+ are shown in Figure 6. The yield of N_4^+ is less than 0.5% and therefore has not been shown. The behavior of the ion yield curves strongly suggests the production of atomic ion at the expense of the molecular ion by the reaction $N_2^+ + N_2 \rightarrow N^+ + N + N_2$. Other sources of N^+—e.g., by the decomposition of N_3^+ ion or dissociative ionization of neutral molecule: $N_2 + e \rightarrow N^+ + N + 2e$—will not contribute appreciably to the observed change of the N^+ ion yield from its initial value in the "normal" glow (large dark space distances) (12). The initial yield is undoubtedly caused mainly by the latter process since the electrons arriving at the glow possess sufficient energy for this process. The contribution of this reaction at other cathode-glow distances is not expected to change appreciably (11).

The data can be treated as before to obtain a cross-section for the reaction. The analysis based on the weighted average ion energy is shown in Figure 7. These results taken over a wide ion energy range indicate an initial increase of the magnitude of the cross-section to a broad maximum, followed by a small decrease at higher energies. Note,

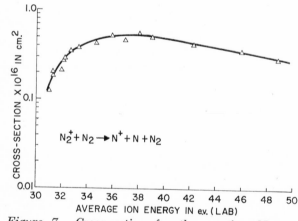

Figure 7.   Cross-section for the reaction $N_2^+ + N_2 \rightarrow N^+ + N + N_2$ calculated as weighted average values

however, that the variation of cross-section with energy does not appear to be as dramatic in this reaction as in the case of the argon ion. Perhaps this is caused by a difference in the nature of the collision which may involve short lived complex formation, possibly highly energized N_4^+ ions which may preferentially yield N^+ ions.

(b) $N_2^+ + O_2 \rightarrow O^+ + O + N_2$, ($\Delta H = 3.1$ e.v.). A more complex system, in which the dissociative charge transfer of molecular nitrogen occurs to both neutral nitrogen and oxygen molecules, has been studied to demonstrate its complexity and the limitations of the general data treatment in the absence of the specific reaction responsible for a particular product.   Figure 8 shows the ion yield at the cathode of a glow discharge in nitrogen containing 1% oxygen.   A number of product ions of varying yields are observed in such a mixture.   The ionic yield of the molecular

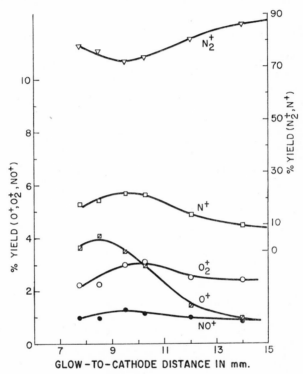

*Figure 8.   Glow discharge in a mixture of 99%
nitrogen and 1% oxygen*

*Pressure = 0.3 mm Hg; nickel cathode.   The yield curve
for $NO_2{}^+$ ions, not shown here, corresponds closely to that
of NO^+ ion;   % yield refers to % total ions observed*

oxygen appears greater than its neutral gas composition, apparently owing to the charge-exchange process between $N_2{}^+$ and neutral oxygen molecule.   The production of nitrogen atomic ion through dissociative charge transfer with $N_2{}^+$ is still prevalent as in the previous example, although its yield is somewhat reduced, owing to other discharge products—namely, O^+, NO^+, and $NO_2{}^+$.   Among the latter products, by far the greatest change with variation in ion energy distribution appears in O^+ ion yield which can be argued as arising mainly by the reaction, $N_2{}^+ + O_2 \rightarrow O^+ + O + N_2$.   The process of dissociative ionization of electrons on molecular oxygen is, however, expected to contribute to the yield of O^+ ion, and the data should be corrected before final analysis.

The corrected data thus obtained could be used to evaluate the variation of the cross-section of the dissociative charge-transfer reaction with ion energy.

Two other products of the discharge—namely, NO^+ and NO_2^+—could apparently arise from the reaction of both molecular and atomic nitrogen ions with oxygen. Since these reactions are exothermic, one one would expect them to occur throughout the discharge including the "glow" region from where they would drift toward the cathode. Under such a condition, the data cannot be used for cross-section calculations.

Studying the relative ion abundances at the cathode of glow discharges could provide information on the variation of the cross-section of endothermic ion-molecule reactions, provided that the abundance measurements could be reliably assigned to specific reactions. Where gaseous impurities severely interfere or the results could be ascribed to several reactions which are equally probable, the data is difficult to interpret. In cases where both endothermic and exothermic reactions could give rise to a particular product ion, an assumption on the variation of cross-section with energy for the two reactions may be helpful in interpreting the data.

Corona Discharges

Corona discharges are formed at low currents with a wide gas pressure range of a few millimeters mercury (Townsend discharges) to beyond 1 atmosphere. Generally, the most stable form of a corona discharge is established around a fine wire, placed at high positive potential with respect to a coaxial cylindrical cathode. A high voltage power supply together with a limiting resistor usually ensures a stable corona with most gases. In such a system, the gas molecules are ionized primarily near the central wire since the electrons gain sufficient energy from the field only at small distances from the wire. Thus, at low currents where the effect of space charge is minimized, the system may be assumed to be similar to a line source for generating positive ions, which then move perpendicular to the axis toward the cylindrical cathode in an almost constant field. The magnitude of this field depends on the square root of the ratio of the current to the mobility of the ion (15). The pressure-reduced electric field E/P, however, is considerably smaller in this system than in most experiments with high pressure mass spectrometry. This characteristic—namely, the low values of E/P (<50 volt/cm. mm. Hg) which dominate the greater distance of the ionic path and the high frequency of resonance charge transfer processes which occur at the pressures usually employed in these systems—is expected to maintain ion energies close to thermal energies.

A second consequence of the relatively high pressures used in these systems is the simultaneous occurrence of many side reactions of the ions with trace quantities of impurity gases. Two of the most serious side reactions are charge transfer processes and fast ion-molecule reactions which often interfere with the reaction under study. Indeed, in systems where atmospheric gases are involved, these side reactions often constitute the most dominant processes *(13)*, and their detailed study should provide interesting information concerning these processes.

Results. An example of the role of minute quantities of impurity gases in corona discharges in atmospheric gases is shown in Figure 9. The ions which reach the cathode at various concentrations of water vapor in a corona discharge in air at 1 atmosphere pressure appear to be hydrated protons with the general formula of $(H_2O)_nH^+$ where $n = 1,2,3$ etc. At water vapor concentrations lower than 5.5×10^{-2} mole % other ionic species of the discharge (e.g., O_2^+, NO^+, and NO_2^+ and their simple hydrated forms $O_2^+(H_2O)_n$, $NO^+(H_2O)_n$, and $NO_2^+(H_2O)_n$) begin to appear in the mass spectrometer.

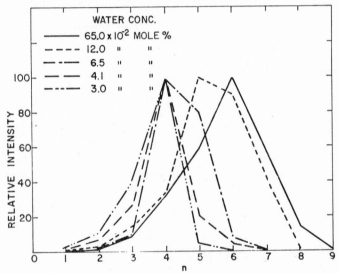

Figure 9.   Corona discharge in air at atmospheric pressure
for different concentrations of water

n denotes the number of water molecules in a hydrated proton cluster
$(H_2O)_nH^+$

To study the processes responsible for converting the primary ions (e.g. N_2^+) to the final forms observed in the mass spectrometer, investigations were extended to the lower limit of the discharge pressure in order to isolate the intermediate species. The yields of various ionic species which arrive at the cathode for different discharge pressures of nitrogen containing 1.0×10^{-2} mole % of water vapor are shown in Figure 10. The disappearance of the species N_2^+, N_2H^+, and N_4^+ and the appearance of H_2O^+, H_3O^+, and $H_5O_2^+$ as the pressure is increased are well demonstrated in these systems. These data could be used to obtain information on the cross-sections for various reactions which give rise to these product ions.

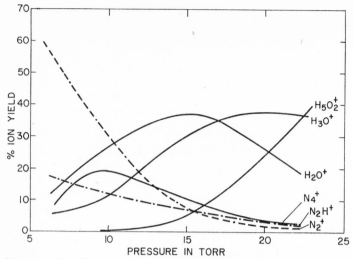

*Figure 10. Corona (or Townsend) discharge in nitrogen
containing 1 × 10⁻² mole % of water vapor*

*The ion yields of O_2^+ arising from 3.3×10^{-2} mole % oxygen im-
purity in the gas are not shown since its contribution at maximum
pressure is less than 3%.   % Ion yield refers to % total ions observed*

Kinetic Analysis. The following reaction scheme is proposed to
account for the observed ionic yields shown in Figure 10 in a system primarily composed of nitrogen and water vapor.

$$N_4^+ \xleftarrow{Q_6} N_2^+ \begin{array}{c} \xrightarrow{Q_8} N_2H^+ \xrightarrow{Q_2} \\ \xrightarrow{Q_1} \\ \xrightarrow{Q_4} H_2O^+ \xrightarrow{Q_5} \end{array} H_3O^+ \xrightarrow{Q_3} H_5O_2^+$$

The values of Q denote average cross-sections for the prevailing ion
energy distribution for the respective reactions.   All the reactions above
involve a water molecule except Reaction 6 which involves a neutral
nitrogen molecule.   The reactions of N_3^+ and N_4^+ with water to yield
N_3H^+ and N_4H^+ were not included since their contribution is negligible
within the pressure range studied.   Side reactions, if any, of some of
these species, (e.g., N_2^+, N_4^+, N_2H^+, and probably H_2O^+) with trace
amounts of oxygen through either simple charge exchange or ion-molecule
reactions should also be included in the scheme.

In deriving the kinetic equation describing the arrival of various
ionic species at the cathode, it is assumed that the primary species N_2^+
is formed at the central wire at a constant rate, and during its passage in
the direction x perpendicular to the axis its concentration is modified
by various reactions.   In this treatment both ion diffusion and ion-ion
or electron-ion recombination processes are neglected because the geometry of the discharge tube and the presence of an electric field would

effectively reduce any ion diffusion, and the low level of ionization within the system would make any contribution from recombination processes negligible.   Therefore,

$$\frac{d(N_2{}^+)}{dx} = -Q_1 n(N_2{}^+) - Q_4 n(N_2{}^+) - Q_6 P(N_2{}^+) - \gamma(N_2{}^+)$$

where n and P denote the density of water vapor and nitrogen gas, respectively, and γ is the product of the cross-section and the density of any other gas (e.g. O_2) which may react with $N_2{}^+$ ions.   Similarly,

$$\frac{d(N_4{}^+)}{dx} = Q_6 P(N_2{}^+) - Q_7 n(N_4{}^+) - Q_8 n(N_4{}^+) - \beta(N_4{}^+)$$

$$\frac{d(N_2H^+)}{dx} = Q_1 n(N_2{}^+) - Q_2 n(N_2H^+) + Q_8 n(N_4{}^+) - \delta(N_2H^+)$$

where β and δ again denote possible side reactions with oxygen.   If we introduce a second series of variables which denote the ratios of the ionic yields—e.g.,

$$R_1 = \frac{(N_4{}^+)}{(N_2{}^+)}, \quad R_2 = \frac{(N_2H^+)}{(N_2{}^+)}, \quad \text{etc.,}$$

it follows that:

$$\frac{dR_1}{dx} = Q_6 P + Q \cdot \alpha P \cdot R_1 - (\beta - \gamma) R_1 \tag{6}$$

where $\quad Q = Q_1 + Q_4 + \dfrac{Q_6}{\alpha} - Q_7 - Q_8$ and $\alpha = n/P$.

It is often possible to neglect the third term in Equation 6 since it involves differences in the reactivity of the two species toward a neutral molecule which may be present in very small quantities—e.g., O_2.   Then it follows that:

$$R_1 = \frac{Q_6}{\alpha Q} (e^{\alpha P Q x} - 1) \tag{7}$$

Similarly after approximating the exponential terms, it can be shown that:

$$\frac{R_2}{P} = \alpha Q_1 x + \frac{\alpha x^2}{2} (\alpha Q_1 Q^1 + Q_6 Q_8) P \tag{8}$$

where $Q^1 = Q_1 + Q_4 + \dfrac{Q_6}{\alpha} - Q_2$.   Under these conditions the data for R_1 and R_2 can be treated to obtain information on Q_6 and Q_1.   Similar expressions could also be obtained for other products—e.g., $R_3 = \dfrac{(H_2O^+)}{(N_2{}^+)}$.

Table I. Measured Reaction Cross-Sections for the Formation of Secondary and Tertiary Ions at E/P between 10 and 40 volts/cm. mm. Hg.

Reaction	Cross-Section $\times$ 10^{16} in sq. cm.	
	This Work	Others[a]
$N_2^+ + H_2O \rightarrow N_2H^+ + OH$	115	16–32 (3)
$N_2^+ + H_2O \rightarrow H_2O^+ + N_2$	13	
$N_2^+ + N_2 \rightarrow N_4^+$	0.01	0.07 (3)
$N_2H^+ + H_2O \rightarrow H_3O^+ + N_2$	440	

[a] Calculated from the measured rate constants.

Using α as an experimental variable, information concerning other reaction cross-sections will also become available. Some of the values of the cross-sections obtained by this technique are summarized in Table I, clearly demonstrating that much useful information can be obtained from the detailed studies of these simple discharge systems.

Literature Cited

(1) Batey, P. H., Court, G. R., Sayers, J., *Planetary Space Sci.* **13**, 911 (1965).
(2) Davis, W. D., Vanderslice, T. A., *Phys. Rev.* **131**, 219 (1963).
(3) Fite, W. L., Rutherford, J. R., Snow, W. R., Lint, V. A. J., *Discuss. Faraday Soc.* **33**, 264 (1962).
(4) Giese, C. F., Maier, W. B., *J. Chem. Phys.* **39**, 197 (1963).
(5) Knewstubb, P. F., Tickner, A. W., *J. Chem. Phys.* **36**, 674, 684 (1962); **37**, 2941 (1962).
(6) Lechenby, R. E., Robbins, E. J., Tyeualion, P. A., *Proc. Roy. Soc.* **A280**, 409 (1964).
(7) Little, P. F., VonEngel, A., *Proc. Roy. Soc.* **A224**, 209 (1954).
(8) Light, J. C., *J. Chem. Phys.* **40**, 3221 (1961).
(9) Light, J. C., Lin, J., *J. Chem. Phys.* **43**, 3209 (1965).
(10) Maier, II, W. B., *J. Chem. Phys.* **41**, 2174 (1964).
(11) Peterson, J. R., "Atomic Collision Processes," ed. M. R. C. McDowell, p. 465, John Wiley & Sons, Inc., New York, 1964.
(12) Shahin, M. M., *J. Chem. Phys.* **43**, 1798 (1965).
(13) Shahin, M. M., to be published.
(14) Stein, R. P., *Phys. Rev.* **89**, 134 (1953).
(15) VonEngel, "Ionized Gases," Oxford University Press, London, 1965.

RECEIVED April 25, 1966.

INDEX